The Platonic S
And Some Othe

John Parker
Formerly Head of Mathematics,
Riddlesdown School, Purley
and Deputy Director, Schools' Council
"Mathematics for the Majority" Project
1970-1972

Table of Contents

Published by
Cressar Publications, Ludgvan,
Penzance, Cornwall, TR20 8XG
01736 351920

www.cressar.co.uk

ISBN 0 9535399 1 1

Published by
Cressar Publications, Ludgvan,
Penzance, Cornwall

Printed by Headland Printers, Penzance
TR18 2EQ

Corrigenda

In some diagrams in the early chapters of this book, mysterious lines appear which seem to be part of the frame of the diagram. Even using the marvels of modern electronics, it has not proved possible to erase these lines. The publishers apologise and hope that these lines will not prove too much of a distraction to the reader.

In two diagrams, fig. 41 on page 19 and fig. 155 on page 52, arrows are missing. The correct diagrams appear below.

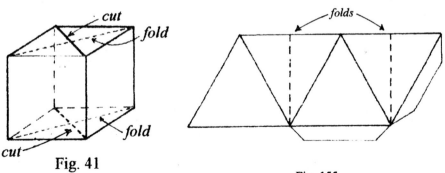

Fig. 41

Fig. 155

The bottom flaps in fig.44 have been shown in the wrong positions. Please note the amended and correct diagram below.

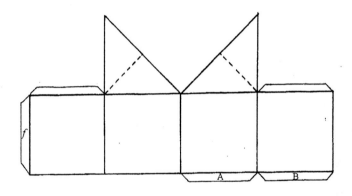

Chapter 1

THE PLATONIC SOLIDS

This book deals primarily with the five *regular polyhedra,* the so-called *Platonic* solids, named after the Greek philosopher Plato (427-347 B.C.). These are the cube (or regular hexahedron), the regular tetrahedron, the regular octahedron, the regular dodecahedron, and the regular icosahedron. Although Plato himself did not discover these solids, he wrote about them with such open admiration that his name has become permanently linked with them. A later Greek, the mathematician Euclid, investigated the properties of the Platonic solids in one book of his *Elements* and proved that there could be five and no more than five regular polyhedra. Appropriately the names by which we still know the solids today, save for that of the cube, are pure Greek. "Hedron" (plural "hedra") means "face", and "tetra", "hexa", "octa", "dodeca" and "icosa" indicate the numbers four, six, eight, twelve and twenty respectively, while "poly" means "many". However "cube" has also come to us indirectly from the Greek "kybos", "a die", *via* the Latin "cubus".

As for Plato, Morris Kline says, in his *Mathematics in Western Culture*, page 66, that "Plato admired these figures so much that he could not conceive of God not making use of them. He therefore elaborated on one Greek school of thought, which affirmed that all objects are composed of four elements, earth, air, fire, and water, by adding that the fundamental particles of fire had the shape of the tetrahedron, those of air had the shape of the octahedron, those of water the icosahedron, and those of earth, the cube. The fifth shape, the dodecahedron, God reserved for the shape of the universe itself".

Two thousand years after Plato, Kepler used the five solids to explain the configuration of the solar system. "The earth's orbit," he wrote, "is the measure of all things; circumscribe around it a dodecahedron, and the circle containing this will be Mars; circumscribe around Mars a tetrahedron, and the circle containing this will be Jupiter; circumscribe around Jupiter a cube and the circle containing this will be Saturn. Now inscribe within the earth an icosahedron, and the circle contained in it will be Venus; inscribe within Venus an octahedron, and the circle contained in it will be Mercury. You now have the reason for the number of planets." It was well for Kepler's peace of mind that he did not live to see his neat scheme disturbed by the subsequent discovery of further planets.

We shall not let these Platonic or Keplerian attributions influence us at all in this book, although we hope that some of Plato's admiration for the beauty and symmetry of the solids will communicate itself to the reader and to his or her pupils. The very beauty of the solids themselves should in fact compel us to treat them with respect and to take the greatest possible care in constructing them, sharpening our powers of accurate drawing and our other manual skills in the process, and enhancing our spatial awareness. Their beauty should also spur us on to try to understand their hidden internal structure, and to investigate how the solids are related one to another.

From this point on, indeed, we shall be strictly technical, looking at the solids from an entirely mathematical point of view. So we note that each solid has faces which are congruent *regular polygons* all of the same type; the faces of the cube are *squares*; the faces of the tetrahedron, of the octahedron and of the icosahedron are *equilateral ("equal-sided") triangles*; while the faces of the dodecahedron are *regular pentagons*. Where the sides of adjacent polygons meet they form the *edges* of the polyhedra, while the edges themselves meet at *vertices* (singular *vertex*) of the polyhedra. We shall study other properties of the solids in detail as we meet them.

Later chapters of the book deal with polyhedra which, while not themselves Platonic, nevertheless are closely related to the Platonic solids, as many of their names suggest. Thus the *cuboctahedron* combines the six faces of the cube with the eight faces of the octahedron, while the *icosidodecahedron* combines the twenty faces of the icosahedron with the twelve faces of the dodecahedron. In these later chapters we also consider transformations of the five solids by

1

truncation and by *stellation*. Stellation generates four more regular polyhedra, the small and the great stellated dodecahedra, discovered by Kepler in the early seventeenth century, and the great dodecahedron and the great icosahedron, discovered by Poinsot two hundred years later, and known collectively as the *Kepler-Poinsot* polyhedra. These, like the five Platonic polyhedra, are technically regular polyhedra, although two have "star" faces and two have "star" vertices (see pages 187–191).

The five Platonic solids are all *convex* polyhedra. A straight line joining any two points on the surface of a convex polyhedron lies either wholly within the polyhedron or on its surface. The Kepler-Poinsot polyhedra are not convex.

This book is addressed primarily to teachers, seeking to offer them a reasonably full account of the mathematical properties of the solids, and suggesting a variety of activities to be undertaken by pupils either in the classroom or at home. Teachers must be prepared to tailor these activities to the ages and abilities of their pupils, but the activities are all feasible, and all have a proper place in the mathematical canon. The average pupil, given a certain amount of guidance, can make many of the less complicated models described here, and should be given every help and encouragement to do so. Other models are perhaps best made by the teacher (or by the mathematical technician, should such a being anywhere exist) for use as demonstration models.

Frequent reference is made in this book to another publication, *Mathematical Models* by H. M. Cundy and A. P. Rollett, which has long been a comprehensive handbook and a source of inspiration for mathematical model-making in schools.   The present book in no way seeks to supplant *Mathematical Models*, but attempts rather to complement it in a modest way, in particular by giving detailed instructions for drawing nets, by indicating where flaps may best be placed on those nets, and by looking closely at dissections of the Platonic solids and others.

[*Note 1*: no account of how to generate computer images of geometrical solids is attempted in this book. This is not to say that the opportunity to view on screen the various configurations of the solids as they rotate is of no value. Such an opportunity should be seized whenever possible, but the techniques involved in this work are outside the scope of the present book.]

[*Note 2*: Chapter 11, "The Rhomboid and its Parts", was the basis of an article of the same name written by the current author and published in January 1998 in *Mathematics in School. Mathematics in School* is a journal produced by The Mathematical Association and the chapter is reproduced here by kind permission of the Editor-in-Chief of the Association.]

Chapter 2

WHY FIVE?

As has been said already, a Platonic solid is a convex polyhedron whose faces are congruent regular polygons all of the same type. As we shall show below, these faces/polygons can take the form only of equilateral triangles, squares or regular pentagons. The same number of faces must meet at each vertex of the polyhedron; and at least three faces must meet at each vertex if the solid is to exist in three dimensions, that is, if it is to enclose or occupy space.

The simplest regular polygon is the equilateral triangle. In fig. 480, page 187, we see eight equilateral triangles meeting at the point D on the stella octangula, but this solid is not convex, and only three or four or five equilateral triangles can be fitted together so that the point at which they all meet is the vertex of a convex solid. To demonstrate this, draw and cut out a regular hexagon with its three diametral diagonals dividing it into six equilateral triangles (fig. 1). (Instructions for drawing all such figures will be found in chapter 4, on page 11 f.) It is clear at once that no convex polyhedron can have as many as six equilateral triangular faces meeting at each vertex.

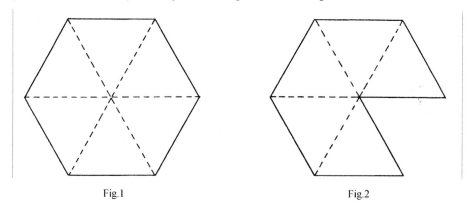

Fig.1   Fig.2

Next fold the hexagon carefully along each of the three diagonals in turn. Flatten the hexagon again, cut away one triangle and discard it (fig. 2), and then close the gap. This brings the five remaining triangles together to form five of the faces and one vertex of a regular icosahedron. Now cut away a second triangle (fig. 3) and close the gap again. This gives four faces and a vertex of a regular octahedron. With a third triangle cut away (fig. 4) the remaining three triangles will fold together to give three faces and a vertex of a regular tetrahedron. If a fourth triangle is cut away, the remaining two triangles cannot be folded to make the vertex of any polyhedron but will simply fold flat one against the other.

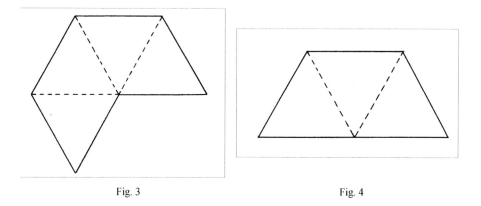

Fig. 3   Fig. 4

[*Note:* two congruent regular tetrahedra (tetrahedra having the same length of edge) can be fitted together so that they form a solid with six equilateral-triangular faces, nine edges and five vertices (fig. 5). However, since at each of two vertices *three* faces meet, while *four* faces meet at each of the other three vertices, this solid is not *regular* and so does not qualify as a *Platonic* solid.]

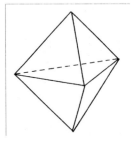

Fig. 5

Next cut a square from paper, fold opposite sides together twice to make a smaller square, and then open it out flat. The two folds divide it into four smaller squares (fig. 6). It is clear at once that no convex solid can have four squares meeting at each vertex. If we cut away one square (fig. 7) and fold the other three to close the gap, we have three faces and one vertex of a cube. If we cut away and discard a second square, we see, as we saw with the two equilateral triangles, that two squares also simply fold flat one against the other and cannot form the vertex of a polyhedron.

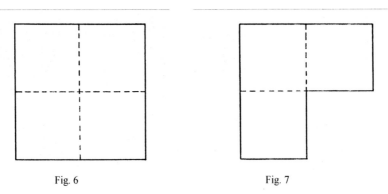

Fig. 6   Fig. 7

Fig. 8 shows three congruent regular pentagons joined along their edges so that they all meet at one point. (The best way to draw this figure for cutting out is either to photocopy it or to use a sharp point to copy its corners on to a sheet of paper placed beneath it, as suggested on page 7.) It should be clear that no more than three pentagons will fit together to meet at a point; and furthermore that two pentagons alone cannot form the vertex of a solid. The three pentagons will fold to give three faces and one vertex of the fifth regular polyhedron, the regular dodecahedron.

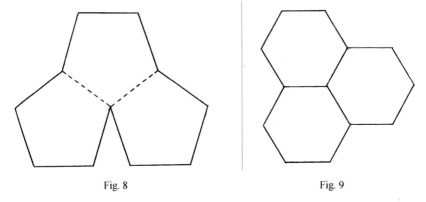

Fig. 8   Fig. 9

Fig. 9 shows three regular hexagons fitting together at a point, all lying necessarily in the same plane. It is clear from this diagram that no polyhedron can have three regular hexagonal faces meeting at a vertex. From this it follows that three regular polygons with seven or more sides cannot meet at a point in the plane nor can they furnish the vertex of a polyhedron.

Schläfli Symbols

So far we have found five possible ways of obtaining the vertices of regular polyhedra from regular polygons. If we wish to confirm that these five ways are the only ways possible, we may proceed as follows. We label each of the five possibilities with a *Schläfli symbol* {p, q} where p denotes how many sides there are to each polygonal face, and q how many such faces meet at a vertex. The regular polyhedra and their Schläfli symbols are:

Tetrahedron	{3, 3}
Cube	{4, 3}
Octahedron,	{3, 4}
Dodecahedron	{5, 3}
Icosahedron	{3, 5}

The Schläfli symbol {4, 3} for the cube, for example, signifies that each of its faces has four sides and that three of these faces meet at each vertex. The symbol for the regular dodecahedron, {5, 3}, signifies that each face has five sides and that three faces meet at each vertex. We know that neither p nor q can be less than 3, since no polygon has fewer than three sides and at least three polygons must meet at a vertex. On the other hand the sum of the angles of the corners of the polygons which meet at a vertex cannot be as much as 360° (or 4 right angles), since this was the total angle at the point where six triangles and four squares met in the plane.

In a regular polyhedron with Schläfli symbol {p, q}, each face has p sides. The interior angle of a regular polygon with p sides is (2p - 4)/p right angles. At each vertex of the polyhedron the number of such angles which meet is q, and their total value must be less than 4 right angles. We can express these conditions by an inequality:

$$q(2p - 4)/p < 4 \;\Rightarrow\; q(2p - 4) < 4p \;\Rightarrow\; q < 4p/(2p - 4) \;\Rightarrow\; q < 2p/(p - 2).$$

The table below shows all the values of p and q which satisfy this inequality and also the inequalities $p \geq 3$ and $q \geq 3$, with the understanding that both p and q must be integers.

p	3	4	5	6
2p/(p − 2)	6	4	$3^{1}/_3$	3
	5	3	3	
q	4			
	3			

From this table we see that the possible values of {p, q} are {3, 5}, {3, 4}, {3, 3}, {4, 3}, and {5, 3}, which are the five pairs of values we have found already.

We can also confirm that these are the only possible values for {p, q} by drawing a graph (fig. 10) on which are marked the three lines p = 3, q = 3 and q = 2p/(p – 2). The points which are ringed show the solutions to the three inequalities p ≥ 3, q ≥ 3, and q < 2p/(p - 2), where both p and q are integers. These solutions lie at the five points – (3, 3), (3, 4), (3, 5), (4. 3) and (5, 3) - whose coordinates are the pairs of numbers in the Schläfli symbols above.

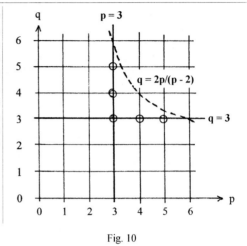

Fig. 10

H. Steinhaus, in *Mathematical Snapshots*, page 252 f., attempts to deduce how many regular polyhedra there are by marking points (representing vertices) on the surface of a sphere, and joining them with lines (representing edges) to enclose regions (representing faces). All vertices have to be of the same *order*, that is, with the same number of lines meeting at each vertex: all regions must have the same number of sides. Fig. 11 shows an example representing a regular tetrahedron, with four vertices of order 3, and six lines enclosing four regions, each with three sides.

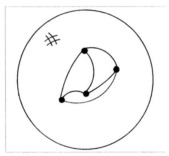

Fig. 11

Steinhaus uses Euler's rule (see page 33), V + F = E + 2, at the centre of his argument. He suggests that if there are V vertices and if v lines meet at each vertex, the total number of lines L will be Vv/2, bearing in mind that each line joins two vertices. Hence 2L = Vv and V = 2L/v. Similarly, if there are F faces or regions, and if f lines form the boundary of each face, then the total number of lines will be Ff/2, since each line is the boundary between two faces; so that 2L = Ff and F = 2L/f. By Euler's theorem therefore, 2L/v + 2L/f = L + 2: dividing through by 2L we have 1/v + 1/f = ½ + 1/L. Steinhaus goes on to show that, since v, f and L must be integers, and since none of these can equal 1 or 2 if the regions on the sphere are to represent the faces of regular polyhedra, then the only solutions {v,f,L} possible are {3,3,6}, {3,4,12}, {4,3,12}, {3,5,30} and {5,3,30}. The v and f values are the same as the p and q values we obtained above; and these five solutions give us the same Schläfli symbols for the five possible regular polyhedra.

[*Note*: the configuration of lines and vertices in fig. 11 is an example of a topological *network*, in which distance and shape are irrelevant. The vertices are *nodes* of the network, while the lines are *arcs*, enclosing *regions*. We use these terms occasionally in later pages when discussing *Schlegel* diagrams of polyhedra, these diagrams being themselves topological networks.]

Chapter 3

MODEL BUILDING

All but a handful of the models described in this book can be made in the classroom from paper or card. Paper should be of reasonably good quality, not easily torn; cartridge paper is very suitable. Card should not be too thick.

A pattern of connected polygons from which a solid is to be made is known as a *net*. Each net must be drawn as accurately as possible, using a sharp and fairly hard pencil (HB will do, H or 2H is better) and a ruler without too many nicks in its edge! The skills needed for accurate drawing have to be carefully taught, and hints on how to draw accurately appear in chapter 4.

Cutting out the Net

Once a net has been drawn on paper or card, with flaps added where needed (see page 8 below), it has to be cut out. Nets for demonstration models should be cut out using a sharp knife and a metal ruler. Nets for models made for the teacher's or the pupil's own purposes can be cut out with scissors.

Once the net has been cut out, its lines must be prepared for folding. These lines will become the edges of the solid, so they must be folded cleanly and with care. On thin paper, the pencil point, if sharp enough, will already have scored, that is, partly cut through, each line, and the net can be folded easily and cleanly along these lines. Using thicker paper or thin card, we need to score firmly along each line of the net, and we do so by using a ruler to guide a scoring tool. Beginners need clear guidance on how to do this.

The scoring tool should not be too sharp. It may be a fine-grade ball-point pen which has run out of ink, or it may be the back of the blade of a pair of scissors, but perhaps the best tool is the point of a pair of compasses inclined almost flat in the direction of travel (fig. 12). It is essential to press down on this point only gently, taking great care not to tear the paper or card, or to cut it to a depth of more than half its thickness.

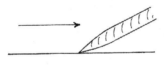

Fig. 12

Copying a Net

We may wish to copy a net from one piece of paper or card to another, or to copy a net from a book. Sometimes photocopying or using tracing paper is the answer, but it is often convenient to use the original drawing as a template.

1. Take an instrument with a sharp point, such as a pair of compasses or dividers. (For copying from thin paper a hard pencil point may be sharp enough.)
2. Place the pattern to be copied over a blank piece of paper or card, and press the sharp point gently through each vertex (i.e., each point at which lines meet) of the net in turn, taking care not to miss any vertices. The vertices of the pattern will appear as a set of small depressions or holes on the copy material.
3. Mark each of these carefully with a sharp pencil, and then join them with straight lines to reproduce the pattern on the upper sheet. This can be done very accurately, since we can place the pencil point in one hole at the start of a line, and shall know that we have reached the far end of the line when we feel the point sink into the mark made at that end.

Flaps

Most of the nets shown in this book have flaps drawn on their edges. These flaps are used to stick together edges of the net to form edges of the solid. The flaps should not be drawn so small that it is difficult to spread glue on them. The lines between the flaps and the net polygons must be scored with the same care used in scoring the other lines of the net, and the flaps must be cut at an angle, to ensure they do not foul any other faces or flaps of the model when it is folded into shape. For most models, a flap angle of 45° will be enough (fig. 13). In nets of the regular tetrahedron and of other solids with equilateral triangles as faces, at least 60° should be cut away from each end of the flap (fig. 14).

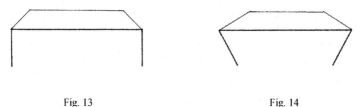

Fig. 13   Fig. 14

In the pages which follow, wherever flaps are shown on a net, the flaps have been positioned in such a way as to make it easy to stick the edges of the net together in the right order as the solid is made up. On the other hand, there are often several possible flap arrangements for a given net, all equally good. In particular, if flaps are drawn on alternate edges of the net, there will be just enough flaps in the right positions for sticking the edges of the model together. This arrangement however will not always ensure that faces are stuck down on to flaps, which should be the aim, since it is not easy to stick flaps *under* faces. For this reason, a firm rule is that the last face to be stuck down should be free of flaps, so that each of its edges sticks down on to a flap. On many nets in this book an *f* marks the first flap to be stuck.

Glue

The quality of glue available for sticking flaps has improved greatly in recent years. Glues of the Copydex type are highly efficient and are particularly easy to use. Surplus glue can readily be rubbed away without marking the surface of the model or of the table or of the user.

Other Materials

It is possible, and sometimes preferable, to make models from materials other than paper or card. Several proprietary kits on the market allow models to be built from clear or coloured plastic sheet; or they allow the bare edges of a solid to be built up, using strips or rods of plastic to make a sort of skeleton, so that we can view the interior and see, for instance, how the internal diagonals of a solid are related to its edges and faces. Skeleton models can be made from lengths of drinking straw held together at their ends by short inserts of pipe-cleaner bent to the appropriate angle, or threaded together with shirring (elastic) thread. Using thread allows us to test the rigidity of the skeleton in space; we find, for example, that the skeleton of the octahedron is rigid whereas that of the cube is not, and that we can in fact flatten the cube skeleton completely. Some models described in this book can be made from cocktail sticks or matchsticks, either glued together at their ends or fixed into small balls of clay or plasticine.

Cundy and Rollett in *Mathematical Models*, page 79 f., have a section headed "Materials and Construction". This contains ideas and suggestions further to those given here, some of which perhaps are of interest more to the technician than to the layman teacher.

Chapter 4

CONSTRUCTIONS

This chapter contains detailed instructions for drawing some of the polygons which make up the nets of polyhedra. Skill in drawing has to be learned by the pupil and therefore has to be taught by the teacher, and the account which follows tries first to identify some of the problems the learner faces and then to suggest ways in which these problems may be overcome.

The need for accuracy in model-making arises from the inescapable fact that an inaccurately-drawn net will not fold into an entire and properly-shaped solid. This means that before we ask pupils to make models of most of the solids described in this book, either in paper or in card, and without the aid of a template or of a tracing, we should make sure that they know how to draw simple geometrical shapes. The tools needed are a reliable pair of compasses which have a sharp point and which will retain their radius as long as we want them to, a hardish pencil with a sharp point (HB will do but H or 2H is better), a ruler marked clearly in centimetres and millimetres, and a protractor in good condition. With these we (and they) should be able, with a little practice, to make accurate enough drawings, accurate, that is, to within, say, half a millimetre and half a degree.

[*Note*: in the following pages the term "compass point" refers to the point of a pair of compasses.]

Drawing a Circle

Drawing a circle is not an easy task for some beginners, who may need help and practice. The pencil has to lean in the direction of motion, the finger and thumb have to grasp the knurled knob found at the top of most compasses, and between them the finger and thumb, ideally without help from the other hand, have to turn the compasses, making sure the pencil point traces a single clear and unbroken line, at the same time putting pressure on the compass point so that it does not slip. If the pencil is a long one, it is better to grasp and turn the top of the pencil rather than the knob of the compasses.

A "Flower" Pattern

1. Put a sharp pencil into a pair of compasses; check that when the compasses are closed the compass point and the pencil point are level; and set the compasses to a given radius, say 3 cm, measured carefully on the ruler. Take a piece of paper at least 12 cm by 12 cm, choose a point at or near its centre, place the point of the compasses on it, and draw a circle. Mark the centre of the circle O.

2. Mark a point A on the circumference of the circle, as near the top of the circle as can be judged by eye.

3. Draw a second circle of the same radius with its centre at A (fig. 15). (It is a useful habit always to leave the compasses set at a given radius until all circles and arcs with that radius have been drawn, or until a different radius needs to be set. All circles drawn in the present construction will have the same radius.) If there is any doubt that the compasses are still set at the required radius, then check, before beginning to draw the second circle, that the (sharp) point of the pencil in the compasses will pass through the small hole at O made by the compass point when the first circle was drawn. The circle with centre A will cut the first circle at two points, B and C.

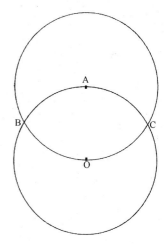

Fig. 15

4. Draw two circles with centres at B and C. These will both pass through A and through O and will also cut the first circle again at two new points, D and E.

5. Draw two circles centred at D and E. These circles should both cut the first circle again at the same point F at the bottom. The degree to which these circles do both pass through F is a useful measure of accuracy.
6. Draw a circle with its centre at F to complete the "flower" pattern (fig. 16).

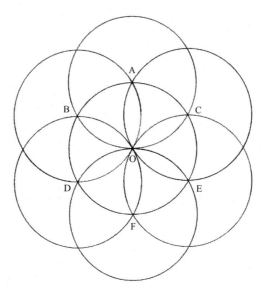

Fig. 16

The "flower" pattern gives a base on which several other useful and/or decorative patterns may be drawn. In fact most of the geometrical constructions we use are based on patterns such as the flower pattern, with the difference that instead of drawing circles for these constructions, we usually draw only parts or *arcs* of circles. The designs in figs. 17 and 18 are two examples of patterns contained in the flower pattern and created by omitting parts of its circles.

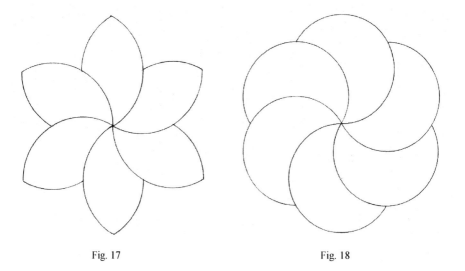

Fig. 17   Fig. 18

A Regular Hexagon

The base pattern for our present purpose, that of drawing a regular hexagon, appears in fig. 19. The circle is the first circle we drew in fig. 16, and the points A to F are the points where the six later circles cut this first circle. Once again, for this construction the compasses are kept at the same radius throughout.

1. Draw a circle centre O. Mark a point A at the top of the circle.
2. Place the compass point on A and draw two arcs to cut the circle at B and C.
3. Place the compass point on B and draw an arc to cut the circle at D.
4. Place the compass point on C and draw an arc to cut the circle at E.
5. Place the compass point on D and draw an arc to cut the circle at F. Place the compass point on E and draw an arc to cut the circle again at F as a check on accuracy.
6. Join adjacent points on the circumference of the circle with straight lines to make a regular hexagon (fig. 20). Each side of the hexagon is equal in length to the radius of the circle, and the circle itself is known as the *circumcircle* of the hexagon.

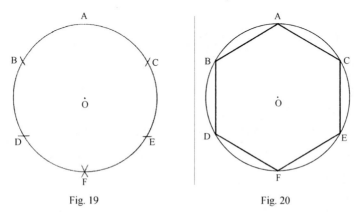

Fig. 19   Fig. 20

[*Note*: beginners are sometimes tempted to join the ends of the arcs rather than the points where they cut the circle. The temptation to do this can be lessened if pupils are encouraged to mark clearly with a pencil the points A to F where the arcs cut the circle before joining them up.]

[*Note*: from now on, the instruction to "join two points" means "join them with a straight line".]

An alternative, and slightly more accurate, method of drawing a regular hexagon is as follows:

1. Draw a circle centre O. Mark a point A at the top of the circle.
2. From A draw a diameter of the circle (passing through O) to meet the circle again at F.
3. Keeping the same radius on the compasses, place the compass point on A and draw two arcs to cut the circle at B and C.
4. Still keeping the same radius, place the compass point on F and draw two arcs to cut the circle at D and E. Erase AF.
5. Join adjacent points on the circumference of the circle to make a regular hexagon (fig. 21).

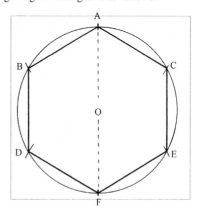

Fig. 21

Equilateral Triangles in a Regular Hexagon

The regular hexagon can be divided into six regular or *equilateral* (equal-sided) triangles by joining opposite corners, that is, points on the circumcircle which lie *diametrically* opposite (fig. 22). The three lines which join these points are diameters of the circumcircle, each passing through the centre. This is one of the patterns we used in chapter 2 (fig. 1) when investigating how many different Platonic solids exist.

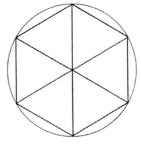

Fig. 22

Two Circles and a Rhombus

1. Draw a straight horizontal line AB, say, 5 cm long.
2. Place the compass point on A and the pencil point on B, so that the compasses are now set at a radius of 5 cm. (If they are not set exactly at 5 cm, it does not matter. The important thing is that the first circle to be drawn should pass through B. If it does not, then move B along the line to meet the circle.)
3. Draw a circle.
4. Move the compass point to B and draw a circle of the same radius passing through A. The two circles cut at C above the line AB and at D below AB.
5. Join A and B to both C and D to make two equilateral triangles. These triangles together form a *rhombus* ACBD, a four-sided figure (*quadrilateral*) with all sides equal, but with its four angles not all equal (fig. 23). (If the angles were all equal, the figure would be a square.)

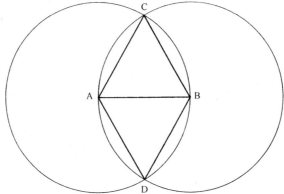

Fig. 23

The Protractor

This is a good point at which to introduce the use of the protractor. Place the centre of the protractor on A in fig. 23 so that the bottom line from 0 to 180 lies along AB, with this line (on a clear plastic protractor) visible across the middle of the 0. If the drawing is accurate, the angle BAC will measure 60°. Now move the protractor sideways to the right so that its centre is at B and check that the angle ABC is also 60°. Note however that this 60° appears on a different scale of the protractor.

Now turn the protractor so that its centre lies on B and its bottom line lies along BD. Check that the angle DBC is 120°, taking the opportunity to clear up any confusion pupils may have about which scale on the protractor is being used. Make it clear that any measurement has to start from 0 on either scale and discuss if need be the difference between *acute* angles (less than 90°) and *obtuse* angles (greater than 90°).

An Equilateral Triangle

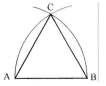

Draw a line AB, as in fig. 23. Draw two arcs, each with radius equal to AB, with one arc centred on A and the other on B, to cut at C above AB. If the two arcs do not meet, make one or both arcs longer so that they do meet. Join C to A and B (fig. 24). ABC will be an equilateral triangle, with all three sides equal in length, and all three angles 60°.

Fig. 24

Perpendicular Lines

We next return to the rhombus in fig. 23 and join CD. We now have a rhombus with its two diagonals (fig. 25). These diagonals have the properties, first, that they are *perpendicular* to each other, that is, they cross or *intersect* at right angles; and secondly that each diagonal *bisects* the other, that is, cuts it into two equal parts. Each diagonal is also a line of mirror (reflective) symmetry of the rhombus.

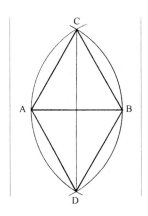

Fig. 25

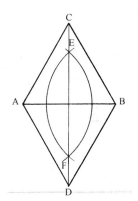

Fig. 26

If we now draw two circles (or, as in fig. 26, two arcs of circles) centred on A and B respectively but with radius a little less than the length of AB, we shall find that these two new circles or arcs meet on the diagonal CD in two points (E and F in fig. 26). In fact, any pair of circles or arcs of circles centred on A and B and both with the same radius, which must be more than half the length of AB, will meet on CD (or on CD *produced*, that is, drawn longer). We use this fact to find the *mediator* or *perpendicular bisector* of a line, that is, a second line which bisects the first line at right angles.

The Mediator of a Line

1. Take or draw the line whose mediator is to be found (AB in fig. 27).
2. Place the compass point on A, set any radius which is clearly longer than half AB, and draw an arc whose ends are to the left of where the mid-point (centre) of AB is judged to be.
3. Draw a similar arc, that is, an arc of the same radius, with centre at B, long enough to cut the first arc in two points. With a little experience it is easy to draw the arcs so that each meets the other in this way without either arc being excessively long.

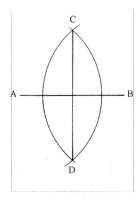

If the arcs meet at C and D, then the line CD is the mediator of AB (and AB is also the mediator of CD).

Fig. 27

A Square

The method described above of constructing a mediator can be adapted for drawing a square.

1. Draw a line AB the length of the side of the required square.
2. Draw the mediator of AB to cut AB at O, making the mediator a little longer than AB.
3. Draw a circle centre O with radius OA. This circle will pass through B, and will also cut the mediator at C and D (fig. 28). Rub out the circle and the two arcs ("construction lines") used to find the mediator.
4. Draw arcs of circles with radius OA and with centres at A, B, C and D to meet in pairs (fig. 29). The points where these arcs meet are the four corners PQRS of a square.

AB and CD divide this square into four quarters, each of which is itself a square. There is no need to draw long arcs: pairs of short cutting arcs will mark the corners of the large square perfectly well.

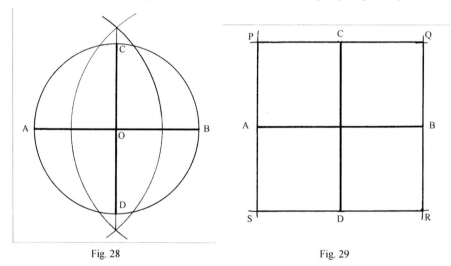

Fig. 28   Fig. 29

Another Square

To draw a square on a given base line, we need to know how to draw a line at right angles to the base line at one end of it, rather than as a mediator at its mid-point. To do this we refer back to the flower pattern (fig. 16, page 10). Fig. 30 opposite shows this pattern redrawn and rotated through 30°, so that two points on the circumference of the first circle are in line horizontally with the centre O. The two lines OA and OB are at right angles to each other.

To draw OB at right-angles to OA we need only that part of the pattern drawn with heavy lines.

1. Draw the base of the square OA (fig. 31).
2. Draw an arc of any radius centred on O, cutting OA at C, passing above O and extending well to the left of O.
3. With compass point on C, draw an arc with radius OC to cut the first arc at D.
4. With compass point on D, draw another arc with radius OC to cut the first arc at E.
5. With centres at D and E respectively draw two arcs of the same radius as each other to cut at B. Join OB. Then OB is at right angles to OA.

To draw a square with base OA use compasses to mark F on OB so that OF = OA. Then draw two arcs with radius OA and centred at A and F to cut at G. OFGA is a square.

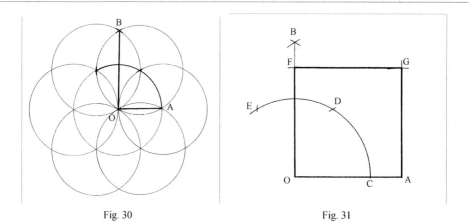

Fig. 30   Fig. 31

A Regular Hexagon and a Square and two Equilateral Triangles

Some solids have nets in which a hexagon is to be drawn with a given line as one side (see, e.g., fig. 71, page 26).

1. Draw a line the length of the side of the required hexagon (AB in fig. 32).
2. With radius AB and with centres at A and B, draw two arcs to cut at C.
3. With radius AB draw a circle with centre at C. This circle will pass through A and B.
4. Extend the arcs AC and BC to cut this circle at D and E.
5. With radius AB, draw two arcs centred on D and E to cut the circle again at K and L. ABDKLE is a regular hexagon (fig. 32).
6. Join AL and BK. These lines will cut the arcs BE and AD at P and Q respectively. APQB is a square.
7. With radius AB, draw arcs centred on P and Q to cut at R below PQ. R should lie on the circumcircle of the hexagon.
8. Produce EA and DB to meet at F. ABF is an equilateral triangle.

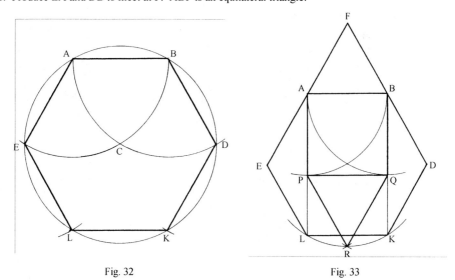

Fig. 32   Fig. 33

A Right-angled Triangle

We may need to draw a triangle ABC with, say, AB = 7 cm, BC = 3 cm, and with a right angle at C.

1. Draw AB 7 cm long and find its mid-point M, either by measuring or by drawing the mediator.
2. With radius AM and centre M, draw a semicircle on AB (fig. 34).
3. Draw an arc of radius 3 cm, centred on B, to cut the semicircle at C. Join AC and BC. The angle ACB is a right angle, being the *angle in a semicircle*.

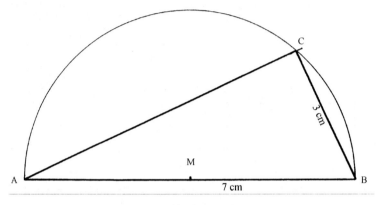

Fig. 34

Other Polygons

Later we shall consider how to draw other polygons such as the regular pentagon and the regular octagon, which we shall need for the nets of some of our models. For the time being we shall be content with the few basic constructions explained here, constructions with which we need to be familiar before we can begin making even the simplest models with any degree of success.

Chapter 5

THE CUBE

We learn at an early age that cubes are solids of a very special shape. If as children we are given a box of cubes to play with, we soon discover that we can use them to build a tower which is reasonably stable, and which will not fall over easily until we push it or try to make it too tall. When we are tired of building towers we find that the cubes will pack neatly and closely together back into their box. Cubes rightly deserve a prominent place in our mathematical studies of shape and space.

A Folding Cube.

The net in fig. 35 can be cut out and folded into a rigid cube. The model is best made from cartridge paper ruled in centimetre squares.

1. Take a piece of squared paper measuring about 17 cm by 11 cm.
2. Draw the net, noting its "Christmas Tree" shape, and cut it out. All the squares have sides 3 cm long.
3. Score all the lines of the net, and fold them cleanly.
4. Fold back the two outside squares (A) at the top of the net until they are at right angles to the square B between them.
5. Fold the other squares and triangles in turn around and outside these three squares. At the finish the bottom square C will fold on top of square B. As the net is folded, the triangles fold in turn over the A squares, with each triangle folding over the one before it and holding it in place.
6. Tuck each triangle E through a slot under the corresponding triangle D (fig. 36). The cube is now rigid and can be handled without collapsing or unfolding. If the folds have been scored and creased correctly, the cube will have sharp edges, and its faces will be flat and will not bulge or be rounded.

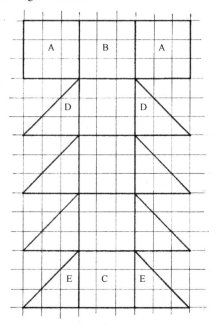

Fig. 35

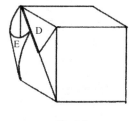

Fig. 36

17

The folding cube can be coloured so that it appears to be built from small cubes of two alternating colours, say, green and yellow (fig. 37). The colouring is most easily done when the cube is unfolded and the net laid flat, but care must be taken. It is best first to make up the cube and then to mark each small square with a dot of the right colour.

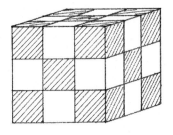

How many small cubes appear to be making up the large cube? How many of these are green (shaded)? How many are yellow (unshaded)? Are there any small cubes hidden inside the large cube? If so, how many are there, and what colour(s) will they be if the alternating colour pattern is continued inside? (For answers and an extension of this investigation, see page 205.)

Fig. 37

Cundy and Rollett, *op. cit.*, page 155, show a net of squares which can be "plaited" to give a rigid cube, together with a number of other nets which can be plaited to give other polyhedra.]

Collapsible Cubes

A. The folding cube we have just described can be unfolded and stored flat, but it cannot be said to be *collapsible*. A cube which can be made to collapse and which can be stored flat in an exercise book or folder is made as follows.

1. Draw the net of squares shown in fig. 38. All the squares have sides 3 cm long. Cut out the net with its flaps and score and fold all its lines.
2. Draw a 3 cm square on a page of the exercise book (fig. 39).
3. Stick the two flaps marked A in the net on to the spaces marked A in the book.

The cube will be rigid when the side squares are tucked in (fig. 40), but can be made to collapse when these squares are untucked.

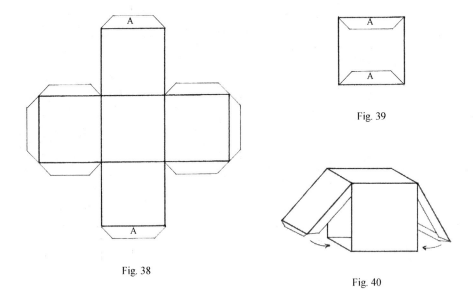

Fig. 38

Fig. 39

Fig. 40

B. Fig. 41 shows a cube with parallel diagonal cuts made on two opposite faces. If the triangular parts of each cut face are folded along the other diagonal, then the cube can be made to collapse. The net for making this collapsible cube contains four squares and four 45° isosceles triangles (fig. 42).

1. Cut out the net, score and fold it along all its lines, including the broken ones.
2. Stick flap *f* first, and then stick the triangles on to the other flaps. This can best be done when the cube is folded flat, when it will appear as in fig. 43.

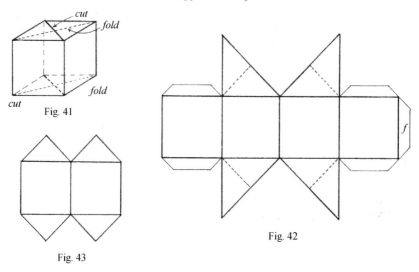

Fig. 41

Fig. 42

Fig. 43

C. A collapsible cube which "pops up" can be made from a modification of the net shown in fig. 42.

1. Redraw fig. 42 with the two flaps at the bottom moved inwards to replace the two triangles (fig. 44).
2. Fold a piece of card in two and mark where the bottom two flaps will stick (fig. 45). Each flap will stick at 45° to the line of the fold.
3. Make up the net as before, and stick the bottom flaps in position on the piece of card. The cube will fold flat when the card is folded and will "pop up" when the card is opened.

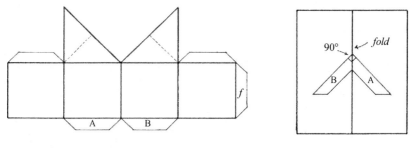

Fig. 44   Fig 45

Instructions for making "pop-up" cubes, with elastic bands fixed inside, are to be found in *Up-pops* by Mark Hiner (Tarquin Publications). This book also includes instructions for making "pop-up" tetrahedra and octahedra.

Nets of Cubes

A rigid cube is made from a net of six squares. Flaps are added where needed, and the net is cut out, folded up and the flaps stuck. Six squares connected along their sides form a *hexomino*, a name derived from "domino", but reflecting the fact that a hexomino is made from six squares instead of from just two.

The hexomino shown in fig. 46 is one possible net of a cube. It will need seven flaps. The seven lines show which pair of sides will be joined by each flap. The letters show which squares will appear as opposite faces when the cube is made up.

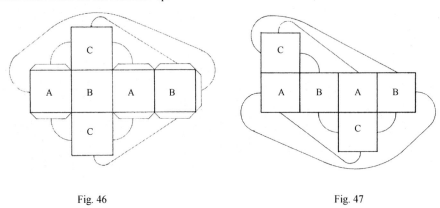

Fig. 46   Fig. 47

Fig. 47 shows another hexomino which is a possible net of a cube. Again, the letters show opposite faces, and the seven lines show which pairs of sides must be joined by flaps. Note that the first of these seven lines must join two sides which meet at right angles, as in fig. 48; we then work outwards from these sides. For example, a line will join side P in fig. 49 either to side Q or to side R; which will it be? We may have to experiment to find the right pattern of lines, bearing in mind that no line may cross another line.

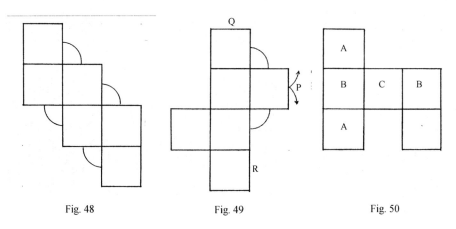

Fig. 48   Fig. 49   Fig. 50

Fig. 50 shows a hexomino which is *not* a possible net of a cube. If we try to fold this hexomino into a cube, we find that the faces marked A and B will be opposite, but that C will have no face opposite, while the sixth square will occupy the same position as the lower square marked A.

Problem 1. (Solution on page 39.)

Six squares will fit together to form hexominoes in 36 distinct ways, but of these 36 hexominoes only eleven are nets of cubes. Find these eleven nets and draw them. Label the squares of each net with letters to show which squares will be opposite faces of the cube, and draw lines joining pairs of sides which will be stuck together with flaps. (Note: each of the hexominoes in fig. 51 is the net of a cube, but the two hexominoes are not different or *distinct*. Each is a *reflection* of the other and if we cut one out and turn it over, the two will be seen to be identical. We cannot make a hexomino "different" just by turning it over or sideways or upside-down.)

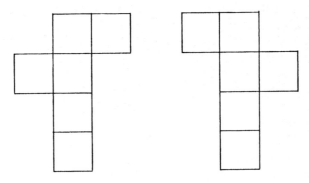

Fig. 51

Planes of Symmetry

The net shown in fig. 52 is that of a half-cube, a *cuboid* or *square prism*. When two of these half-cubes are placed together with two square faces meeting, they make a cube (fig. 53), and the two faces which meet lie on a *plane of symmetry* of the cube. Each half-cube is a mirror-image of the other, with the plane of symmetry acting as the mirror (fig. 54).

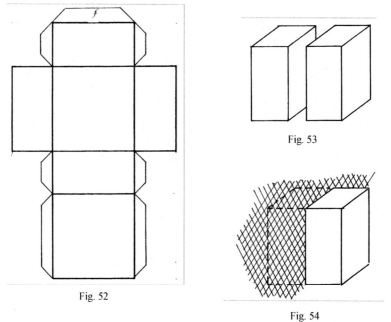

Fig. 52

Fig. 53

Fig. 54

[*Note*: the net shown in fig. 52 is not the only net possible for a half-cube: there are eleven of these, each adapted from one of the eleven possible nets of a cube. It is a good exercise in spatial thinking for pupils to be invited to design their own nets for a half-cube, either by examining a model or by adapting the net of a whole cube, when they will have to decide which lines stay the same length and which must be halved. The pupils can then cut out their nets from paper and see if these assemble properly into half-cubes.]

We can see perhaps more clearly how a plane of symmetry acts as a mirror if we make a "triangular" half-cube from the net shown in fig. 55. The length of BE is the length of the diagonal of a face of the complete cube.

1. Draw a square ABCD, the size of one face of the cube.
2. Extend the line AB some distance to the right, place the compass point on B and the pencil on D, and draw an arc to meet AB produced at E.
3. Draw the central rectangle and the right-hand square, drawing arcs to find the positions of the missing corners (see page 14, fig. 29).
4. Draw the upper triangle by using compasses again, so that BF = BA and EF = EG. Check that F lies on DB produced. Draw the lower triangle in a similar way.
5. Draw flaps where shown. Stick flap *f* first.

Two of these *right-angled isosceles triangular prisms* will fit together to form a cube, the rectangular faces meeting and lying on the new plane of symmetry (fig. 56).

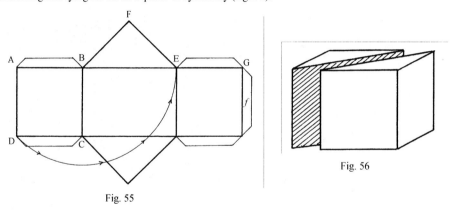

Fig. 55

Fig. 56

More Problems (Solutions on page 37.)

Problem 2. How many planes of symmetry does a cube have?

Problem 3. While we are on the subject of symmetry, we can work out the *symmetry number* of the cube. We imagine that we have a cube sent us as a present, fitting neatly into a cubical box (fig. 57). The *symmetry number* of the cube is the number of different ways in which the cube can be fitted back into its box. This is either 6 or 12 or 24 or 48. Which of these is it?

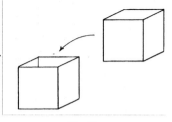

Fig. 57

Problem 4.

Every plane of symmetry divides the cube into two *congruent* parts, each identical in shape and size to the other. By cutting a cube vertically downwards through the two diagonals on a horizontal face, we can divide the cube into four congruent parts (fig. 58). Can we divide a cube into three congruent parts? Or into five congruent parts? If so, how?

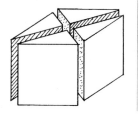

Fig. 58

Trisecting a Cube.

One way of dividing a cube into three congruent parts or pieces is not obvious, but is easily demonstrated in a model. Each of the three pieces will be a pyramid on a square base, but these pyramids will be unlike pyramids as commonly envisaged, that is, as *right pyramids* with the apex (top) directly above the centre of the base. Instead the apex of each of these three pyramids will be vertically above one corner of the square base. Two faces of the pyramid will be right-angled *isosceles* triangles, with two sides equal; and two faces will be plain or *scalene* right-angled triangles (fig. 59) with no two sides equal.

The net for one of these pyramids is shown in fig. 60.

1. Draw a square ABCD. (This is the square base.)
2. Produce BA and DA in the direction of the points E and F, and of G and H.
3. Both AE and AF must be equal in length to AB. With centre A and radius AB, draw arcs to fix the positions of E and F.
4. Join DE and BF. Both BG and DH must be equal in length to BF. With centres B and D and radius BF, draw arcs to fix the positions of G and H. Join C to both G and H.

Flap *f* is stuck first, and the triangle DCH is stuck down last of all.

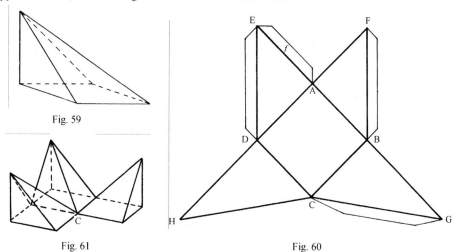

Fig. 59

Fig. 61   Fig. 60

Three of these pyramids may be taped together or stuck down on to an L-shaped base of three squares (fig. 61) with the points C on the base of each pyramid all meeting. The three pyramids will fold together to make a cube. The volume of the cube is the area of the base multiplied by the vertical height, and the volume of each pyramid is one-third of this. The model illustrates the general rule that the volume of any pyramid is one-third the area of the base multiplied by the vertical height.

A collapsible or fold-flat model of one of these pyramids can be made from the net in fig. 62.

1. Draw AB the length of one side of the square base. Produce AB to C so that BC = AB.
2. Draw the mediator of AC. On it mark D and E so that BD = BE = AB. (See fig. 28, page 14.)
3. Join AD, AE, and CE. Produce DA to F so that AF = AB.
4. Draw CG so that D, C and G all lie on the same straight line and CG = AB.
5. Produce CA to H so that AH = AD. Check that FH = AB and EF = EG.
6. Draw flaps as shown and cut out the net. Fold the isosceles triangles ABD and AFH in half along BJ and FK. These two triangles together make the square base of the pyramid.

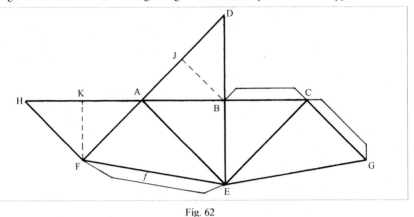

Fig. 62

Six Pyramids make a Cube.

Any regular polyhedron or solid can be dissected into congruent *right* pyramids, each of which has a face of the solid as its base and has its apex at the centre of the solid. The slant edge of the pyramid will be half the length of the internal diagonal from one vertex of the polyhedron to the opposite vertex, and the problem is to determine this length.

It is not difficult to solve this problem for the cube. If the edge of the cube is 1 unit long, then by Pythagoras the diagonal of a face is $\sqrt{2}$ units long, and again by Pythagoras, the interior diagonal of the cube is $\sqrt{3}$ units long (fig. 63). The length of the slant edge of the pyramid (fig. 64) will therefore be $\frac{1}{2}\sqrt{3}$ units.

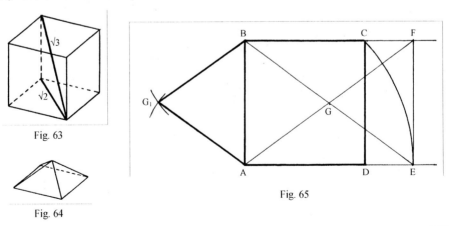

Fig. 63

Fig. 64

Fig. 65

In fig. 65 ABCD is a (square) face of the cube, with each side 1 unit long. AC is the length of its diagonal = $\sqrt{2}$ units.
1. Use compasses to copy AC onto AD produced to find the position of E. AE = AC.
2. Complete the rectangle ABFE. Draw the diagonals AF and BE to cross at G.
3. AF and BE are each $\sqrt{3}$ units long and are the length of an internal diagonal of the cube. AG is half this length, and is therefore the length of the slant edge of the pyramid in fig. 64.
4. Use compasses to draw the reflection G_1 of G in AB, with $AG_1 = BG_1 = AG$.

The isosceles triangle ABG_1 is a face of the pyramid, so the net of the pyramid will be the square ABCD with a triangle congruent to ABG_1 attached to each side (fig. 66).

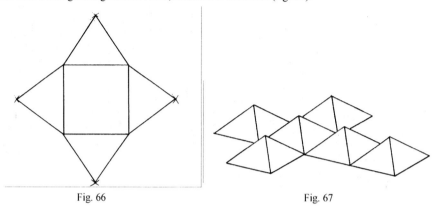

Fig. 66   Fig. 67

Six of these pyramids with their bases joined together in the configuration shown in fig. 67 (or in any other of the eleven configurations of the net of a cube), and then folded inwards so that their apexes meet, will make a cube.

[*Note*: if the model in fig. 67 is folded so that the apex of each pyramid faces *outwards* rather than inwards, with the six square faces meeting around an internal cube, the twenty-four triangular faces will combine in pairs to form the twelve faces of a *rhombic dodecahedron*. This solid has the important property that, like the cube, it will "tessellate" in space, that is, it will fit together with other rhombic dodecahedra of the same size to fill space, with no gaps in between (see page 139 f.).]

A Further Dissection of the Cube.

Another cut can be made which will divide a cube into two congruent parts, although this cut does not lie along any plane of symmetry of the cube. If the cube is held between finger and thumb by two opposite vertices, one vertically above the other, the cut in question will lie along the horizontal plane passing midway between the two vertices (fig. 68). The cut passes through the mid-points of six of the twelve edges of the cube (fig. 69), and the two faces exposed by the cut are regular hexagons.

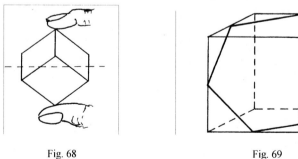

Fig. 68   Fig. 69

The net of each of the two (identical) pieces is not too difficult to draw. First however we have to decide what length is to determine the size of the model. This could be either the length of the edge of the cube or the length of the side of the hexagon. If the latter, then there is no problem, since the framework on which we draw the net uses the side of the hexagon as its basic unit of length. If on the other hand the edge of the cube has to be of a certain length, then the basic unit of length on the net will be the length of the edge of the cube divided by √2 (or multiplied by √2/2). For example, if the cube is to have an edge 5 cm long, the net will have to be based on a unit length of 5/√2 ≈ 3.54 cm.

1. Draw a square with sides three times the basic unit of length.
2. Divide each side of the square into three equal parts and draw a three-by-three grid of squares (fig. 70). Draw diagonal lines as shown.
3. Set the basic unit of length on a pair of compasses, and with the compass point first on A and then on B, draw arcs to cut at O, which is the centre of the circumscribing circle of the hexagon. Draw the hexagon within this circle, with AB as one side (see page 15, fig. 32).
4. On the grid, draw more firmly the lines which will form the net shown in fig. 71, including the hexagon drawn within the circle. Erase any lines which are not needed, and draw flaps where shown. Point C will be a vertex of the cube.
5. Score the lines, and cut out and fold the net and its flaps in the usual way. Stick flap *f* first, and finally stick the hexagon down on to five flaps (fig. 72).

Two of these models together make the complete cube.

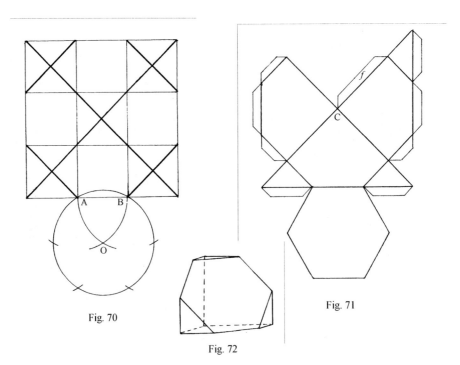

Fig. 70

Fig. 71

Fig. 72

[***Note***: in chapter 11 we look at the geometry of the cube when it is deformed into a *rhombic hexahedron* or *rhomboid*, with each face changed from a square into a rhombus with angles of 60° and 120°. A hexagonal cut, similar to that made here on the cube but made instead midway between two opposites vertices of the rhomboid, will give two solids, each of which can be dissected into a *regular tetrahedron* and a *truncated tetrahedron*.]

We can make the hexagonal cut on the cube in four different ways, which is to say that we can draw four separate hexagons on the surface of the cube by joining the mid-points of adjacent edges. Fig. 73 shows the pattern made on the cube by these four hexagons. Four lines in the form of a square appear on each face of the cube. Each of these four lines belongs to a different hexagon, and the four hexagons together mark the edges of a *cuboctahedron* contained within the cube. We have more to say about the cuboctahedron in chapters 14 and 15.

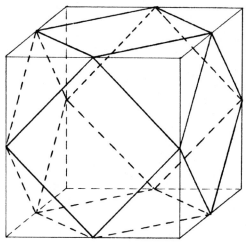

Fig. 73

In chapter 14 we shall also meet the *truncated octahedron*. We can make this solid not only by truncating, that is, by cutting the corners from, a regular octahedron, but also by fitting together the eight pieces obtained if we dissect four congruent cubes in the manner we have described above (fig. 74). The truncated octahedron shares with the cube and the rhombic dodecahedron the rare property of being able to "tessellate" on its own to fill space. The fact that it can be built from dissections of cubes, which have this same property, may help us to understand why and how it tessellates. It will certainly help us to calculate the volume of a truncated octahedron. Taking the length of one edge of the truncated octahedron to be b units, we can readily work out the volume as $4 \times (\sqrt{2}b)^3 = 8\sqrt{2}b^3$ cubic units. (The edge of the dissected cube is $\sqrt{2}$ times the length of the side of the hexagon.)

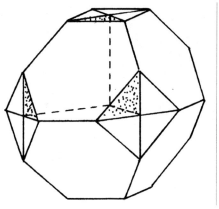

Fig. 74

Cubes from Straws and Shirring Thread.

We can make the *skeleton* of a cube from short lengths of straw, which may be cut either from drinking straws or from straws specially marketed for model-making, joined with "shirring" elastic threaded through them. Twelve equal lengths of straw are needed for one cube. First thread four lengths together as a square and tie them off; then thread the other eight in turn to form the cube and tie them off also (fig. 75).

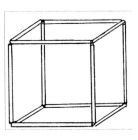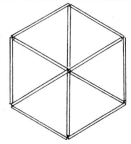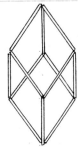

| Fig. 75 | Fig. 76 | Fig. 77 |

Unlike the skeletons of "deltahedra" such as the tetrahedron and the octahedron, whose faces are all triangles, the skeleton of the cube is not rigid, and by allowing it to take up different positions we may learn more about the cube itself. In particular the skeleton will collapse flat into the shape of a regular hexagon with three diagonals (fig. 76); and if we pull two opposite vertices of the cube apart a little, the square faces will deform to become rhombuses (fig. 77), and the skeleton will then be that of a "rhombic hexahedron". When the angles of each rhombus are 60° and 120° (are all the rhombic faces necessarily congruent?), then this hexahedron will be the "rhomboid" whose properties we examine in some detail in chapter 11.

Drawing Cubes

When we come to draw a cube or any other solid figure, we encounter the difficulty of representing a three-dimensional object by a two-dimensional drawing. At best we may draw a view of the solid when looked at from a particular direction.

Seen from directly in front or from the side or from on top, the cube appears simply as a square. These views are respectively the front and side *elevations* and the *plan* view. To make the cube look more like a cube we have to draw more than one face. To do this we look at the cube *obliquely*, from a different direction, usually from slightly above and to one side of the front face, and we can then draw an *oblique* view.

We may do this on squared or on plain paper.

1. On squared paper draw a square of side, say, six small squares.
2. Draw a line from each of the top corners of the square and from the right-hand bottom corner, to a point, say, three small squares along to the right of each corner and one square up. These lines will all be parallel and of the same length.
3. Join the ends of the three lines to obtain an oblique view of the cube (fig. 78).

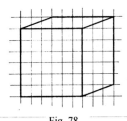

Fig. 78

(The fact that the three sloping lines are parallel makes this a *parallel* view rather than a *perspective* drawing, in which the three lines would tend to converge towards a *vanishing point* on the horizon.)

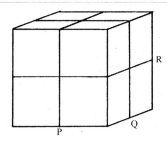

Fig. 79

We can mark the mid-points of all the lines in the drawing and join them in such a way that the cube now appears to be made up of eight smaller cubes (fig. 79). By dividing the lines into any chosen number of equal parts, we can draw the cube so that it appears to be made up of different numbers of smaller cubes, as, for example, in fig. 37, page 18. (See also pages 205 f.)

If we draw a fourth line in fig. 78 the same length as the three sloping lines and parallel to them, starting from the bottom left-hand corner and passing as it were behind the front face, we may then draw further lines to indicate where the hidden edges of the cube lie. In fig. 80 these hidden edges are shown as broken lines. (In general, any broken line in a diagram in this book represents a hidden line, unless otherwise stated.)

If we firm in these broken lines (fig. 81), it is no longer clear which of the two squares represents the front face of the cube and which represents the back face. This drawing is a well-known optical illusion, in which we cannot be sure whether we are looking at the (skeleton) cube from a point slightly above the front face or from a point slightly below it.

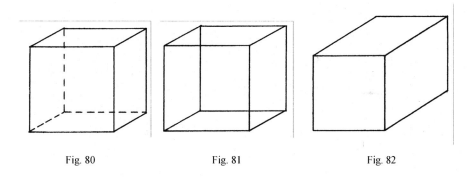

Fig. 80   Fig. 81   Fig. 82

We may vary the length and direction of the sloping lines. In particular if we make these lines the same length as the sides of the square face in fig. 78, the drawing will be an *oblique projection* of a cube (fig. 82). By looking at an actual cube from different angles we should be able to decide whether or not this oblique projection gives a realistic view of the solid.

[*Note*: in this book, when we say we "look directly at" a face, edge or vertex, we mean that we look along the axis of rotational symmetry of the solid which passes through the centre of that face or through the mid-point of that edge or through that vertex. The view we see will have reflective symmetry usually in a vertical line passing through the point at which we are looking.]

We can also work on plain paper as long as we ensure that the sloping lines are parallel and are of equal length.

1. Draw the square ABCD.
2. Draw BE the chosen length and at the chosen angle to AB.
3. Use a set-square sliding along a ruler (fig. 83) to draw lines parallel to BE from C and from D, making each of these lines a little longer than BE (fig. 84).
4. Again using a set square and ruler, draw a line through E parallel to BC to meet the line from C at F (fig. 85).
5. Draw a line through F parallel to DC to meet the line from D at G (fig. 86). Erase the unwanted parts of lines beyond F and G.

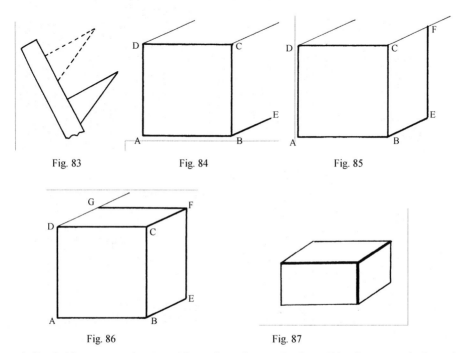

Fig. 83   Fig. 84   Fig. 85

Fig. 86   Fig. 87

In a similar fashion we may draw an oblique view of any *cuboid*, a solid at least two of whose six faces are rectangles rather than squares. In fig. 87 the three bold lines define the cuboid; all other lines in the drawing will be parallel and equal in length to one or other of these three lines.

To show a large cube divided into eight smaller cubes, as in fig. 79, page 29, use the set square and ruler to draw extra lines parallel to the edges of the large cube. There is no need to mark the mid-points of more than three edges (P, Q and R in fig. 79). Lines drawn through these three mid-points parallel to the appropriate edges will meet three other edges at their mid-points, and from these mid-points the remaining lines can be drawn. This method may of course be used to draw a view of a cube divided into any number of smaller cubes. For each view only three edges of the large cube need be divided into the appropriate number of equal parts.

An Isometric Projection

We may draw an *isometric projection* of a cube on *isometric* paper, which is a grid of equilateral triangles.

1. Draw a vertical edge of the cube; then draw the four other edges which meet this edge (fig. 88). All edges must be the same length, and the angles between the vertical and sloping edges will be either 60° or 120°.
2. Complete the projection as in fig. 89.

In this projection the three visible faces of the cube appear as rhombuses, and the boundary of the projection is a regular hexagon. This is more or less the view we see of the cube when we look at it along an axis of rotational symmetry passing through a vertex (see fig. 95, page 32, and page 33). If we now mark the position of the hidden edges with broken lines (fig. 90), we see a regular hexagon divided into six equilateral triangles which is the pattern we saw earlier when we flattened the skeleton cube made from drinking straws (fig. 76, page 28).

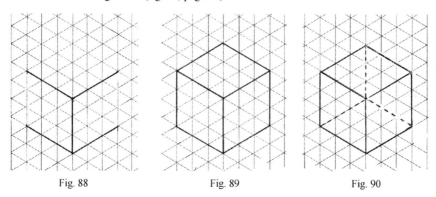

Fig. 88   Fig. 89   Fig. 90

Fig. 91 shows six of these "isometric" cubes in a stack, together with side and base panels drawn to fill in the gaps. But are there only six cubes in the picture? If we turn the page upside down we can see seven.

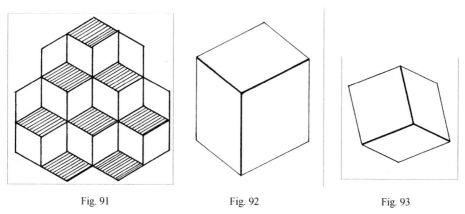

Fig. 91   Fig. 92   Fig. 93

We are of course free to vary the methods we use for drawing cubes to suit our own particular purposes. Figs. 92 and 93 show two different oblique views of a cube, each of the completed views being determined by the length and direction of the three edges drawn with bold lines.

Other Views of a Cube

We noted on page 28 that the plan of a unit cube (one whose edges are all one unit long) and its front and side elevations are all squares whose sides are one unit long. If we look directly at the edge of a unit cube (see note on page 29), we see a rectangle divided in half by this edge (fig. 94). The rectangle is one unit high but its base is the length of the diagonal of the bottom face (and top face) of the cube, that is, $\sqrt{2}$ units.

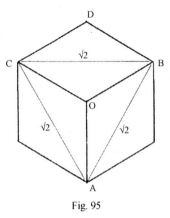

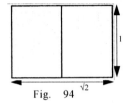

Fig.   94

Fig. 95

If we look at the vertex of a unit cube directly along the axis of rotational symmetry which passes through that vertex (see page 33), we see a regular hexagon (fig. 95), divided into three rhombuses. (The hexagon is a *Petrie* hexagon of the cube, see page 76.) This view is identical to the isometric view in fig. 89 on page 31. However all the edges of the cube are in fact sloping away from us, and the only lengths which are true lengths in the drawing are AB, BC and CA. These are all diagonals of faces of the cube and each is $\sqrt{2}$ units long. ABC is an equilateral triangle, with its centre at O, and OA bisects the angle BAC which is 60°. The drawn length of AO is therefore not 1 unit but $\sqrt{2}/2 \div \cos 30° = \sqrt{2}/2 \div \sqrt{3}/2 = \sqrt{(2/3)} \approx 0.8165$ units. This is also the length of CD, which is both a side of the boundary hexagon and an edge of the cube. The points A and D, which are opposite vertices of the cube, are end-points of an interior diagonal of the cube. In reality this diagonal is $\sqrt{3} \approx 1.732$ units long, but it is also sloping away from us and AD is in fact just twice the length of AO, or only 1.633 units long.

The Trigonometry of the Cube

This is a suitable point at which to consider the internal trigonometry of the cube. We have calculated already by Pythagoras (page 24) that the length of the internal diagonal of the unit cube, the diagonal which joins opposite vertices, is $\sqrt{3}$ units long, and from this we can work out that the angle it makes with the base (fig. 96) is $\sin^{-1} 1/\sqrt{3} = 35.26°$. The face diagonals are $\sqrt{2}$ units long and make an angle of 45° with the sides of the faces; and the *dihedral* angle between adjacent faces is 90°.

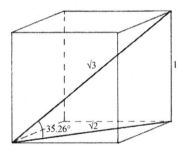

Fig. 96

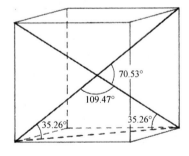

Fig. 97

Fig. 97 shows two internal diagonals joining the ends of two opposite edges of a cube. The diagonals bisect each other at the centre point of the cube, crossing at an angle of 2 x 35.26° ≈ 70.53°, or alternatively at an angle of (180 – 70.53)° = 109.47°. (This latter angle is the *Maraldi* angle, important in natural structure.)

By using the cosine rule, we can calculate that $70.53° = \cos^{-1} \frac{1}{3}$, while $109.47° = \cos^{-1} (-\frac{1}{3})$. (Also $\sin 70.53° = 2\sqrt{2}/3$ and $\tan 70.53° = 2\sqrt{2}$.) The angle $70.53°$ is the face angle at the apex of each of the six pyramids which make up the cube, that is, the angle BG_1A in fig. 65, page 24.

More Questions and their Answers

We have looked at different ways of making cubes, of dissecting them and of drawing them. We now look at some problems concerning complete cubes.

1. How many faces, edges and vertices does a cube have? How are these numbers connected?

A cube has six faces, twelve edges and eight vertices. These numbers are connected by the rule, formulated by Leonard Euler (1717-1794), and mentioned in chapter 2, which states that for any polyhedron the sum of the number of faces (F) and the number of vertices (V) is always two more than the number of edges (E), that is, $F + V = E + 2$ or $F + V - E = 2$. This is certainly true for the cube, since $6 + 8 - 12 = 2$; we shall see later that it is true also for the four other Platonic solids.

2. Fig. 98 shows one *axis of rotational symmetry* of a cube. It is of *order four*, that is to say, if we rotate the cube about this axis, we can make it occupy the same space in four different ways. How many axes of rotational symmetry does a cube have altogether?

A cube has three axes of symmetry passing through the centres of pairs of opposite faces (fig. 99), four axes of symmetry passing through pairs of opposite vertices (fig. 100), and six axes of symmetry passing through the midpoints of pairs of opposite edges (fig. 101), a total of thirteen in all. (It may be worth noting here that thirteen is half twenty-six, which is the sum of the numbers of faces, edges and vertices of the cube. Is this a coincidence or does it happen with other solids?)

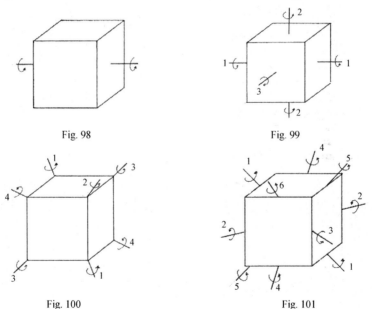

Fig. 98   Fig. 99

Fig. 100   Fig. 101

Note that the order of rotational symmetry about each axis varies. The symmetry about axes through the faces is of order 4, that about axes through the edges is of order 2, while that about axes through the vertices is of order 3. If we hold a rigid cube with finger and thumb at opposite vertices and rotate it slowly, we see how the three edges leading from each of the vertices we are holding indicate the rotational symmetry of order 3 we have mentioned (see fig. 95, page 32). We have to rotate the cube through $360° \div 3 = 120°$ to exchange one edge for the next.

If we hold the cube gently with finger and thumb at opposite vertices and then blow on one side of it, we can make it rotate. When it rotates fast enough, it gives a new "solid of revolution", with a cone at the top and bottom and with a concave curved surface in the shape of a *hyperboloid* between them (fig. 102). Steinhaus illustrates this solid of revolution on pages 171-2 and in fig. 202 of *Mathematical Snapshots.*

blow

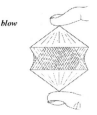

Fig. 102

3. A spider at one vertex S of a cube walks along the edges of the cube to catch a fly at the opposite vertex F (fig. 103). What is the least number of edges the spider must walk along in order to get to the fly? How many such "shortest routes" are there from one vertex to the opposite vertex? How many such shortest routes are there from any vertex of the cube to the opposite vertex?

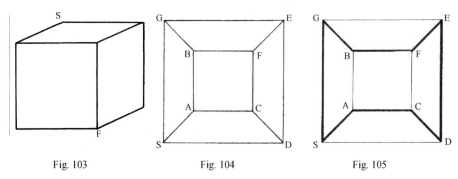

Fig. 103   Fig. 104   Fig. 105

To help solve this problem we use a *Schlegel* diagram of the cube (fig. 104). This is a view of the inside of the cube seen through a window replacing the front face of the cube. At the far end we see the square opposite (back) face, and around this we see four trapezia representing the four (side) faces joining the front and the back faces. Any problem involving the relationship of the edges and faces of the cube, though not their measured lengths or areas, can generally be transferred on to and solved on the Schlegel diagram.

Let us imagine the spider starts at S on the Schlegel diagram. The fly is at the opposite vertex, F. The spider has an initial choice of three edges to walk along: let us suppose he chooses to walk first to A. At A he is faced with a choice of two edges: let us suppose he chooses to walk to B. From B he must walk directly to F if he is to follow the shortest route. His route has taken him along three edges. He could have chosen five other routes, SACF, SDCF, SDEF, SGBF, SGEF, all of them exactly the same length, three edges long.

The following argument can be used to confirm that there are six possible shortest routes, not only from S to F but from any vertex of the cube to the opposite vertex. At the start the spider has three choices of edge. At the next vertex he has two choices, while at the third vertex he has only one choice, the edge which leads directly to the fly. The number of different routes he can choose is therefore 3 x 2 x 1 = 6.

4. What is the length of the shortest route along the edges which starts at one vertex, passes through all the other vertices once only, and then returns to the start?

Again we solve this problem on the Schlegel diagram, following the progress of our spider. Since he has seven vertices to visit in turn, and must then return to the eighth, he must pass along at least eight edges. Fig. 105 shows that there is at least one way in which he can do this, say, SACDEFBGS, so eight edges is the length of his shortest route.

5. What is the length of the shortest route which starts at one vertex, passes along each edge at least once, and then returns to the start?

This problem needs some thought. Since on the Schlegel diagram lines or *arcs* correspond to edges on the cube, and *nodes* correspond to vertices on the cube, it is possible to work with the arcs and nodes of the Schlegel diagram, and then apply any conclusions to the edges and vertices of the cube.

A rule concerning networks such as the Schlegel diagram states that if a network contains only even nodes (transferred to polyhedra, "even nodes" refers to vertices at which an *even* number of edges meet), then it is possible to trace a route around the network which starts at any node, passes along each arc once only, and returns to the start. If the network has just two odd nodes (vertices at which an *odd* number of edges meet) then any route which passes along all the arcs must start at one of these odd nodes, and finish at the other. (Two is the minimum number of odd nodes which can exist in any network; no network can have only one odd node.) The Schlegel diagram for the cube has eight odd nodes, with three arcs meeting at each node. How is the shortest route to be found and how long is it?

Since the required route has to return to the starting point, we need to add extra arcs to the diagram so that all nodes become even nodes. Since there are eight nodes and each arc joins two nodes, just four extra arcs are needed. In fig. 106 we have chosen to add the extra arcs to duplicate the four arcs joining the two squares. This has the effect of making each of the edges represented by these arcs a "two-way" edge, along which we must pass twice, once in each direction. The numbers in the diagram in fig 106 show one possible order in which we may pass along the arcs: the total journey is sixteen arcs (edges) long. This solution is only one among many possible solutions: we may add four extra arcs in many different ways, and we may traverse the resulting network in many different ways, but all our journeys on the cube will be just sixteen edges long.

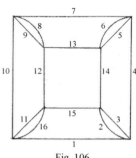

Fig. 106

6. How much distance does the spider save if he is allowed to walk across the faces of the cube to get to the opposite vertex? How can he find the shortest route across the faces?

We can no longer use the Schlegel diagram since now we are dealing with measured lengths on the cube. We shall assume for simplicity that the edges of the cube are all one unit long, so that the spider's journey along three edges will be three units long.   However, when the spider arrives at A from S in fig. 107 he can save his legs by cutting diagonally across the last face and going directly to F rather than going through B or C. By Pythagoras the distance AF is $\sqrt{2}$ units, so the distance saved is $2 - \sqrt{2}$ units, or about 0.59 units, which is nearly 20% of the journey by way of the edges.

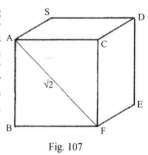

Fig. 107

But the spider could do even better than this. First we have to agree that the length of a journey from a point on one face of a solid across an edge to a point on an adjacent face is not affected by the angle which one face makes with the other, the *dihedral* angle. The length of the journey remains the same if the two faces are set flat, edge to edge, on the same plane. This means we may now in fact work on a net of the cube. In fig. 108, which shows two squares of such a net, S, A, B, C and F are vertices of the cube, with S and F being opposite vertices. Clearly the shortest route from S to F lies along the straight line joining them. This line crosses the

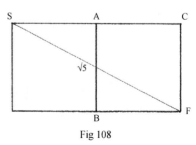

Fig 108

35

edge AB at its mid-point, and by Pythagoras is $\sqrt{(2^2 + 1^2)} = \sqrt{5}$ units long. Fig. 109 shows two such routes on the reconstructed cube. The saving in distance is now $3 - \sqrt{5} \approx 0.76$ units or over 25% of the journey by way of the edges.

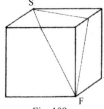

Fig. 109

There are six different shortest routes by which the spider at S may reach the fly which he knows to be at F, although at the start he cannot see it. When the spider leaves S he must head for the mid-point of an edge on the far side of any face in sight. Here the isometric projection of the cube shown in fig. 89 on page 31 is useful. In fig. 110 we see the six (mid-) points from which the spider has to choose; once he reaches any one of these he is halfway to the fly and in sight of it.

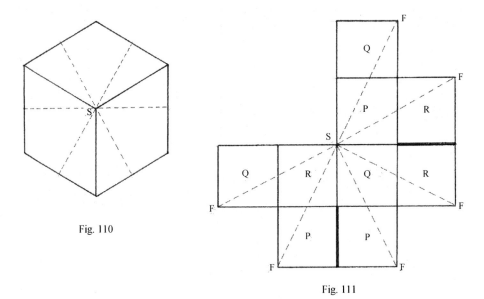

Fig. 110

Fig. 111

We can "flatten" the cube to show these six different (but equal in length) routes. They appear as broken lines in fig. 111, which can be thought of as a composite of parts of possible nets of cubes featuring faces labelled P, Q and R, faces with the same letter being either the same face or opposite faces. If S is the vertex where three faces P, Q, and R meet and from which the spider starts, the points marked F are the six possible points at which the fly may be sitting. All of these of course represent the same point on the reconstructed cube. If we cut out the diagram, fold the lines, and make a cut along the thick lines between the two squares labelled P and the two labelled R, we can fold the whole into a cube with the outside P, Q and R squares overlapping, and with the corners marked F all meeting at the vertex opposite to S.

7. If we refer back to fig. 69 on page 25, we can see that the angle between the two lines AB and BC in fig. 112, where A, B and C are the mid-points of edges of the cube, is 120°, because the two lines are adjacent sides of a regular hexagon which can be drawn on the surface of the cube. Fig. 113 shows a cube with two face diagonals drawn on it. What is the angle between the two diagonals?

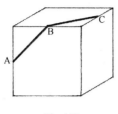
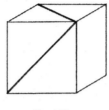
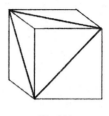

Fig. 112   Fig. 113   Fig. 114

We could solve this problem by considering the internal trigonometry of the cube, but there is a much easier way. If we turn the cube around so that we can see the ends of the diagonals, and join them by drawing a diagonal across a third face (fig. 114), we see that the three diagonals form an equilateral triangle, the angle between any two of whose sides is 60°.

Some More Answers

On pages 22 and 23 we asked some questions about symmetry. Here are some answers.

Problem 2. How many planes of symmetry does a cube have?

The plane of symmetry in fig. 54, page 21, passes through the mid-points of four edges of the cube. Since a cube has twelve edges, it must have three such planes of symmetry. Another plane of symmetry passes diagonally across two faces and through two opposite edges of the cube (fig. 56, page 22). Since the cube has six pairs of opposite edges it must have six such planes of symmetry. The cube has no other planes of symmetry apart from these nine.

Problem 3. What is the symmetry number of the cube?

To fit the cube back into its box, we must push one face in first. There are six faces to choose from, and we can fit each face into the box with any of its four sides facing us, giving a total of 6 x 4 = 24 different ways. So 24 is the symmetry number of the cube.

Problem 4. Can we divide a cube into three congruent parts which are not pyramids? Or into five congruent parts?

We can cut a cube into three congruent parts which are not pyramids by cutting it into three slices of equal thickness as in fig. 115. In a similar manner we can slice it into five congruent parts or into any number of parts we choose, within reason. (The present discussion is not about practicalities. We are talking about theory, and we do not suggest that there is any need actually to make models of any other than the simplest dissections of the cube. For this reason, we leave the design of nets of more complex dissections to the interested reader.)

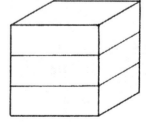

Fig. 115

One way of cutting the cube into six congruent parts which are not pyramids is to cut it horizontally into three slices and then vertically into two slices (fig. 116).

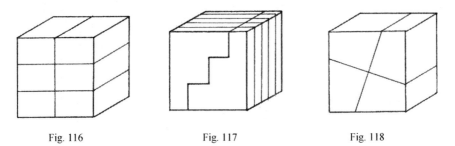

| Fig. 116 | Fig. 117 | Fig. 118 |

This opens the route to an infinite number of ways of cutting a cube into various numbers of congruent parts. We first make any cut which divides one face into two congruent parts which are related by *rotational symmetry of order 2*, and then slice the cube with cuts parallel to this face. Fig. 117 shows a cube divided in this way into ten congruent parts.

Since there is an infinite number of ways of cutting a square into two congruent parts which are related by rotational symmetry of order 2, it follows that there is an infinite number of ways of cutting the cube into any *even* number of congruent parts, by first cutting symmetrically through a face and then slicing. There is also an infinite number of ways of cutting a square into congruent parts which have rotational symmetry of order 4, as in fig. 118, which means that there is an infinite number of ways of cutting and slicing the cube into any number of congruent parts which is a multiple of four.

As we have seen on page 23, we can dissect a cube into three congruent pyramids, but we can dissect it into another odd prime number of congruent parts only by slicing it, making cuts parallel to a single face. We can however cut the cube into a *non-prime* odd number of congruent parts by making cuts parallel to more than one face . For example, three slices in one direction, three in another and five in a third, will divide the cube into 3 x 3 x 5 = 45 congruent parts. If the odd number is a square number, we can cut the cube into that number of square prisms; if it is a cube number, we can cut it into that number of smaller cubes.

In fig. 69 on page 25 we showed how a cut made through the mid-points of six edges of the cube will divide the cube into two congruent parts each with a hexagonal face. If we place one of these two pieces with its hexagonal face flat on a table and view it from above (fig. 119), we see a shape which has rotational symmetry of order 3. Cuts made vertically downwards through each of three edges (marked by thick lines) will divide the piece itself into three congruent parts.

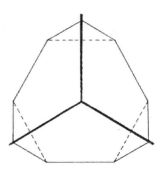

These cuts do not have to be made through the edges; we can rotate the cuts and so divide the piece into three congruent parts in an infinite number of ways, as long as the cuts are made vertically downwards from the apex and at an angle of 120° to one another, as in fig. 120 opposite. By dissecting

Fig. 119

each of the two pieces identically in this way, we shall have dissected the cube into six congruent parts. Can we fit together pairs of corresponding parts, one part taken from each of the two different pieces, so as to dissect the complete cube into three congruent parts? Since there is an infinite number of ways of making the cuts, there may well be an infinite number of ways of dissecting the cube into three congruent parts in this way. If there is, can we make the cuts on a cube without first making the cut through the mid-points of six of its edges?

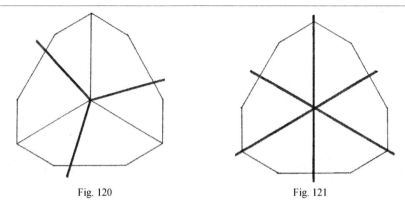

Fig. 120   Fig. 121

Note that if each of the three parts in fig. 119 is cut in half by cuts made vertically downwards along the extended line of the three top edges of the half-cube (fig. 121), each half-cube will then have been cut into six congruent parts and the whole cube into twelve congruent parts. However, if these cuts are now rotated slightly, the six parts will no longer be congruent, although the cuts will still divide the *base hexagon* into six congruent parts.

Nets of Cubes

On page 21, we stated that there are exactly eleven distinct hexominoes which are the nets of cubes, and we asked the reader to find these eleven. They are shown below. In figs. 122a and 122b only, squares which become opposite faces on the cube are labelled with the same letter (*cf.* figs. 46 and 47, page 20).

(i) Six nets contain a row of four squares, with the other two squares in various positions one above this row and one below it. They are:

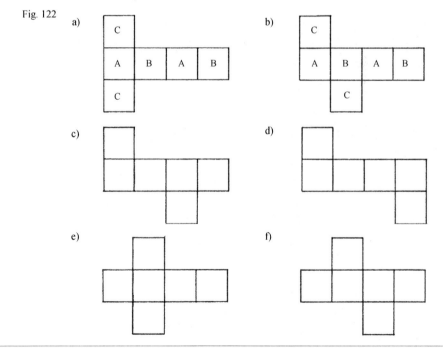

(ii) Three nets have a row of three squares, with two squares below it in a fixed position and the sixth square in different positions above it:

Fig. 122   g)   h)

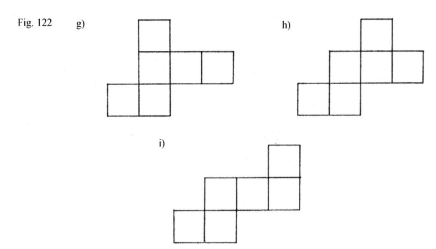

i)

(iii) One net has three rows of two squares:

Fig. 122   j)

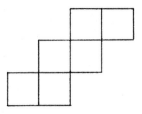

(iv) One net has two rows of three squares:

Fig. 122   k)

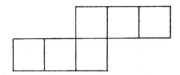

Of these eleven nets the cruciform net (e) is a popular one, favoured by Cundy and Rollett, *op. cit.*, page 85. The last net shown (k) is possibly the most economical of material if a number of nets are to be cut out of the same sheet of paper or card. (Which squares become opposite faces on this net?)

On page 86 we consider the like problem of how many different *octiamonds* (patterns of eight joined equilateral triangles) can form the net of a regular octahedron.

Further aspects of the cube are discussed in Appendix B, page 205 f.

Chapter 6

THE REGULAR TETRAHEDRON

A well-known puzzle asks how four triangles can be made from six matchsticks. This cannot be done if the matchsticks are laid flat; instead three matchsticks must be raised above the other three so that the six together form the edges of a tetrahedron (fig. 123).

Fig. 123

The regular tetrahedron, with only four faces, is the simplest of the five regular Platonic solids, but, despite its simplicity, on close study it displays some interesting features. (From now on, for the sake of brevity, we shall generally refer to the regular tetrahedron simply as a "tetrahedron".)

Models of a Tetrahedron

We can fold a regular tetrahedron from a rectangle of paper (A4 and A5 are both suitable).

1. Fold the paper down the centre of the sheet. Unfold it to reveal a crease (fig. 124a).
2. Bring the right-hand bottom corner A of the sheet up to a point on this crease such that when the sheet is folded now, the new fold will exactly meet the bottom left-hand corner of the sheet at B (fig. 124b).
3. Bring the edge DC over to meet the edge CB. The new fold will lie along AC (fig. 124c).
4. Fold over the small triangle at the top left of the paper and tuck it in out of sight, to give an equilateral triangle (fig. 124d).
5. At the back of this triangle there is a crease TS. Fold the triangle along this crease to obtain a trapezium made from three equilateral triangles (fig. 124e). Fold P to meet S and Q to meet T, then allow the three uppermost triangles to spring up to form a regular tetrahedron.

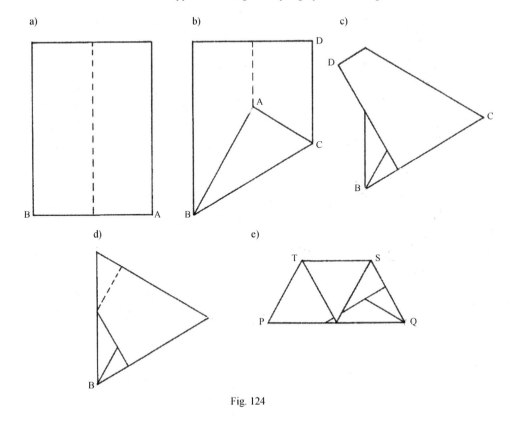

Fig. 124

At this stage pupils can be invited to explore various properties of the tetrahedron with the help of a worksheet. (The content of the sheet may need to be adjusted to the abilities of the pupils, and it is left to the teacher to decide just how this is to be done.)

A REGULAR TETRAHEDRON

1.   Count how many faces, edges and vertices the tetrahedron has.   Write these numbers down and find out how they are connected.

2.   Fold in half the edges of the tetrahedron you have made, and so find their *mid-points*. Mark the mid-points clearly, and make up the tetrahedron. Join each mid-point to the two opposite vertices of the tetrahedron with straight lines. Write down how many *planes* of symmetry a regular tetrahedron has.   How many *axes of rotational symmetry* does it have?

3.   Draw the net of a regular tetrahedron.   Find as many *distinct* nets for the tetrahedron as you can.

4. (a) Choose one net, cut it out of paper, colour each face a different colour, and make up the tetrahedron.

   (b) Make a second regular tetrahedron which is very slightly larger than the tetrahedron you have made in (a), but leave one face open. Find out in how many different ways the first tetrahedron will fit inside the second one.

5.   In how many *distinct* ways can you colour a regular tetrahedron using the same four colours, one colour to each face?

6.   Draw a regular tetrahedron from several different points of view, including from in front, from the side and from above.   Draw an *oblique view* of a regular tetrahedron.

7.   Make a regular tetrahedron which can be made rigid but which can also be folded flat.

8.   Find four points on the edges of a regular tetrahedron which are the four corners of a square.

9.   Draw a Schlegel diagram of a regular tetrahedron.

10. What is the *dual* of a regular tetrahedron?

11. If each edge of a regular tetrahedron is one unit long, what is the length of the shortest path which:

   (a) starts at one vertex, visits all the other vertices at least once, and returns to the start?

   (b) starts at one vertex, travels along each edge at least once, and returns to the start?

We shall not give immediate answers to all the questions asked in the worksheet, but answers will be found in the outcome of activities suggested in the sections which follow.

Nets of a Tetrahedron.

The net of a regular tetrahedron consists of four congruent equilateral triangles. There are just two distinct ways of drawing such a net.

A. 1. Draw a line AB twice as long as the edge of the tetrahedron. Mark its mid-point C.
2. With radius CA and centre C, draw a semicircle above AB and joining A and B. If this semicircle does not meet B exactly, move B along the line to meet the semicircle.
3. With radius AB and centres A and B, draw two arcs to cut at D (fig. 125). Join AD and BD.
4. Mark the points where AD and BD cross the semicircle as E and F respectively. Join EF, CE and CF. Draw flaps on AC, AE and BF.

B. 1. Draw a line AB twice as long as the edge of the tetrahedron. Mark its mid-point C.
2. With radius CA and centre C, draw a semicircle above AB and joining A and B. If this semicircle does not meet B exactly, move B along the line to meet the semicircle.
3. With radius AC and centre A, draw an arc to cut the semicircle at D (fig. 126).
4. With radius AC and centre B, draw an arc to cut the semicircle at E.
5. With radius AC and centres B and E, draw two arcs to cut at F. Join DF, checking that this line passes through E.
6. Join AD, CD, CE, BE and BF. Draw flaps on AC, AD and DE

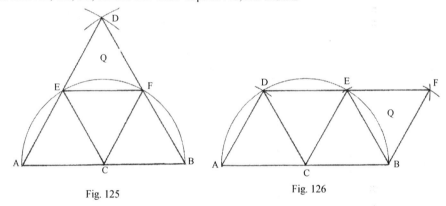

Fig. 125   Fig. 126

For both nets draw flaps as instructed, cut out the nets, and score and fold the lines. Stick the flap on AC first, and then stick down triangle Q on to the other two flaps.

Drawing a Tetrahedron

A careful study of the models we have made will tell us a great deal about the geometry of the regular tetrahedron. Like all tetrahedra, regular or otherwise, the solid has four faces (F), six edges (E) and four vertices (V). These numbers obey Euler's relationship, $V + F = E + 2$, which we met on page 33 when discussing the cube. In the tetrahedron, $4 + 4 = 6 + 2$.

A Plan View

The four faces of the regular tetrahedron are all equilateral triangles, and its six edges are all the same length. From whichever angle we view it, we can see no more than three of its faces at any one time. However, if we can see three of its faces, then we can see all six of its edges and all four of its vertices, and in this respect it differs markedly from every other regular solid. In particular we can see all the edges and vertices of the tetrahedron if we place it on one face and look down on it directly from above to get a *plan* view (fig. 127).

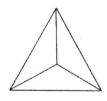

Fig. 127

The plan view of the tetrahedron consists of an equilateral triangle together with portions of its three *medians*, which are lines joining the corners of the triangle to the mid-points of the opposite sides. To draw a plan view:

1. Draw a line AB to represent one edge of the tetrahedron.
2. Draw two circles of radius AB, with their centres at A and B respectively. Mark as C the point where these two circles intersect above AB.
3. Draw a third circle of radius AB with its centre at C. This circle should pass through both A and B.
4. Draw the triangle ABC and label the other points where the circles intersect as P, Q and R (fig. 128).
5. Join AP, BQ and CR and firm in those portions of these lines which appear in the plan view of the tetrahedron in fig. 127.

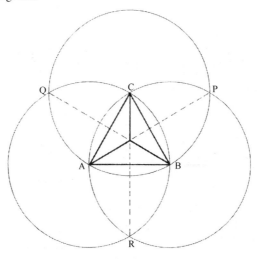

Fig. 128

The medians of the triangle all cross at the *centre* of the triangle, and it is those portions of the medians which join the corners of the triangle to the centre which appear in the plan view of the tetrahedron. If we are to draw accurate views of the tetrahedron from directions other than from directly above, we need to know the lengths of the medians. The fact that the medians of an equilateral triangle meet the sides at right angles allows us to calculate their lengths.

The Trigonometry of the Equilateral Triangle

In fig. 129, CD:
   (a) is a median of the equilateral triangle ABC:
   (b) is a line of symmetry of the triangle:
   (c) measures the *height* of the triangle: and
   (d) bisects the angle ACB.
D is the mid-point of AB, and the angles ADC and BDC are both right angles. If we take the sides of the triangle ABC to be two units long, then AD is one unit long and by Pythagoras CD is $\sqrt{(2^2 - 1^2)} = \sqrt{3}$ units long. If AB, etc, were just one unit long, the height CD of the triangle would be $\frac{1}{2}\sqrt{3}$ or $\sqrt{3}/2$ units.

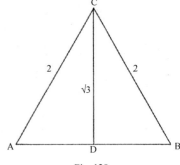

Fig. 129

44

In fig. 130 ABC is an equilateral triangle with two of its medians, AE and CD, intersecting at P. The medians meet BC at E and AB at D and bisect the angles at A and C respectively. Angle CAD is 60°; angle PAD is half 60°, or 30°. For ease of calculation, we take AC to be two units long and AD one unit long, so that by Pythagoras CD (= AE) = $\sqrt{(2^2 - 1^2)}$ = $\sqrt{3}$ units long. Now CD (= $\sqrt{3}$) is also 1 x tan 60°, so tan 60° = $\sqrt{3}$; PD is 1 x tan 30°, and tan 30° = 1/tan 60° = $1/\sqrt{3}$ = $\sqrt{3}/3$, so PD is one-third the length of CD. We can confirm this by considering the similar triangles ACD and PCE: AC/AD = PC/PE = 2, so CP (= AP) = 2PE (= 2PD) ⇒ PD = $\frac{1}{3}$CD. (Note that if AC is taken to be 1 unit long, then CD = $\frac{1}{2}\sqrt{3}$ units long.)

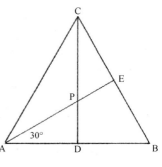

Fig. 130

We may make a further check on this result by considering the relative areas of the triangles ABC and ABP in fig. 131, where CD is a median and AP and BP are partial medians of the equilateral triangle ABC. By the symmetry of fig. 128 opposite, the triangle ABP has one-third the area of triangle ABC. The two triangles stand on the same base AB, and since triangles on the same base have areas which are proportional to their heights, it follows that PD is one-third the length of CD.

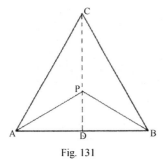

Fig. 131

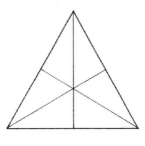

Fig. 132

In fact the point P at which all three medians intersect divides each median in the ratio of 1:2, so that P lies one-third of the way along each of them. (This is true of all triangles and not of equilateral triangles only. However this fact has no bearing on the present discussion.)

The three medians divide the whole triangle into six congruent triangular parts (fig. 132), which can be proved to be congruent by considering the fact that each median meets the mid-point of a side at right angles. With reference to Euclid, each triangle shares with the others two equal corresponding sides and a right angle.

Views of the Regular Tetrahedron

A Side View

We are now ready to draw the side view or side *elevation* of the tetrahedron, as seen from the direction E in the plan view in fig. 133. This side view is shown in fig. 134 overleaf, where ABC is an isosceles triangle with AB = AC. AB is the length of a median of the base of the tetrahedron; AC is a median of a face, while BC is an edge of the tetrahedron. Hence AB = AC = $\frac{1}{2}\sqrt{3}$ x BC. Note that the triangle ABC also represents a cross-section of the tetrahedron, revealed by a cut made vertically downwards through the points A, C and B in fig. 133. Such a cut dissects the tetrahedron into two congruent parts.

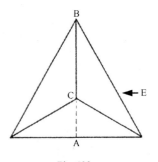

Fig. 133

A Front View

To draw a *front elevation* of the tetrahedron we need to know its height, which is CD in fig. 134. C lies vertically above D, which is the centre of the base face and which lies one-third of the way along the median AB from A. The angle ADC is a right angle, so that as well as being the *altitude* of the triangle ABC, CD also measures the *height* of the tetrahedron. If BC = 1 unit, then AB = AC = ½√3 units and AD = $^1/_3$ AB = $^1/_3$ x ½√3 = √3/6 units. By Pythagoras CD = √({½√3}² − {√3/6}²) = √(¾ − $^3/_{36}$) = √($^{24}/_{36}$) = √($^2/_3$) ≈ 0.816 units long.

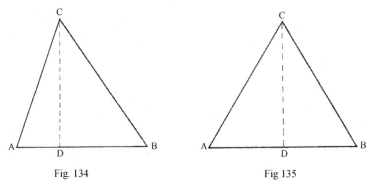

Fig. 134   Fig 135

The front elevation of the tetrahedron (fig. 135) is an equilateral triangle slanting away from us slightly as we look at it, so that when drawn it will be not equilateral but isosceles. If its base AB is one unit long, then its height CD as we saw above will be √($^2/_3$) ≈ 0.816 units long; and by Pythagoras AC = BC = √($^2/_3$ + ¼) = √($^{11}/_{12}$) ≈ 0.957 units long.

An Oblique View of the Regular Tetrahedron

It is very difficult to draw a realistic oblique view of the regular tetrahedron, such as we did for the cube (e.g., fig. 78, page 28). However it will be useful to have an oblique view as a working diagram which we can use when illustrating, for example, dissections of the tetrahedron, and to draw this we proceed as follows.

   1. Draw an equilateral triangle ABC representing the front face of the tetrahedron (fig. 136).
   2. From B draw a short line BD sloping upwards and to the right.
   3. Join CD and AD as shown.

It is clear, as can be seen by looking at an actual tetrahedron, that this drawing of the tetrahedron gives a very inaccurate, if not impossible, view of the solid. In particular the line AD is much too long. This does not matter too much however, given the few and simple uses to which the drawing is normally put.

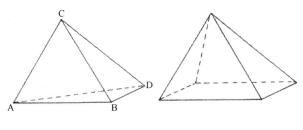

Fig. 136   Fig. 137

Another problem with this view is that it differs very little from the oblique view of a square-based pyramid (fig. 137), and only by showing the hidden edges as broken lines can we distinguish between the two.

[*Note:* strictly speaking, in oblique views both of the tetrahedron and of the square-based pyramid the top vertex should be placed vertically above the centre of the base. Figs. 138 and 139 opposite show how oblique views of the two solids should be drawn following this rule. In fig. 138 the medians of the base are shown as broken lines, each joining a corner to the mid-point of the opposite side. Note that the front face of each solid drawn in this way is now clearly no longer an equilateral triangle. Note also that the two solids have been drawn here with the same height. If the square-based pyramid were part of an oblique view of a regular octahedron (see fig. 218, page 73), then its height would be somewhat less than that of a tetrahedron with the same length of edge, although the visual confusion between the solids referred to above would still remain.]

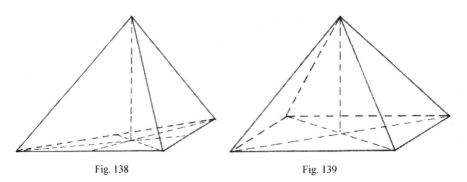

Fig. 138   Fig. 139

The Internal Trigonometry of the Tetrahedron.

Before we can begin a detailed investigation into how to dissect the regular tetrahedron into congruent parts, which we pursue on page 52, we need to know still more about its internal trigonometry.

We have already described a dissection into two congruent parts (fig. 133, page 45). We can cut the regular tetrahedron symmetrically in half by any cut which passes through the midpoint of any of its six edges and along the length of the opposite edge. Each cut will lie along a plane of symmetry (fig. 140). The tetrahedron has no other planes of symmetry apart from these six.

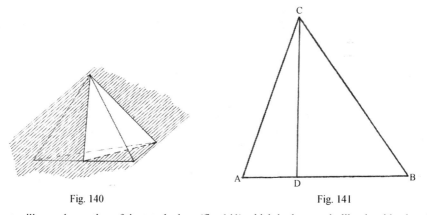

Fig. 140   Fig. 141

Each cut will reveal a section of the tetrahedron (fig. 141) which looks exactly like the side elevation seen in fig. 134. To see clearly what we mean by the *height* of the tetrahedron, we can make a model of the half-tetrahedron, and on it mark the height (or *altitude*) CD. One net for such a model appears in fig. 142 overleaf (but see also fig. 156, page 53). On this net the points marked A, B, C and D correspond to the points marked accordingly in fig. 141.

To draw the net:

1. Draw EF twice the length of an edge of the tetrahedron. Mark its mid-point B. With radius EB and with centre B, draw a semicircle on EF.
2. With radius EB and centre F draw an arc to cut the semicircle at G. With radius EB and centre E draw a second arc to cut the semicircle at H. Join BG.
3. With radius EF and centres E and F, draw two arcs to cut below the semicircle at K. Join FK. The line FK should pass through G.
4. Join BK and GH and mark the point where they intersect as A.
5. With radius AK and centre A, draw two arcs to cut the semicircle at C and L. Join CL and mark the point where CL cuts BK as D. Join CB and CA. Erase EB, DL and AH to finish with the net in fig. 142. Draw flaps on BF, FG and AC. Stick the flap on BF first.

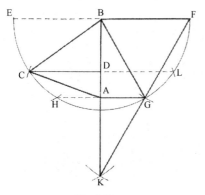

Fig. 142

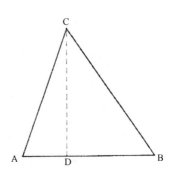

Fig. 143

We now revise our earlier calculations of the proportions of the cut face ABC in fig. 134, page 46. In fig. 143, which copies fig. 134, we take AB to be three units long, so that AC is also 3 units long and AD is 1 unit long. By Pythagoras CD is $\sqrt{8} = 2\sqrt{2}$ units long, and BC, an edge of the tetrahedron, is $\sqrt{12} = 2\sqrt{3}$ units long.

We note at this point that the angle CAB is the angle between two faces, the *dihedral* angle. This angle is $\cos^{-1} \frac{1}{3} = 70.53°$, which incidentally (or coincidentally?) is the angle at which two interior diagonals of the cube meet (see page 32). We also note in passing that the sides DB, DC and CB of the triangle BCD are in the ratio of $1:\sqrt{2}:\sqrt{3}$, which are the ratios also of the sides of the triangle drawn inside a cube in fig. 96, page 32.

The Centre of the Tetrahedron

In fig. 144 we have drawn fig. 143 again, and have added BE as a second altitude of the tetrahedron, cutting the altitude CD at F. By symmetry BE = CD, and also EF = DF. The point F is the centre (sometimes known as the *centroid*) of the tetrahedron, a point equidistant from the vertices, from the centres of the faces and from the mid-points of the edges. We must find out exactly where this point is before we can begin to dissect the tetrahedron further into congruent parts.

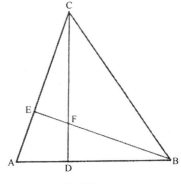

Fig. 144

The distance we need to find is DF, which we shall call a. DF is part of CD which as we have seen on page 48 is √8 units long, as is BE. The triangles FDB and AEB are similar, since they have the angle ABE in common, and both contain a right angle.　　FD/DB = AE/EB ⇒ $a/2 = 1/√8$ ⇒ $a = 2/√8 =$ $(2√8)/8 = ¼√8$. F is therefore one-quarter of the way along CD from D and also one-quarter of the way along BE from E. Both D and E represent the centres of faces, so we may say that the centre of the tetrahedron lies one-quarter of the way up each *altitude* of the tetrahedron, the line joining the centre of a face to the opposite vertex.

We can confirm the position of the centre of the tetrahedron as one-quarter of the way up an altitude by considering volumes. In fig. 145 the centre F of the tetrahedron is joined to each of the four vertices. These lines represent the edges of four congruent triangular pyramids, non-regular tetrahedra, into which the regular tetrahedron can be dissected. One of these is shown separately in fig. 146. The volume of a tetrahedron, or of any pyramid, is one-third of the base area multiplied by the vertical height. The two tetrahedra in figs. 145 and 146 stand on the same base, and so their volumes must be directly proportional to their heights. By symmetry the four small tetrahedra are all congruent and together they make the large tetrahedron. Each must have a volume one-quarter that of the large tetrahedron, and so each must have a height one-quarter the height of the large one.

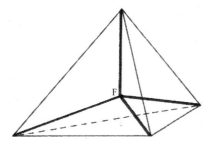

Fig. 145

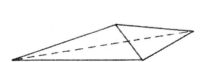

Fig. 146

Fig. 147 is an augmented copy of fig. 144, but with a changed scale. CB, an edge of the tetrahedron, which earlier we took to be 2√3 units long, is now taken to be 1 unit long, so all other lengths have to be divided by 2√3.

a) AC = AB = 3/(2√3) = √3/2 ≈ 0.866 units long;

b) CD = BE = 2√2/(2√3) = √2/√3 = √(2/3)
　　　≈ 0.8165 units long;

c) CF = ¾CD = ¾√(2/3) = √(3/8) ≈ 0.612 units long,

d) AD = 1/(2√3) = 1/√12 ≈ 0.289 units long;

e) DF = ½√2/(2√3) = ¼ x √(2/3) = 1/√24
　　　≈ 0.204 units long.

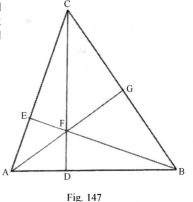

Fig. 147

We shall make use of these particular lengths when we come to make models of dissections of the tetrahedron.

In fig. 147, as well as the altitudes CD and BE, we have also drawn a median AG of the triangle. This median passes through F and is also an altitude of the triangle ABC. By Pythagoras both AF and FG are √(1/8) = 1/2√2 ≈ 0.354 units long, while AG = 1/√2 ≈ 0.707 units long and F is its mid-point. Since A and G can be taken to mark the mid-points of two opposite edges of the tetrahedron, it should come as no great surprise to discover that the centre of the tetrahedron lies halfway along the line joining these two points.

The Volume of a Regular Tetrahedron.

We are now ready to calculate the volume of a regular tetrahedron, measured in terms of the length of its edge, a.

As stated on the previous page, the volume of any tetrahedron is one-third of the area of its base multiplied by its vertical height or altitude. The base of a regular tetrahedron of edge a units is an equilateral triangle, whose area is $\frac{1}{2} a^2 \sin 60°$, or $\frac{1}{2} a^2 \times \sqrt{3}/2 = \sqrt{3}a^2/4$ square units. The altitude of the tetrahedron (see page 49) is $\sqrt{(2/3)}a$ units, so its volume will be $\frac{1}{3} \times \sqrt{3}a^2/4 \times \sqrt{(2/3)}a = \sqrt{6}a^3/12\sqrt{3} = \sqrt{2}a^3/12 \approx 0.118a^3$ cubic units. This means that a regular tetrahedron has just under one-eighth the volume of a cube with the same length of edge.

Further Activities

We return to look at other ways of dissecting the regular tetrahedron into congruent parts on page 52, using the results we have obtained above, but for the present we look at other aspects of the solid.

Planes of Symmetry

If we make a tetrahedron following the instructions on page 41 and draw lines on it in the way suggested in paragraph 2 of the worksheet on page 42, and then open the model flat, it will appear as in fig. 148. On each triangular face three lines appear, each lying on a plane of symmetry of the tetrahedron. There are four faces, so there are twelve lines altogether; but on the reconstructed model (fig. 149) each line lies on the same plane as one other line, so there are not twelve planes of symmetry but only $12 \div 2 = 6$, confirming the result we obtained earlier on page 47.

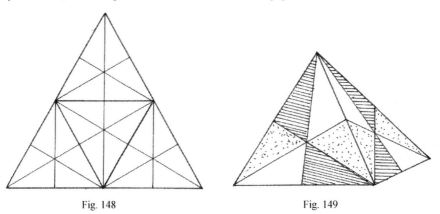

Fig. 148   Fig. 149

A Colouring Problem

We can colour the regions of fig. 148 in such a way that the tetrahedron appears to be made up of twelve pieces (fig. 149). Regions meeting at an edge belong to the same "piece" and so must be the same colour, but otherwise we stipulate that no two regions of the same colour may touch except at their corners. Ideally we should need to use only three colours, and regions on each face which are *vertically opposite* should be the same colour, as shown in fig. 149. Is it possible to colour the whole tetrahedron in this way?

More Symmetry.

Besides six planes of symmetry the tetrahedron also has seven *axes* of rotational symmetry, around which it will rotate symmetrically. Three axes of symmetry pass through the mid-points of opposite edges (fig. 150) and each has rotational symmetry of order 2. Each of the other four axes of symmetry passes through a vertex of the solid and the centre of the opposite face (fig. 151) and has rotational symmetry of order 3.

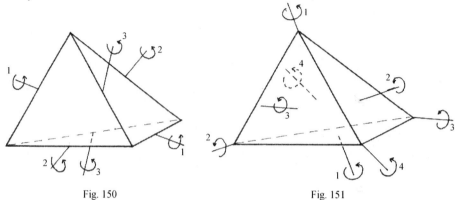

Fig. 150   Fig. 151

When we were considering the symmetry of the cube (page 33), we asked whether the fact that the cube had thirteen axes of rotational symmetry was linked to the fact that the sum of the number of its faces, edges and vertices was 26, which is twice thirteen. The tetrahedron has a total of seven axes of symmetry, and the sum of the numbers of its faces, edges and vertices is $4 + 6 + 4 = 14$, which is twice seven. It looks as if there may in fact be a connection here. Is there a connection, and if so, what is the reason for it?

The Symmetry Number of the Regular Tetrahedron

The symmetry number of the regular tetrahedron, the number of distinct ways in which we can place a regular tetrahedron into another regular tetrahedron, (or into a regular-tetrahedron-shaped hole), is 12. We may push any one of the four vertices of the tetrahedron into the hole, and we may then rotate the face opposite to this vertex, the face which is facing us, so that it takes any one of three different orientations: $4 \times 3 = 12$.

Another Colouring Problem

To colour each face of a regular tetrahedron a different colour, we need four colours. However with these four colours we can colour the tetrahedron in two and only two distinct ways. To demonstrate this we suppose that we have coloured the four faces yellow, red, green and blue. We place the tetrahedron with the yellow face downwards and with the red face facing away from us. We can then see either the green face on the left and the blue face on the right, or the blue face on the left and the green face on the right (fig. 152a, b). This gives the only two distinct ways possible of colouring the faces of the tetrahedron in this manner.

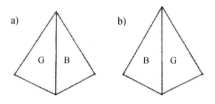

Fig. 152

Other Models of Tetrahedra

Cundy and Rollett, *op. cit.*, page 154, describe a method of "plaiting" a regular tetrahedron from a net, reproduced here in fig. 153, of nine equilateral triangles.   The five extra triangles in the net give rigidity to the model when it is folded up together.   The last triangle is tucked in under another triangle to finish off the model.

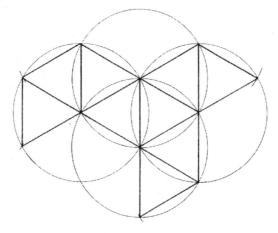

Fig. 153

The net is part of a pattern of three overlapping hexagons together with their main diagonals, and can be drawn on the framework of the flower pattern shown in fig. 16, page 10.

Collapsible Tetrahedra

It is also possible to make from paper or card a *collapsible* model of a tetrahedron which will fold flat, yet which can instantly be made up again into a tetrahedron.   In the finished model, one edge is cut along its length and two faces are folded in half.   The net is either a rectangle enclosing three equilateral triangles, the middle triangle being folded, together with two half equilateral triangles (fig. 154); or four equilateral triangles with two folds (fig. 155).   Both nets can easily be drawn by adapting the net of a tetrahedron shown in fig 126 on page 43.

fold

folds

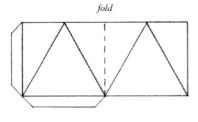

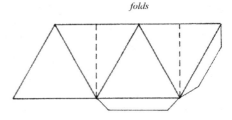

Fig. 154

Fig. 155

Dissections of the Regular Tetrahedron.

Two parts.

(a)   We have described already on page 48 how to make a model of a half-tetrahedron on which is drawn a line representing the *height* of the tetrahedron.   We can show how a tetrahedron can be dissected into two congruent parts along a plane of symmetry by making the other half of the tetrahedron and placing the two halves together. The net is the same for each half and is shown in fig. 156, which is a symmetrical alternative to the net shown in fig. 142, page 48.

1. Draw AB the length of an edge of the tetrahedron.
2. Draw two arcs with radius AB, centred on A and B, to cut at C and D. Join AC and BC. Draw CD as a construction line to cross AB at M, its mid-point.
3. Draw arcs with radius CM, centred on A and B, to cut at E, and also to locate the points F and G above A and B. Two more arcs with radius AM, centred on C, will fix the positions of F and G. Join AE, BE, AF, FG (to pass through C) and BG. Draw flaps where shown.

The two halves are identical but fit together to form a complete tetrahedron (fig. 157).

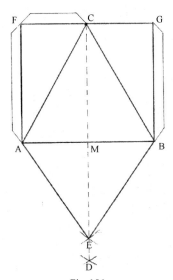

Fig. 156

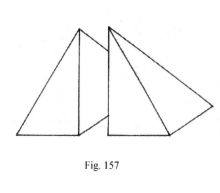

Fig. 157

(b) It is not difficult to find four points on the edges of a regular tetrahedron which are the corners of a square. First draw a view from directly above the tetrahedron when it is resting symmetrically on one edge. This edge is shown as a broken line in fig. 158. The view is a parallel projection of the tetrahedron which ignores perspective, and the outer boundary is a square (the *Petrie* polygon of the tetrahedron, see page 77). The projection of the top edge crosses that of the bottom edge at right angles and bisects it, just as one diagonal of a square bisects the other diagonal at right angles. And just as the mid-points of the sides of a square are themselves the corners of a smaller square, so the midpoints of the four edges of the tetrahedron which join the top and bottom edges are the four corners of the square we are looking for (fig. 159). We can see two sides of this square when we look down on the tetrahedron; the other two sides are on the hidden faces and are shown here as broken lines.

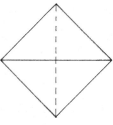

Fig. 158

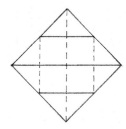

Fig. 159

If we make a regular tetrahedron from the net of four equilateral triangles in a row (fig. 126, page 43), we can draw the four sides of this square on the net as a straight line, equidistant from its top and bottom edges (fig. 160). If we use the net which is four triangles in the shape of a larger triangle, (fig. 125, page 43), this line will appear on the net split into two parallel but unequal parts (fig. 161).

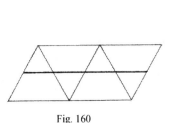

Fig. 160

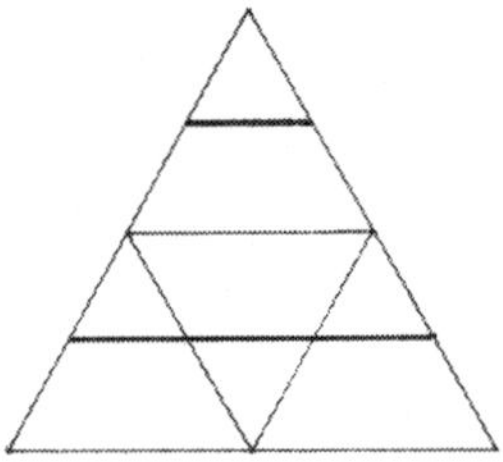

Fig. 161

We can draw three such squares on the surface of a regular tetrahedron, and the sides of these squares will then divide each face of the tetrahedron into four congruent equilateral triangles (fig. 162). Each square lies on a plane which, although not a plane of symmetry of the tetrahedron, will nevertheless cut the tetrahedron into two congruent parts. [On the other hand these squares *do* lie on the planes of symmetry of the regular octahedron which can be inscribed within the regular tetrahedron, and are in fact the three "equatorial" squares of this regular octahedron. We study these matters in detail on pages 69 and 147.]

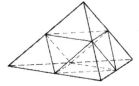

Fig. 162

We may make a model showing the regular tetrahedron divided into two congruent parts by a cut made through the sides of one of these squares. For the net of each part:

1. Draw a square ABCD.
2. With radius AB draw four three-quarter circles outside the square centred on A, B, C, and D. These part-circles will intersect at P, Q, R and S (fig. 163).
3. With radius AB and centres Q and S, draw arcs to cut the three-quarter circles at K, L, M and N.
4. Draw the equilateral triangles ABP and CDR.
5. Draw the trapezia BCLK and ADMN. Draw flaps on AN, BK, KL, CL and DM. Stick the flap on KL first.

How to fit the two parts together to form a regular tetrahedron is a well-known puzzle.

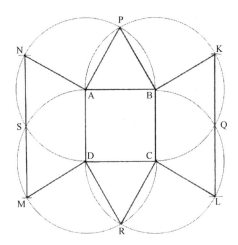

Fig. 163

A less well-known puzzle is to divide each of these two parts themselves into two congruent parts, four of which will then fit together to make a regular tetrahedron. The cut on each part is made perpendicular to the square face through a diagonal (fig. 164).

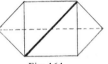

Fig. 164

Cundy and Rollett, *op. cit.*, page 202, give a net for making one of these four parts: it consists of a rhombus with two equilateral triangles and two isosceles right-angled triangles.

1. Mark two points A and B. The length AB will be half the length of edge of the complete tetrahedron.
2. With radius AB, draw two circles centred at A and B. The circles will intersect at C and D (fig. 165).
3. With radius AB and centre D, draw two arcs to cut the circles at E and F. Join CE, CF and EF. CEF is an equilateral triangle, and D lies on EF.
4. Join AD and BD.
5. Place a straight-edge to join E and B. This line extended will meet a circle at G. Join BG.
6. In the same way, find H in line with F and A. Join AH, EH and FG.

Add flaps where shown in fig. 166. Flap *f* is stuck first.

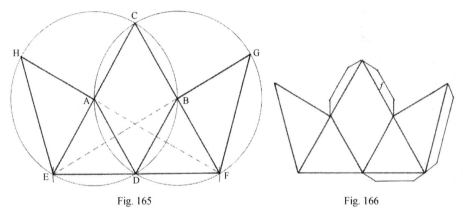

Fig. 165   Fig. 166

Three Parts.

In the first dissection of the tetrahedron into two congruent parts described above, a cut was made along the line of symmetry of the base equilateral triangle shown in fig. 167. There are many different ways of dividing an equilateral triangle into three congruent parts, and here we use two of these ways to dissect the tetrahedron into three congruent parts. These two ways are derived from the pattern of the three medians of the triangle seen in fig. 132, page 45, and are shown in figs. 168 and 169.

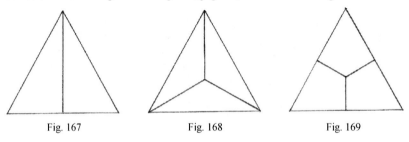

Fig. 167   Fig. 168   Fig. 169

The nets for each dissection are shown in figs. 170 to 174.

a) Fig. 170 shows the net for the dissection which divides the base as shown in fig. 168.

1. Draw an equilateral triangle ABC. This triangle is a face of the tetrahedron.
2. Draw the three medians of the triangle, AD, BE and CF. The medians cross at G.
3. With radius AE, and with centres at E and D, draw semicircles on AC and BC.
4. With radius AG, draw arcs centred at A and B to cut at H (fig. 170). The triangle ABH is one-third of the base triangle of the tetrahedron
5. With radius AG, draw arcs centred at A and B to cut the semicircles at I and J.
6. Join AI and BJ, and CI and CJ. The angles CIA and CJB are right angles. Both CI and CJ represent an altitude of the tetrahedron.

Draw flaps where shown in fig. 171 and stick flap *f* first.

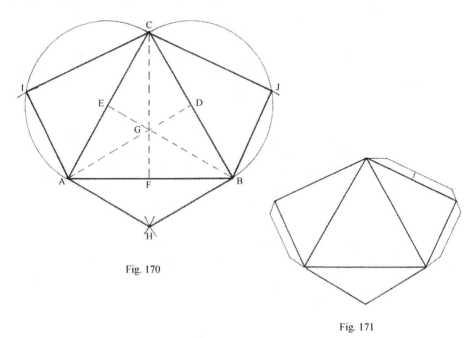

Fig. 170

Fig. 171

b) Figs. 172-174 opposite show the net for the dissection which divides the base as shown in fig. 169. In these three figures AB is the length of an edge of the tetrahedron.

1. Draw equilateral triangles ABC and ABD, one on either side of AB, and find the two medians AE and AF of these triangles. Join CD to meet AE at G (fig. 172).
2. Erase AC, CE, AD and FD. Produce AE and FB as shown in fig. 173. Find the mid-points H and I of AE and AF respectively. With radius AH, draw semicircles on AE and AF, centred at H and I.
3. With radius EG draw a semicircle centred at E to find the position of J on AE produced. Mark as K the point where the two semicircles intersect.
4. With radius EG draw an arc centred at F to cut the semicircle on AF at L.
5. Join AK, KE, AL and LF. The angles AKE and ALF are right angles.
6. With radius BF draw a semicircle centred at B to find the position of M on FB produced. Join JM and check that the angle JMB is a right angle.

Draw flaps where shown in fig. 174 and stick flap *f* first.

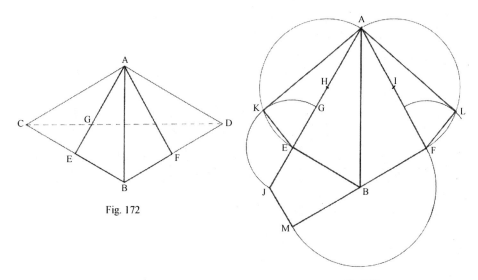

Fig. 172

Fig. 173

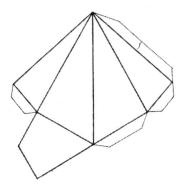

Fig. 174

Four parts.

a) Four Pyramids Make A Regular Tetrahedron.

The regular tetrahedron is made up of four pyramids, each one-quarter of the volume of the large tetrahedron, as shown in figs. 145 and 146 on page 49. Each pyramid has a face of the tetrahedron as its base, and the apexes (or *apices*) of the four pyramids all meet at the centre of the tetrahedron. In fig. 175 we reproduce part of fig. 147 from page 49, in which CD and BE are altitudes of the isosceles triangle ABC. Each of the slant edges on the pyramid will be the length of FB, which, expressed as a fraction of BC, the edge of the tetrahedron, is $\sqrt{(3/8)} \approx 0.612$. The net of the pyramid is shown in fig. 176 overleaf.

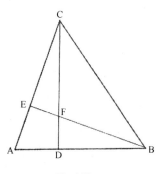

Fig. 175

In fig. 176 AB is the length of an edge of the tetrahedron. EF has to be one-third of this length.

1. Set a radius on the compasses of 1½ times the length of AB. With centres at A and B, draw arcs to cut at C. Join AC and BC.
2. Find D, the mid-point of AB. Join CD.
3. With radius AB, draw arcs centred at A and B to cut AC and BC at E and F respectively as shown in fig. 176, extending the arc AF well to the right of B. Erase CE and CF.
4. With radius AB draw an arc centred at F to cut the arc AF at I. Join BI and FI to give the equilateral triangle BFI, which is one face of the tetrahedron.
5. With radius AB and centre E, draw an arc to cut the arc AFI at G. AG will bisect the angle EAB, and will cut CD at H. Join AH.
6. Join BH, EH and FH. Draw flaps where shown in fig. 177. Stick flap *f* first.

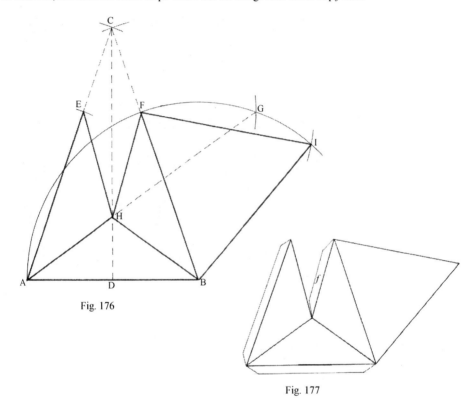

Fig. 176

Fig. 177

When these pyramids are made up, they may appear unexpectedly low in height, but four of them do fit together to form a regular tetrahedron. This can be shown simply either by making a regular tetrahedron with edges 0.1 cm longer than the edge AB in fig. 176, leaving one face open, and fitting the four pyramids into it; or by joining four of the pyramids by their bases in the manner shown in fig. 385 on page 143, and folding them together to form a regular tetrahedron.

We shall meet these pyramids again later. Eight of them fitted one to each face of a regular octahedron will make a rhombic dodecahedron (see page 143). Four of them fitted one to each triangular face of a truncated tetrahedron will make a non-regular solid which, however, like the rhombic dodecahedron, will nevertheless "tessellate" to fill space. This solid is illustrated in David Wells' *The Penguin Dictionary of Curious and Interesting Geometry*, page 234.

b) Four, six and twelve parts.

We can divide the surface of the regular tetrahedron into four regions, each region comprising the points which are nearer to one vertex of the tetrahedron than they are to any of the others. The boundaries of these regions join the midpoints of the edges to the centres of the faces (fig. 178). Viewed from above when the tetrahedron is resting on a face, the boundaries of one region form a hexagon (fig. 179), but when the tetrahedron is placed on an edge and viewed from above, the line joining the centres of the two visible faces appears as a straight line (fig. 180). The boundaries of all four regions can be thought of as six straight lines, each line crossing one edge of the tetrahedron.

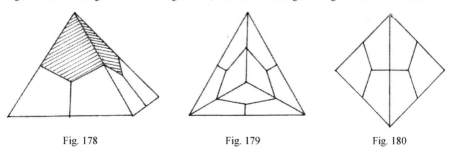

Fig. 178   Fig. 179   Fig. 180

In fig. 181 we suppose that the net of the tetrahedron is to be cut from a tessellation of equilateral triangles. The lines we are talking about will be part of the tessellation of regular hexagons whose corners are at the centres of the triangles.

Cuts made along the boundaries of these regions in towards the centre of the tetrahedron dissect the solid into four congruent parts.

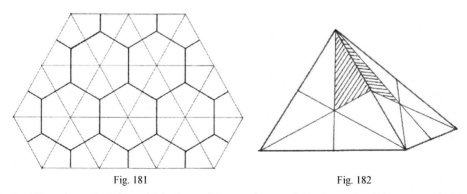

Fig. 181   Fig. 182

In fig. 182 we have shaded one-third of one of these regions, and this figure should be compared with fig. 149 on page 50, in which we saw how we might colour the tetrahedron to make it appear as if made up of twelve congruent parts. At present we are talking about a section (or dissection) made up of a combination of three of these twelve parts. We shall in fact consider first how to make a model of just one part, and then of two parts joined together, before considering a model of three of the twelve parts joined together, which will lead to a dissection of the whole tetrahedron into four congruent parts.

i) Twelve parts

For this dissection, we cut, as it were, along all the six planes of symmetry of the solid, that is, along all the lines shown in fig. 182. The cuts will be perpendicular to the edges, and one face of each of the twelve resulting parts will be in the form of a kite with two of its angles right angles. These twelve faces will meet at the centre of the tetrahedron, at a point a quarter of the way along each of its altitudes. This is the point F at which the bold lines meet in fig. 145, page 49.

Fig. 183 shows one of these twelve parts. It is the part shaded in fig. 182, cut out and viewed slightly from below. AB is half the edge of the tetrahedron, and E is the centre of the tetrahedron. The net has to contain two portions, ABC and ABD, of two faces of the tetrahedron. The angles ABC, ABD, ACE, and ADE are all right angles. CE and DE are both one-quarter the length of an altitude; AE is three-quarters the length of an altitude. A net for fig. 183 can be drawn as follows.

1. Draw an equilateral triangle ACD and its median AB (fig. 184). AB will be half the edge of the tetrahedron in the model, and it is convenient to make AB 1 unit long. AC, AD and CD must therefore be drawn as $2/\sqrt{3} \approx 1.155$ units long (see fig. 129 on page 44). If for example AB is to be drawn 6 cm long, then AC will have to be drawn about 6.9 cm long.
2. Draw CE at right angles to AC, and DF at right angles to AD. CE, DF, CG and GH all measure the distance of the centre of the tetrahedron from the centres of the faces, which is $1/\sqrt{8} \approx 0.354$ times the length of AD = $1/\sqrt{8} \times 2/\sqrt{3} = 1/\sqrt{6} \approx 0.408$ units long.
3. Join AE and AF. Each line is $\sqrt{(3/2)} \approx 1.225$ units long.
4. Draw CG at right angles to CB and 0.408 units long.
5. BH = BD = $1/\sqrt{3} \approx 0.577$ units long. To find the point H, draw an arc with radius CG and centre G, to cut an arc with radius BD centred at B. When CBHG is drawn, the angle BHG should be a right angle. BG should be $1/\sqrt{2} \approx 0.707$ units long and CH should be 2/3 of a unit long. If for example AB is drawn 6 cm long, then CH should be exactly 4 cm long. CH is the distance between the centres of two adjacent faces of the complete tetrahedron, and by simple geometry is one-third the length of an edge of the tetrahedron.

As usual, flaps are required where shown; flap *f* is stuck first.

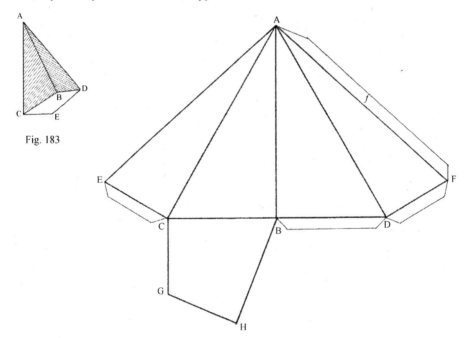

Fig. 183

Fig. 184

ii) Six parts

Fig. 185 opposite is the net of two of the twelfths shown in fig. 183 joined at their kite faces. The resulting piece, shown shaded in fig. 186, contains a complete edge AL of the tetrahedron.

In fig. 185 both ACD and CDL are equilateral triangles.   AECDF is drawn in the same way as in fig. 184.   LJCDK is a reflection of AECDF in CD.   The flaps are best stuck in the order shown.

Six of these pieces will make a whole tetrahedron, while three or four can be assembled in interesting and sometimes decorative ways.

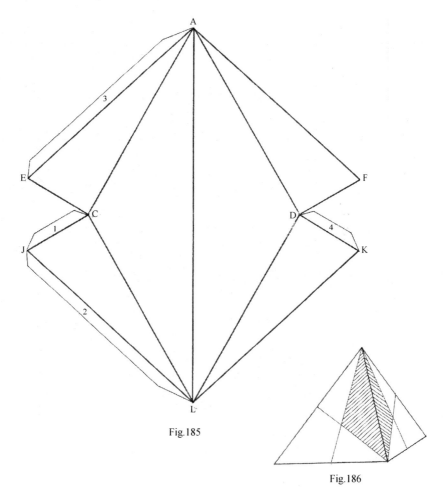

Fig.185

Fig.186

iii) Four parts

We now draw the net of three of these twelfths combined, so as to make a quarter of the tetrahedron, the part shown shaded in fig. 178 on page 59.

The net of each of these parts consists of three kites each representing one-third of a face of the tetrahedron, attached to three other kites representing the hidden cuts made perpendicularly from the mid-points of each edge in towards the centre.   The net is shown overleaf in fig. 187.

1. Draw AB equal in length to the edge of the whole tetrahedron.   Find its mid-point P.   Take AP to be 1 unit long.
2. Draw a semicircle below AB with radius AP and centre P.

3. Using the method for drawing a regular hexagon (see page 11), mark off arcs with radius AP around the semicircle to find the points C and D. Join PC and PD.
4. Draw PE $2/\sqrt{3} \approx 1.155$ units long at right angles to AP to bisect the angle CPD. (Derive the method by considering fig 23, page 12.) Mark the point where PE cuts the semicircle as T (fig. 187).
5. With radius AP and centre T, draw arcs to cut the semicircle at U and V.
6. Draw PF to pass through U and PG to pass through V. Both PF and PG are equal to PE ≈ 1.155 units long. The lines PE, PF and PG are shown as broken since they are not to be folded. PF bisects the angle APC and PG bisects the angle DPB.
7. Join AF and BG, checking that the angles PAF and PBG are right angles.
8. Join FE and EG. FCE and EDG should be straight lines.
9. Produce CE to M with EM = CE = $1/\sqrt{3} \approx 0.577$ units long.
10. Draw EK at right angles to CEM. EK = $1/\sqrt{6} \approx 0.408$ units long.
11. With radius EK and centre K, draw a circle. The points N, Q and L will all lie on this circle.

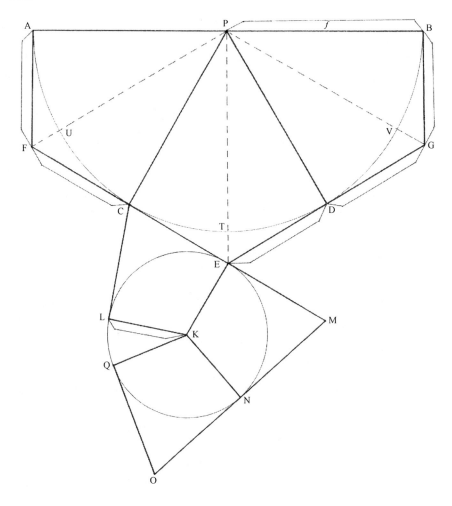

Fig. 187

12. With radius CE and centres C and M, draw arcs to cut this circle to find the positions of L and N. Join CL and LK, checking that the angle CLK is a right angle.
13. Join MN and produce it to O with NO = MN. Join KN, checking that the angle MNK is a right angle.
14. With radius CE and centre O, draw an arc to cut the circle with centre K at Q. Join OQ and KQ. Check that the angle KQO is a right angle. The distance from L to Q should be exactly one-ninth the length of AB.

Draw flaps where shown. Stick flap *f* first.

Further Dissections

We have discussed here only those dissections of the tetrahedron which may be worth our while constructing. It is possible in theory to dissect the tetrahedron into congruent parts in an infinite number of different ways. For example, each face of the tetrahedron has threefold rotational symmetry, and, as we see in fig 188, three lines which meet at the centre of a face at an angle of 120° to one another in any orientation will dissect the triangular face into three congruent parts. Cuts made along these lines perpendicular to this face will dissect the tetrahedron into three congruent (pyramidal) parts. Again, if the line which cuts in half the piece shown in fig. 164, page 55, is rotated about the centre of the square to any position such as in fig. 189, then cuts on the two halves of the tetrahedron made along this line perpendicular to the square face will divide the tetrahedron into four congruent parts. The small pyramid in fig. 146 on page 49, as well as any other dissections of the tetrahedron which have threefold rotational symmetry about some axis, can also be cut into three congruent parts in an infinite number of different ways.

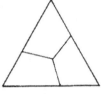

Fig. 188   Fig. 189

We shall return later (page 128) to consider a modification of the net shown in fig. 187 to produce a solid model, four of which will fit together to make a hollow tetrahedron which encloses a space of the right shape, size and orientation to contain the small tetrahedron which is dual to the large one.

Journeys on the Surface of the Regular Tetrahedron.

If we remove one face of the regular tetrahedron and look inside, we see a triangle with three lines (edges) meeting at the centre (fig. 190). This is the *Schlegel* view of the tetrahedron, in which we see all six edges, all four vertices, and three of the faces, the fourth face being represented here by the region surrounding the figure.

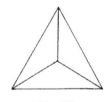

Fig. 190

As it happens the Schlegel diagram is identical with the plan or "bird's-eye" view of the tetrahedron shown in fig. 127, page 43, the view from directly above when the tetrahedron is resting on one face.

On a regular tetrahedron with edges of unit length, the shortest path which visits each vertex at least once before returning to the start is four units long. We see one such path drawn on the Schlegel diagram in fig. 191.

The shortest path which passes along each of the six (unit) edges of the tetrahedron at least once before returning to the start, has to be at least eight units long. The Schlegel diagram for the tetrahedron is not *traversable* (see page 35), having four odd nodes (vertices), and there is no way in which we can travel along each arc (edge) once only and return to the start. To make the diagram traversable, we have to make all the vertices even, and we do this by adding two extra arcs to the figure, each arc joining a different pair of nodes. Fig. 192 shows one way of doing this. These extra arcs allow us to pass along two edges in both directions. The eight arcs of the modified diagram represent the eight units of a journey which passes along all the edges of the tetrahedron and returns to the start, with two edges being traversed twice, once in each direction. Fig. 193 shows one such possible journey.

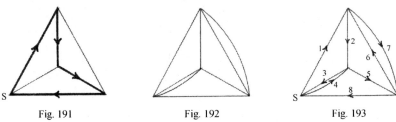

| Fig. 191 | Fig. 192 | Fig. 193 |

No journey between any two points on the surface of a regular tetrahedron need be longer than the distance from a vertex to the centre of the opposite face. Fig. 194 shows the net of a tetrahedron with one face (D) drawn in each of three possible positions, and with its centre each time marked as F. There are three possible shortest routes from V to F, and each route clearly passes through the mid-point of one of the edges separating V from F. When the net is cut out and folded into a tetrahedron, the three faces marked D will come together as the face opposite the vertex at V. If a pin or other sharp point is pushed through this face, preferably close to an edge, each of the three faces will have a small hole in it when the net is flattened, say, at the points marked G in fig. 194. If the distance from V to G_1 looks longer than the distance from V to F, we have only to look at the other positions of G to see that there is at least one other route, shorter than VF, which will take us from V to G (here VG_3).

Fig 195 shows another net of a tetrahedron. When the net is made up, the points V_1, V_2 and V_3 will all come together at one vertex, V, and so F is the centre of the face opposite the vertex V. Any point G on the net is clearly closer than F is to at least one of the points labelled V, that is to say, at least one of the lengths GV_1, GV_2 or GV_3 will be shorter than, say FV_1. Here it is GV_3.

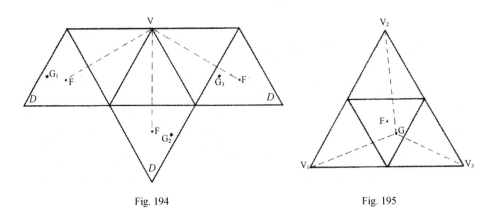

| Fig. 194 | Fig. 195 |

On the other hand, there may be another point H on the surface of the tetrahedron whose distance to G appears to be greater than the distance from F to V_2, as in fig. 196. However, consider the line HG moved by translation to H_1G_1 so that H_1 coincides with V_2. G_1 is still further away from V_2 than F is, but is also still closer to V_3, which is the position of H_1 on the made-up tetrahedron. That is to say, the shortest route from G to H is equal in length to the distance from G_1 to V_3. In fact, no matter where we place G on the surface of the tetrahedron, it will always be closer to V_1 or to V_2 or to V_3, that is, to V, than F is, unless it happens to coincide with F.

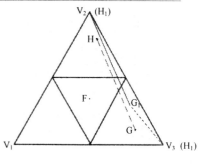

Fig. 196

Rings of rotating tetrahedra

We can fold a rectangular strip of paper in a such a way that, when we twist it, it takes the form of a number of tetrahedra joined at their edges. Fig. 198 is the net for such a model, which will, when folded and stuck and joined at its ends, give a rotating ring of ten tetrahedra.

1. Draw AB ten units long, with marks at unit intervals.
2. Draw the equilateral triangles ACD and EBF, with sides two units long (fig. 197). Join DF and produce DF one unit in each direction to G and H. Mark unit intervals along GH.
3. Join appropriate marks on AB and GH to give a pattern of smaller equilateral triangles and rhombuses.
4. Draw IJ eleven units long and parallel to AB and GH, to pass through the points where the rhombuses meet. Draw the triangles P and Q (fig. 198). Draw flaps where shown.
5. Score and fold the solid lines of the net in the usual way, but score the broken lines on the back of the net so that they fold the other way and form the edges where the ten tetrahedra join.

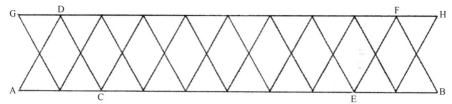

Fig. 197

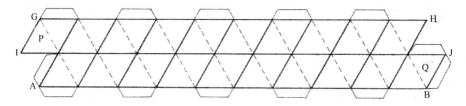

Fig. 198

Note that each flap is stuck to an edge which belongs to its own set of four triangles arranged in a line, as in fig. 199. It should be easy to work out how the end triangles are to be joined once the central tetrahedra have been made. Triangle P is to be stuck last of all.

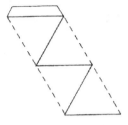

Fig. 199

We can make the net longer or shorter, to produce as many tetrahedra as we wish. Six tetrahedra or more can be joined to form a ring, but a ring consisting of fewer than eight tetrahedra will not rotate. A ring of 22 or more tetrahedra can be knotted.

A rotating model with fourteen tetrahedra appears in *Mathematical Curiosities 3*, Jenkins and Wild (Tarquin), under the title "Seven Colour Rotating Ring", using a net in which the triangles for each tetrahedron are slightly rearranged, and which incidentally makes it easier to make a long strip by joining shorter ones.

Chapter 7

THE REGULAR OCTAHEDRON

Eight congruent equilateral triangles fit together in space to form the regular octahedron. Four triangles meet at each vertex of the solid; two triangles meet along each edge. Since eight triangles have 8 x 3 = 24 sides, the octahedron must have 24 ÷ 2 = 12 edges; and since eight triangles have 8 x 3 = 24 corners, the octahedron must have 24 ÷ 4 = 6 vertices. Euler's relation, V + F = E + 2, holds for the octahedron: 6 + 8 = 12 + 2. (Since in this chapter we shall not meet any octahedron which is not regular, we shall henceforward usually refer to the regular octahedron simply as "the octahedron".)

We can look at the octahedron in two very different ways. First we may look at it when one vertex is placed vertically above the opposite vertex (fig. 200). It can then be seen either as being made from two square-based pyramids, one upside down to the other, joined at their bases; or as being one such pyramid together with its reflection in a mirror lying on the plane of its base. We can take any pair of opposite vertices to be the upper and lower vertices, and there are three such pairs. Halfway between two opposite vertices is a square cross-section of the octahedron framed by four of its edges. The twelve edges of the complete octahedron may be seen as framing three such squares, which we may call "equatorial" squares.

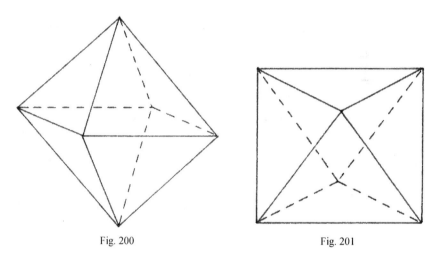

Fig. 200   Fig. 201

Alternatively we can set the octahedron on one of its faces (fig. 201). It then appears as an equilateral triangular *antiprism* with a "top" triangular face and a "bottom" triangular face joined by six other triangular faces. These six "other" faces will form the "ring" of triangles which we shall draw first when we build the octahedron from either of the nets shown in figs. 202 and 204 overleaf.

Models of the Regular Octahedron

We can make a model of an octahedron from a net of eight equilateral triangles which will fold together to enclose space. Out of the thirty-five distinct ways of joining eight triangles along their sides, only eleven will give nets for an octahedron (see pages 86 and 87 for drawings of these nets).

Any net of a regular octahedron may be drawn by joining intersections on a base pattern of overlapping circles (figs. 202, 203). This pattern of circles is simply an extension or overflow of the extended flower pattern shown in fig. 16 on page 10. For practical purposes it is of course enough to draw arcs of circles rather than full circles, as in fig. 204 overleaf.

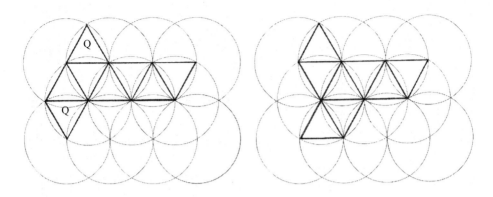

Fig. 202   Fig. 203

The net in fig. 204 can be drawn by a process similar to that used for drawing the net of a regular tetrahedron (see figs. 125, 126, page 43).

1. Draw AECB three units long, marked at unit intervals. Draw the equilateral triangle ACD.
2. With radius AE draw arcs centred at A and C to find the mid-points I and J of AD and DC respectively, and also draw the equilateral triangles CFB and CGB.
3. With radius AE draw arcs centred on B and F to cut at H. Join HB. Join IH, which must pass through J and F, and also join EI and EJ (fig. 204).

Draw flaps where shown and stick flap *f* first.

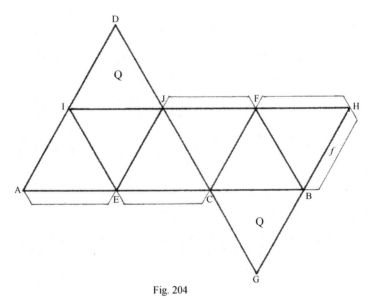

Fig. 204

As we have mentioned earlier, the nets in figs. 202 and 204 have six triangles in a row, and these triangles make the faces of the triangular antiprism, with the triangles marked Q closing the octahedron "on top" and "underneath". In the net in fig. 205 opposite there is no "top" or "underneath" to the model as we assemble it, but this particular net is very economical of material if we are cutting several nets from one sheet of card or paper.

68

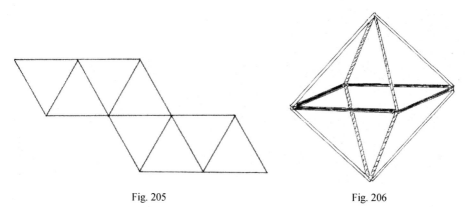

Fig. 205   Fig. 206

We may make a rigid skeleton model of the octahedron from twelve short lengths of drinking straws, threaded with shirring elastic. If we use straws of three different colours, we can show how the octahedron is made from three squares joined at their corners, two squares out of the three meeting at each vertex of the octahedron (fig. 206).

Three Squares Make a Regular Octahedron

We can make a model to show how the octahedron can be built on a framework of its "equatorial" squares.

1. Cut three squares from card, with the side of each square, say, 6 cm long.
2. Cut slots along the diagonals as shown in fig. 207. Square A has a slot from a corner to the centre of the square, and two slots from opposite corners, each slot reaching halfway to the centre. (It is important not to make the slots too wide: ideally each slot should be exactly as wide as the thickness of the card.) Square B has one slot only, from a corner to the centre of the square; while square C is cut in half along one diagonal, each half having a slot cut from the centre of the square half way to a corner.
3. Slot together squares A and B first, and then slot the two half-squares of C on to square A (fig. 208 overleaf). The corners of the model can be fixed with sellotape so that they stay in place and do not come apart.

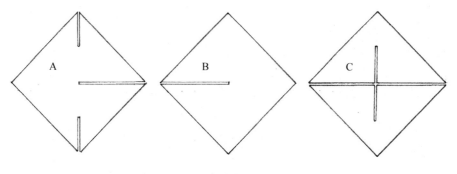

Fig. 207

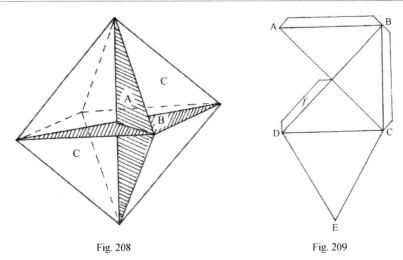

Fig. 208   Fig. 209

We can see clearly how these three squares give a framework to the regular octahedron if we cut out any net of the octahedron and wrap it around this framework, making the edges of the net a millimetre or two longer than the sides of the squares to ensure a proper fit.

If we wish we can fit the triangular faces separately onto the framework. The net in fig. 209 will make a triangular pyramid which will fit into any one of the recesses to give the framework a triangular face.

1. Draw a square ABCD the same size as the squares in fig. 207.
2. Draw the diagonals of the square and erase AD.
3. Draw the equilateral triangle CDE on CD.

Draw flaps where shown and stick flap *f* first. Eight pyramids together will make the complete octahedron, so this is one way of dissecting a regular octahedron into eight congruent parts (see below, page 78).

Views of the Regular Octahedron

A.   A plan view of the octahedron with a vertex uppermost is simply a square together with its diagonals (fig. 210). A side view, looking towards a horizontal edge along the line of symmetry which passes through that edge, shows the octahedron as two isosceles triangles, each the mirror image of the other, reflected in a common base line which is the true length of an edge (fig. 211). To find the height of these two triangles we need to do some trigonometry inside the octahedron.

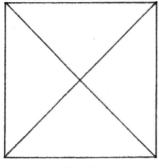

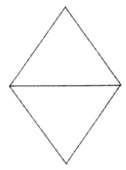

Fig. 210   Fig. 211

The Trigonometry of the Regular Octahedron

The height of the octahedron with a vertex uppermost is equal to the length of the diagonal of any of its equatorial squares. In fig. 212, which shows a section of the octahedron exposed by a cut vertically downwards through the equatorial square ABCD, AC is the length of the diagonal of the horizontal equatorial square, while BD is the height of the octahedron, and together with AC is a diagonal of the vertical equatorial square ABCD. If the edge of the octahedron is one unit long, then by Pythagoras the diagonal of each square will be √2 units long, and this is the combined height of the two isosceles triangles in fig. 211. The height of each separate triangle will be half this, that is, ½√2 ≈ 0.707 units, a length which, using compasses, we

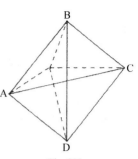

Fig. 212

may copy from the plan view in fig. 210 as the distance from the centre of the square to a corner. This is all we need to know in order to draw the side view shown in fig. 211. The height of each triangle will be ½√2 units, and, again by Pythagoras, the equal sides of the isosccles triangles will each be √3/2 ≈ 0.87 units long.

More Views of the Regular Octahedron

B.   To draw an oblique view of the octahedron which shows as many faces as possible, which from any direction is never more than four, we proceed as follows.

1. Draw a parallelogram to represent the horizontal equatorial square (fig. 213), with the corners of the parallelogram more or less equally spaced horizontally (this ensures that the visible and the hidden lines of the finished view can be seen clearly separated).
2. Draw the diagonals of this parallelogram, and from the point where they cross draw lines vertically upwards and downwards, each half the length of the long diagonal of the parallelogram, finding this length by drawing a semicircle (fig. 214).

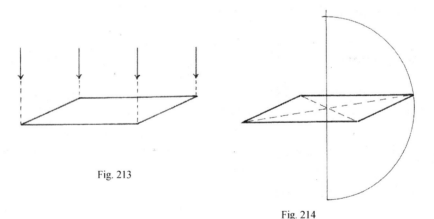

Fig. 213

Fig. 214

3. Join both ends of the vertical line to each corner of the parallelogram to give an *oblique* view of the octahedron. Firm up the eight lines which represent the visible edges of the octahedron, and draw the four hidden edges as broken lines. The finished view shows four visible faces and four hidden faces (fig. 215 overleaf).

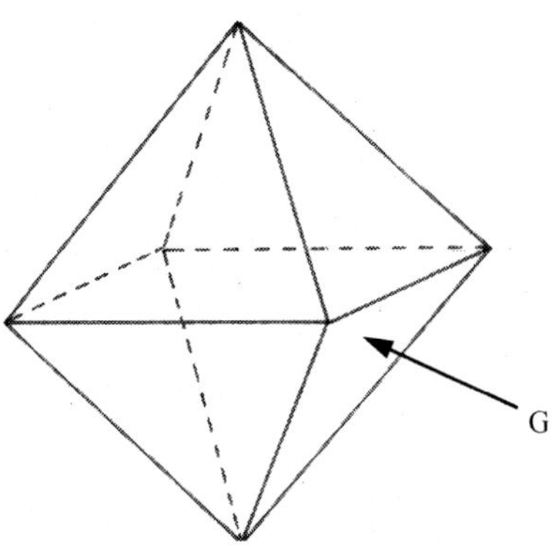

Fig. 215 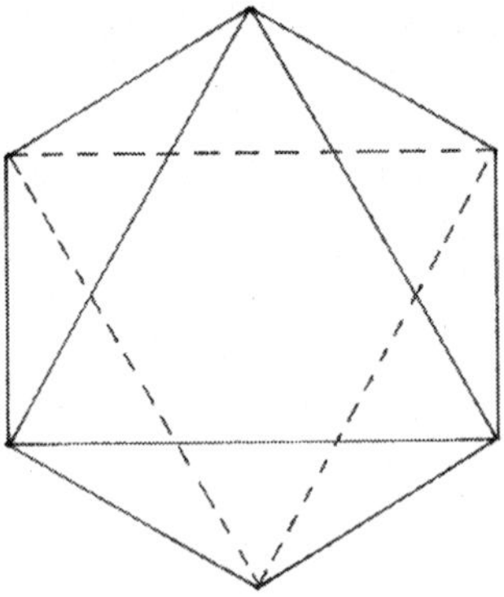   Fig. 216

Note that if we look directly at a vertex along an axis of rotational symmetry (see page 75), that is, from the direction G in fig. 215, we shall see the octahedron again as a square with its two diagonals, as in fig. 210, but standing not on a side but on a corner.

C. Viewed directly from above when it is resting on a face, the octahedron appears as an equilateral triangle within a surrounding hexagon (fig. 216). To draw this view:

1. Draw a circle of a suitable radius, say, 3 cm. Mark six points equally around the circle and draw a regular hexagon (see page 11). This hexagon is the *Petrie* hexagon of the octahedron (see page 76).
2. Join three of these six points alternately to obtain the triangle which is the top face.
3. Join the other three points with broken lines to obtain the triangle which is the hidden face on which the octahedron is resting. The diagram shows all twelve edges of the octahedron, both visible and hidden.

D. We can draw two more views of the octahedron when it is resting on one face. The "front" view will show one face facing us, with two other faces visible, one on either side (fig. 217). The outline of this view will be a rectangle with its base equal in length to the edge of the octahedron, and with its height equal to the perpendicular distance between opposite faces, a distance we have yet to calculate. (The second view appears in fig. 220 opposite.)

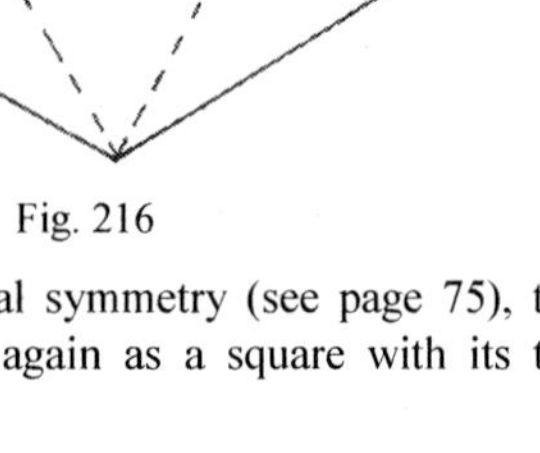

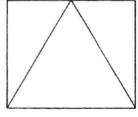

Fig. 217

Some More Trigonometry

The perpendicular distance between opposite faces is the length of a line joining the centres of opposite faces, the line RQ in fig. 218 opposite. B and D are the mid-points of opposite edges, and P is both the centre of the octahedron and the mid-point of RQ.

Fig. 219 shows the cross-section ABCD of the octahedron in fig. 218, which is an "interior" view of the side view shown in fig. 211. BD is one unit long. We know from our study of the regular tetrahedron (page 45) that the centre of a triangle lies one-third of the way along a median from a side, so we see that BR (fig. 218) is one-third of BA, or $\frac{1}{3} \times \sqrt{3}/2 = \sqrt{3}/6$, and BP = ½. By Pythagoras, RP $= \sqrt{(\{\frac{1}{2}\}^2 - \{\sqrt{3}/6\}^2)} = \sqrt{(\frac{1}{4} - \frac{3}{36})} = \sqrt{(\frac{1}{4} - \frac{1}{12})} = \sqrt{(\frac{1}{6})} = 1/\sqrt{6}$. RQ is double this distance or $2/\sqrt{6} = \sqrt{4}/\sqrt{6} = \sqrt{(\frac{2}{3})} \approx 0.816$. So the height of the rectangle in fig. 217 is about 0.82 units.

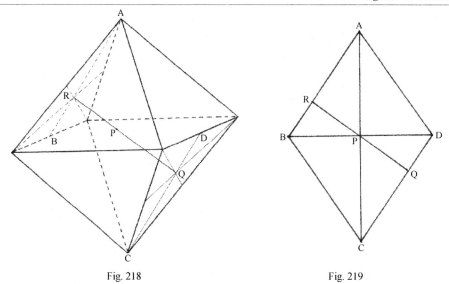

Fig. 218   Fig. 219

Further Views of the Regular Octahedron

E. In fig. 220 we see a "side" view of the octahedron when it is resting on one face. This view, in which we are looking directly at the edge AB, is simply a "tipped-over" version of the view shown in fig. 211 on page 70. This means that we could in fact have used fig. 211 to measure or to calculate the perpendicular distance (RQ in fig. 218) between opposite faces!

Note that this distance, $\sqrt{(2/3)}$, is also the height of a regular tetrahedron of edge 1 unit (see page 49). We shall see later (page 136) how two such tetrahedra fitted one to each of two opposite faces of the regular octahedron form a *rhomboid*, one of whose views is shown in fig. 221. The shaded triangles represent the two tetrahedra attached to the octahedron whose side view appears in fig. 220.

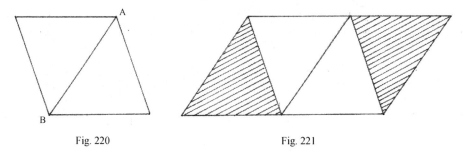

Fig. 220   Fig. 221

The Volume of a Regular Octahedron.

As we have seen, we may regard the octahedron as being made from two square-based pyramids placed base to base. If we take the length of edge of the solid to be a units, then each pyramid will have a base whose area is a^2 square units, and its height, equal to half the diagonal of this base, will be $\frac{1}{2}\sqrt{2}a$ units. The volume of each pyramid will be $(\frac{1}{2}\sqrt{2}a \times a^2)/3$ and the volume of the octahedron will be double this, or $\sqrt{2}a^3/3$ cubic units. This gives it a volume which is $\sqrt{2}/3 \approx 0.47$ times, or just under half, the volume of a cube with the same length of edge, and exactly four times the volume of a regular tetrahedron with the same length of edge (see page 50).

A Collapsible Octahedron

We have seen earlier how to make both a cube and a regular tetrahedron which can be made to collapse or fold flat (pages 19 & 52). Making an octahedron which will fold flat is a much easier task.

1. Inside a circle of radius, say, 3 to 4 cm draw a regular hexagon (see page 11) with one main ("diametral") diagonal horizontal (fig. 222).
2. Divide the hexagon into six equilateral triangles.
3. With the same radius as in 1. above, draw arcs centred at A and B to cut at C. (fig. 223).
4. Draw a circle with centre C to pass through A and B, and inside this new circle draw a hexagon divided into six more equilateral triangles (fig. 224).
5. Erase two triangles from each hexagon. The net has a line of symmetry in AB (fig. 225).

Draw flaps as shown and then cut out the net. Score and fold along all the lines, and fold one half of the net over the other half, sticking all the flaps at once (fig. 226). Press on the vertices at D and E, will make the flat model rise to form an octahedron.

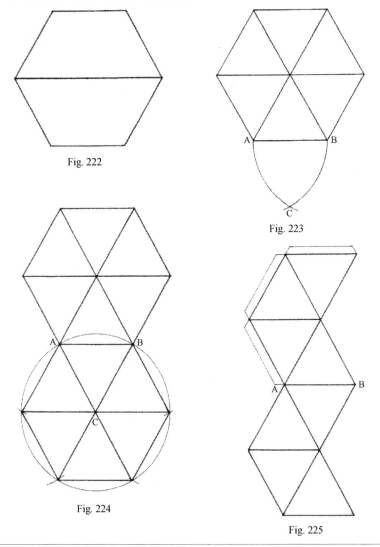

Fig. 222

Fig. 223

Fig. 224

Fig. 225

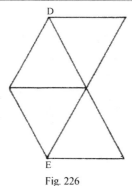

Fig. 226

The Symmetry of a Regular Octahedron

Each of the three "equatorial" squares of an octahedron lies on a plane of reflective symmetry of the solid. Also a plane of symmetry passes through any two opposite vertices and the mid-points of a pair of opposite edges (fig. 227). Since an octahedron has twelve edges, it will have six such planes of symmetry, making a total of nine planes of symmetry in all.

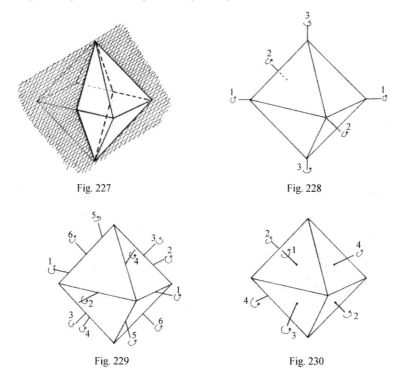

Fig. 227   Fig. 228

Fig. 229   Fig. 230

The octahedron also has thirteen axes of rotational symmetry. Three of these, each of order four, pass through opposite vertices (fig. 228); six axes, each of order two, pass through the mid-points of opposite edges (fig. 229); and four axes, each of order 3, pass through the centres of opposite faces (fig. 230).

Note that thirteen is half the total number of faces, edges and vertices of the octahedron. We asked earlier (pages 33 and 51) if this might be a coincidence. In fact for any regular solid the number of axes of symmetry will be half the total number of its faces, edges and vertices. This is because any axis of symmetry must pass through the surface of the solid twice. For the cube and octahedron, axes of symmetry will pass through opposite pairs of vertices or through mid-points of opposite edges or through centres of opposite faces. For the regular tetrahedron axes of symmetry will pass through the mid-points of opposite edges, or through a vertex and the centre of the opposite face. For every regular solid, each vertex, mid-point of edge, and centre of face will therefore have an axis of symmetry running through it, and it follows that the total number of faces, edges and vertices must necessarily be double the number of axes of symmetry of the solid.

The *symmetry number* of the octahedron is twenty-four. If we pack an octahedron into an octahedron-shaped box, any one of its eight faces may lie against a particular inside face of the box; and this first face can be placed by rotation in any of three different positions. Eight times three is twenty-four.

It is worth noting that the regular octahedron has exactly the same symmetries as the cube, owing to the fact that the cube and the regular octahedron are *dual* to each other. We shall look at this dual relationship in more detail later on (page 121 f.).

Petrie Polygons

W. W. Rouse Ball, in *Mathematical Recreations and Essays*, page 135, has comments to make about the symmetry of the Platonic solids. He first introduces the *Petrie polygon*. "Among the edges of a regular polyhedron, we easily pick out a skew polygon or zig-zag, in which the first and second edges are sides of one face, the second and third edges are sides of another face, and so on. This zig-zag is known as a *Petrie polygon* ... Each finite polyhedron can be ... projected on to a plane in such a way that one Petrie polygon becomes a regular polygon with the rest of the projection inside it." In fig. 95, page 32, we see the Petrie hexagon of the cube; in fig. 158, page 53, we see the Petrie square of the regular tetrahedron; in fig. 216, page 72, we see the Petrie hexagon of the regular octahedron. Later we shall meet the Petrie decagons of the regular dodecahedron and of the regular icosahedron (figs. 272 and 310, pages 93 and 110).

Rouse Ball points out that if h is the number of sides to the Petrie polygon of a polyhedron, the polyhedron will have $3h/2$ planes of symmetry. He also points out that the number of axes of symmetry, $(F + V + E)/2$, is more simply $E + 1$:

$F + V = E + 2 \Rightarrow F + V + E = 2E + 2 \Rightarrow (F + V + E)/2 = E + 1$

Dissections of the Regular Octahedron.

Two Parts

a) We can dissect the regular octahedron into two congruent parts by cutting it along any of its planes of symmetry. If we make the cut through four of its vertices, that is, along the plane of an equatorial square, each part will be a square-based pyramid, whose net is shown in fig. 231 opposite.

1. Draw a regular hexagon inside a circle with one main diagonal vertical. Divide it into six equilateral triangles and then erase two of these to leave the four triangles shown.
2. Produce the line through AC towards E.
3. With radius AB, draw an arc centred at C to find the position of E on AC produced.
4. With radius AB, draw arcs centred at C and D to cut at F. Join DF and EF.

Draw flaps as shown and stick flap *f* first.

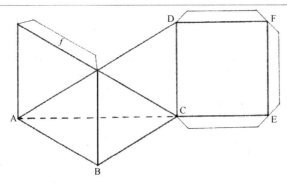

Fig. 231

b) We can also dissect the octahedron into two congruent parts by cutting it through two vertices and the mid-points of a pair of opposite edges, e.g., through ABCD in fig. 218, page 73. Each part will have seven faces, of which one will be a rhombus, two will be equilateral triangles, and four will be 30°-60°-90° right-angled triangles. The net is shown in fig. 232.

1. Draw a line AB equal in length to the edge of the octahedron.
2. With radius AB, draw two circles centred at A and B to intersect at C and D. Produce AB to meet the circles at E and F.
3. Draw the rhombus ACBD and the rhombus ECFD.
4. Produce the sides of the rhombus ACBD to meet the sides of the rhombus ECFD at G, H, I and J.
5. Draw an arc with radius DJ and centred at D, to cut an arc with radius AB centred at J. The two arcs will cut at K.
6. Draw arcs with radius DJ and centred at J and K to cut at L. Draw the rhombus DJLK.

Erase the lines EH, EG, IF and JF. Draw flaps on AH, HC, CI, IB and DG. Stick the flap on AH first and then the flap on IB. The angles of the rhombus DJLK are 109.47° (= $\tan^{-1} {}^-2\sqrt{2}$, which is the *dihedral* angle of the octahedron) and 70.53°.

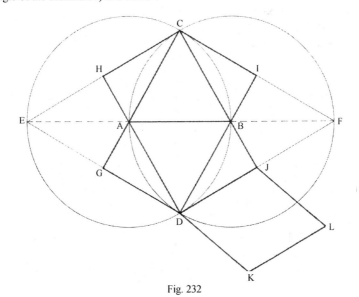

Fig. 232

Eight Parts

a) If we take a square-based pyramid with all its edges equal in length and cut vertically downwards through all its slant edges (that is, with cuts perpendicular to the diagonals of the square base), we shall have four congruent pieces in the shape of triangular pyramids (fig. 233). Eight of these pyramids will fit together to form the octahedron. Each pyramid will have a face of the octahedron as one of its faces; the other three faces will be right-angled isosceles triangles. Its net, with instructions for drawing it, appeared in fig. 209 on page 70, and is shown again in fig. 234.

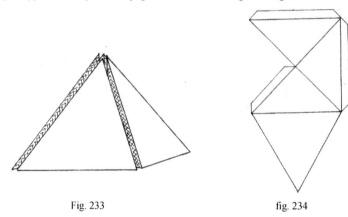

Fig. 233   fig. 234

This pyramid is the same shape as the triangular pyramid whose volume we shall calculate on pages 212 and 213; the answer to the question we ask there is that eight such pyramids make a regular octahedron.

On page 25 we saw how to make a model of six pyramids which folded inwards to make a cube, and which folded outwards to make a rhombic dodecahedron. We can tape together the equilateral faces of eight pyramids, each built from the net shown in fig. 234, in any of the configurations which give a net of the octahedron (see page 88), so that they fold inwards to form a regular octahedron. The resulting model will not however fold outwards to give a named solid, the pyramids being a little too high for their faces to join in the plane to form rhombuses, but the resulting shape is nevertheless quite interesting and decorative.

Each of these pyramids could be dissected into three or six small parts by making cuts perpendicular to the three medians of the equilateral triangular face, giving a total of twenty-four or forty-eight congruent parts into which the octahedron itself could be dissected, but we do not suggest this as a practical task for the classroom.

b) If we take the square-based pyramid we made from the net in fig. 231 and make cuts symmetrically downwards though its slant faces, the cuts passing through the mid-points of opposite edges of its base, we shall have four square-based skew pyramids (fig. 235). Eight of these pyramids will fit together to form the octahedron. The net of one such pyramid is shown in fig. 237.

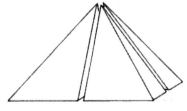

Fig. 235

1. Draw a circle, centre O, with radius equal to half the length of an edge of the pyramid. Draw a horizontal diameter AB. This will be equal in length to the edge of the pyramid.

2. With radius OA, draw two arcs centred at A to cut the circle at C and D. Join AC, CB, AD and DB (fig. 236).
3. Draw two arcs to cut at E, one with radius AB centred at D and the other with radius BD centred at B (fig. 236). Join BE and DE.
4. With radius OA, draw an arc centred at D to cut DE at F. F will be the mid-point of DE.
5. Join BF and produce this line to G, where FG = DF. Draw arcs with radius DF centred at D and G to cut at H, the fourth corner of the square DFGH.

Draw flaps as shown and stick flap *f* first.

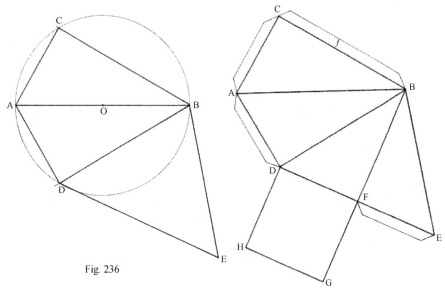

Fig. 236

Fig. 237

The proportions of the various lines in the net are as follows: if AB is 2, then AC = AD = DF = FE = 1; BC = BD = BE = √3; and BF = √2. These four pyramids can also be assembled to form the half-octahedron whose net is shown in fig. 232.

Looking at the plan view of the octahedron, we can see that any straight cut passing vertically downwards through a vertex (fig. 238) will cut it into two congruent parts. Any two such cuts made at right angles to each other (fig. 239) will cut it into four congruent parts. None of these possible cuts, infinite in number, necessarily lies along a plane of reflective symmetry of the solid.

Fig. 238

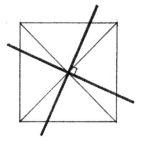

Fig. 239

Other Dissections

a) Another cut, which neither lies along a plane of symmetry nor passes through a vertex of the octahedron, nevertheless divides it into two congruent parts. This cut passes equidistantly between two opposite faces of the octahedron, and is made parallel to the base of the octahedron and at half its altitude when it is viewed as a triangular anti-prism (fig. 240). The two pieces will each have a regular hexagon as one face. [We recall that a cube can also be cut into two parts each of which has a regular hexagon as one face (fig. 69, page 25).] The cut passes through the mid-points of six edges of the octahedron (fig. 241), the net of each part being shown in fig. 243.

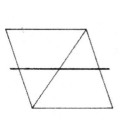

Fig. 240

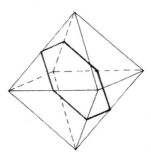

Fig. 241

1. Draw a circle whose radius is equal to the length of an edge of the octahedron. Inside this circle draw a regular hexagon with its three main (diametral) diagonals.
2. Draw an equilateral triangle on the side AB of the hexagon.
3. Find the mid-points of the sides of the hexagon. Join alternate mid-points to obtain two equilateral triangles in the form of a star (fig. 242).
4. Erase appropriate lines to leave the net shown in fig. 243. Draw flaps as shown and stick flap *f* first.

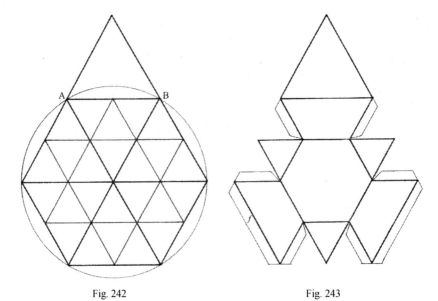

Fig. 242

Fig. 243

Each of these two parts can itself be divided into congruent parts: how many? and how?

Answer: into two parts; or into three (two different ways); or into six (fig. 244). (This is a plan view of the piece when it is resting on its hexagonal face.) This gives a method of dividing the whole octahedron into four or six or twelve congruent parts. We can also divide one piece into three congruent parts in an infinite number of different ways by three cuts which meet at 120° to one another at the centre of the top triangular face (fig. 245).

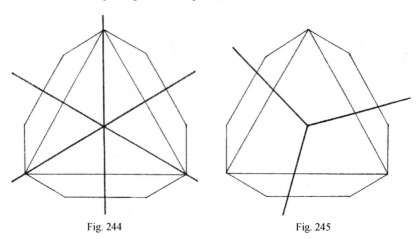

Fig. 244   Fig. 245

Since the octahedron has eight faces, we can make four such hexagonal cuts along planes midway between four different pairs of opposite faces, and we can show each cut by a hexagon drawn on the surface of the octahedron. Any one face is crossed by three hexagons out of the four, and the hexagons divide each face into four equilateral triangles. The four hexagons themselves combine to make the edges of a *cuboctahedron* (fig. 246), as did the four hexagons drawn on the cube (see fig. 73, page 27).

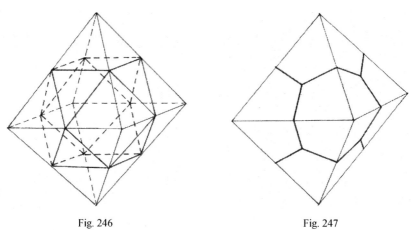

Fig. 246   Fig. 247

b) We can dissect the octahedron into six congruent parts in another way. We draw lines from the centre of each face to the midpoints of the sides of that face (fig. 247). These lines divide the surface of the octahedron into six regions, all the points in any one region being nearer to one particular vertex than to any other. The boundaries of these six regions mark the position of cuts to be made directly towards the centre of the octahedron. The two lines from the mid-point of each edge to the centres of the two faces which meet along that edge together form a straight line, albeit angled at the edge, so that we need simply to make a straight cut between face centres. Fig. 248, which is based on fig. 211, page 70, shows one such cut, PQ. (See also fig. 181, page 59. The remarks made on that page concerning the net of the tetrahedron apply also to the net of the octahedron.)

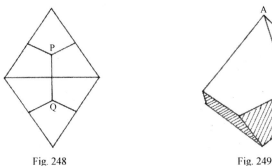

Fig. 248   Fig. 249

Fig. 249 gives a general view of one of these six pieces. A is a vertex of the octahedron, and the shaded faces are the cut faces. The net for one piece of the octahedron is shown in fig. 251 opposite. Six of these pieces will fit together to form the complete octahedron.

In fig. 250 opposite, A is a vertex of the octahedron and B is the mid-point of an edge. For convenience we take the length of AB to be 1 unit.

1. Draw AB vertically. Draw about three-quarters of a circle with centre A and radius AB.
2. With radius AB, mark arcs around the circle from B to fix the positions of C, D, E and F, which, like B, are also mid-points of edges of the octahedron. Join AC, AD, AE and AF.
3. Draw AG $2\sqrt{3}/3$ units ≈ 1.15 units long to bisect the angle BAC. With radius AG, (i) draw about three-quarters of a circle centred at A, and (ii) mark arcs around the circle from G to fix the position of the points H, I and J. The points G, H, I and J mark the centres of faces of the octahedron.
4. Join DH, HG, GI, IJ and JF. These lines will be tangents to the smaller part-circle at D, C, B, E and F respectively (fig. 250).
5. Produce CH to K with HK = HC. Draw two arcs with radius AB (= 1 unit) centred at C and K to cut at L (fig. 251).
6. Draw a circle with centre L and radius LC (= 1 unit). With radius CK, mark arcs around this circle from K to find the positions of M and N. Join KM and MN. P and Q are the mid-points of KM and MN.
7. With radius CK draw an arc centred on C to cut the circle centre L at S. U is the mid-point of CS. With radius CK draw an arc centred on N to cut the circle at R. T is the mid-point of NR. Join NT, UC, LH, LP, LQ, LT and LU.

Draw flaps where shown and stick flap f first.

If the net has been drawn accurately, then TU = $16/9\sqrt{3}$ ≈ 1.03 units in length. For example, if AB = 4 cm, then TU should be 4.1 cm. The angle HCU is the dihedral angle of the octahedron, which is $2\tan^{-1}\sqrt{2}$ (= $\tan^{-1}{}^{-}2\sqrt{2}$, see page 77) ≈ 109.47°.

The adaptation of this net shown in fig. 348 on page 125 will fold into a solid, six of which will appear to fit together and form an octahedron. However this octahedron will in fact enclose a hole in the shape of a cube. This cube has its vertices at the centres of the faces of the octahedron and is the dual of the regular octahedron. One edge of this dual cube will lie along HU and so will be $2\sqrt{2}/3$ ≈ 0.943 units long. It is possible also to make an octahedron model similar to this which has a detachable section, a modification of that shown in fig. 249, which when removed will reveal the dual cube in position inside the octahedron (fig. 350 on page 126).

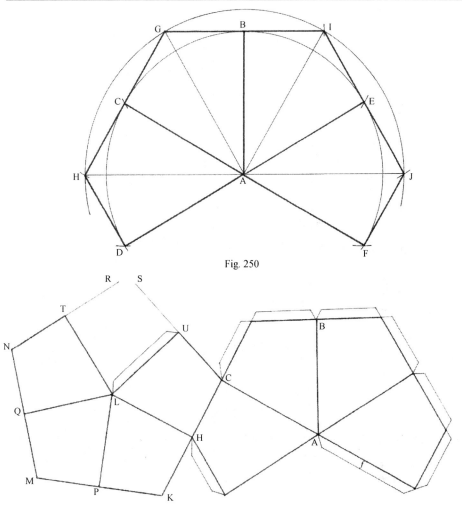

Fig. 250

Fig. 251

Journeys on the Surface of the Regular Octahedron.

We ask first: "What is the shortest path by which a wandering insect may travel from one vertex of the octahedron to the opposite vertex?" taking the length of an edge to be one unit. We solve this problem on a net of the octahedron, such as that in fig. 252 overleaf. The opposite vertices A and B are separated by two faces of the solid, and the shortest path from one vertex to the other lies in a straight line across the two faces. This line is equal in length to twice the vertical height of a face, which is twice $1 \times \sin 60° = 2 \times \sqrt{3}/2 = \sqrt{3} \approx 1.732$ units. No shortest route from A to any other point on the surface of the octahedron is longer than this. For example, the distance from A to E, halfway between B and F, by the cosine rule is $\sqrt{(1^2 + \{1/2\}^2 - 2.1.1/2.\cos 120°)} = \sqrt{(1 + 1/4 + 1/2)} = \sqrt{7/2} \approx 1.323$ units.

In fact we need at most two triangles of the net to draw the shortest path from A to any other point on the surface. On these two triangles the shortest path is the straight line joining that point to A. Note that if we mark a point C on the net in fig. 252, then the shortest distance from A to C on the *solid* is simply that from A to D, since C and D coincide when we fold the net up to make the octahedron. If C does not lie on an edge of the octahedron, then we rotate the triangle containing C until it joins a triangle which has A as a corner (fig. 253), so AC_2 is the shortest distance from A to C.

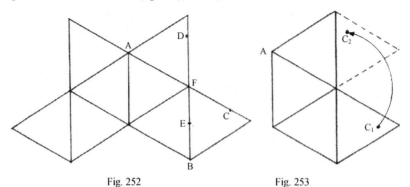

| Fig. 252 | Fig. 253 |

If we ask: "What is the shortest distance from the centre of one face of the octahedron to the centre of the opposite face?" we need fig. 254, which contains four triangles of the net. We take MN to be one unit long. K and L are the two centres, while P is the mid-point of NQ. MK is $2/3 \times \sqrt{3}/2 = \sqrt{3}/3$ units, while PL is $1/3 \times \sqrt{3}/2 = \sqrt{3}/6$ units, and MP = 1.5 units. We translate KL, the distance we wish to find, to RP where MR = $\frac{1}{2} \times$ MK = $\sqrt{3}/6$ units, and then use Pythagoras to calculate RP as $\sqrt{(1.5^2 + \{\sqrt{3}/6\}^2)} = \sqrt{(7/3)} \approx 1.53$ units. Note that this is considerably (12%) less than the shortest distance between opposite vertices.

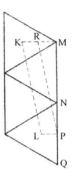

Fig. 254

Next we ask, (a) "What is the length of the shortest journey along the edges of the octahedron which visits all vertices and returns to the starting point?" and (b) "What is the length of the shortest journey which travels along every edge at least once and returns to the starting point?" To answer these questions we use the Schlegel diagram of the octahedron.

The Schlegel Diagram of the Regular Octahedron

If we imagine that the hidden base triangle in fig. 216 on page 72 has shrunk and is now contained entirely within the top triangle, taking with it the lines of the outer hexagon; and if we then firm in all its lines, we shall have the Schlegel diagram for the octahedron (fig. 255).

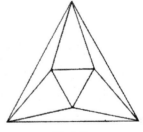

Fig. 255

A reasonably well-proportioned Schlegel diagram can be drawn in the following way.

1. Draw a circle and on it mark six points representing the six corners of a regular hexagon (see fig. 19, page 11).

2. Join alternate points to obtain two equilateral triangles making a six-pointed star (fig. 256). Join alternate corners of the hexagon inside the star to make another smaller star.

3. Join three alternate corners of the hexagon inside the smaller star to give an equilateral triangle (fig. 257). Join each corner of this triangle to the nearest two corners of the triangle ABC, and erase the unwanted lines.

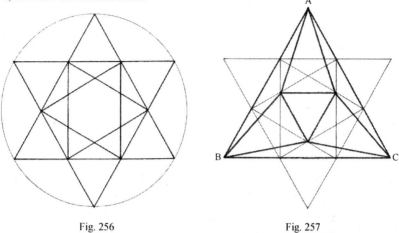

Fig. 256   Fig. 257

Of course, any rough sketch of this diagram will do for practical purposes, as long as it is *topologically* equivalent to fig. 255, with six nodes, twelve arcs and eight regions (seven plus the outside region) clearly shown.

To answer the two questions posed on page 84 we use the Schlegel diagram in fig. 258.

a) Including the starting point there are six vertices to be visited. We need to trace a path on the diagram which visits each vertex in turn and returns to the start. Once we have passed through a vertex, we can erase all lines leading to that vertex save those by which we have entered and left it. Fig. 259 shows the single chain of lines which is left after we have travelled from A to B to C to D to E to F and back to A again. We have visited six vertices and have travelled along six lines of unit length, so our journey is six units long. No other journey through the vertices which satisfies the same conditions need be more than 6 units long.

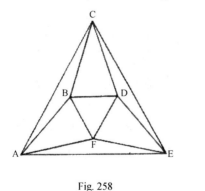
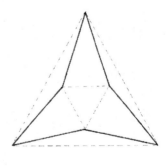

Fig. 258   Fig. 259

b) We next have to travel along each edge at least once and return to the starting point. To do this we do not need to travel over the same edge twice, since the diagram has four lines meeting at each vertex (or four *arcs* at each *node*), and so is traversable. A journey through the following points ABCDBFDEFAECA (fig. 260) is one possible solution among many. [H. E. Dudeney, in *Amusements in Mathematics*, says that there are just 1488 different routes along the edges if we start and finish at a particular vertex.]

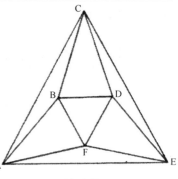

Fig. 260

The Nets of a Regular Octahedron.

In "Mathematics Teaching", no. 42, Spring 1968, A. Sanders and D. V. Smith explain how they arrive at the conclusion that there are just 11 distinct ways of combining eight equilateral triangles to form the net of a regular octahedron. They give details of a method of obtaining the nets both of cubes and of octahedra by cutting the solids along their edges. This method at the same time establishes a one-to-one correspondence between the nets of cubes and the nets of octahedra, and also shows that it is no coincidence that there is the same number of distinct nets for each solid, this being a consequence of the fact that each solid is the dual of the other.

The eleven nets of the regular octahedron are shown in fig. 261. Note that no more than four triangles may meet at a single point. The nets from (a) to (f) have six triangles in a row. When the ends of this row of triangles are joined, the two other triangles are stuck down to close the octahedron "on top" and "underneath". The nets from (g) to (i) have five triangles in a row, with a sixth on top and two more variously arranged underneath. The last two, (j) and (k), have one and two rows respectively of four triangles. Both (i) and (j) have useful reflective symmetry, and either may be used as the net for a collapsible octahedron (see page 74), while (k), being only two rows high, is very economical in material if we are cutting the nets of several octahedra from a sheet of card or paper.

In (a) we have shown by letters which triangles are opposite faces in the complete model, as we did for the cube on page 20, figs. 46 and 47. The lines show which pairs of sides are to be joined with flaps. Pupils can be asked to do the same for the other nets before they cut them out and make them up.

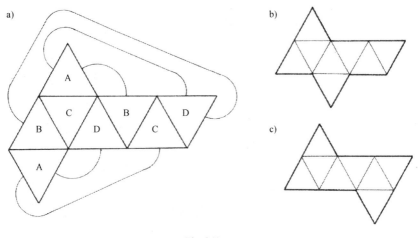

Fig. 261

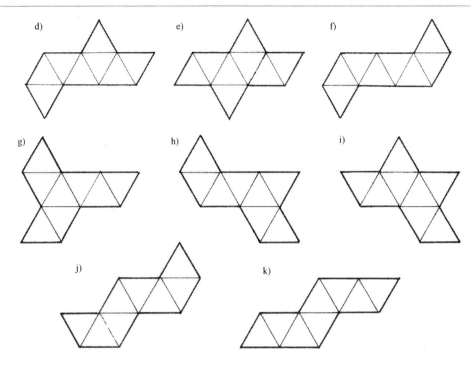

Fig. 261 (cont.)

Octahedra and Dice

Regular octahedra have been used in the past as dice. While dice in the shape of cubes have faces numbered from 1 to 6, octahedral dice have faces numbered from 1 to 8. The numbers on opposite faces of normal cube dice add up to 7; if we follow the same principle, then the numbers on opposite faces of octahedral dice should add up to 9. We may ask the usual probability questions about octahedral dice: what is the largest total we can throw on two dice? what is the most probable outcome when we throw two dice together? and so on.

A Numbering Problem

We are asked to number the faces of the octahedron in such a way that the numbers on faces which meet at the same vertex always have the same sum. Can this be done, and if so, how?

In the first place we can reason that the four numbers we can see must add up to the same total as the four numbers we cannot see, and this total must therefore be half of $1 + 2 + 3 + 4 + 5 + 6 + 7 + 8 =$ half of $36 = 18$. We now list all possible combinations of four numbers from 1 to 8 that add up to 18. These are:

8, 7, 2, 1	6, 5, 4, 3,
8, 6, 3, 1	7, 5, 4, 2
8, 5, 4, 1	7, 6, 3, 2
8, 5, 3, 2	7, 6, 4, 1

As we see, there are eight possibilities, which fall into four complementary pairs of numbers, the visible, as it were, on the left, and the invisible on the right. Since there are only six vertices to the octahedron, we need only three of these pairs at a time, and we can choose these three pairs in four different ways simply by omitting one of them.

First we choose, say, 8, 7, 2, 1, and begin numbering the faces. This is where the Schlegel diagram is useful. We place the 8 in the central triangle (any starter number will do, but we choose 8 because it is the largest). Since 7 only occurs once in combination with 8, we cannot have 7 sharing two vertices with 8, that is, on adjacent faces, so we must place 7 in an outer triangle. Each of 2 and 1 goes in an inner triangle (fig. 262).

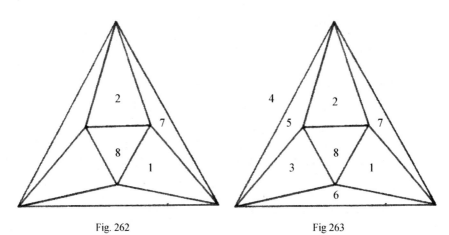

Fig. 262   Fig 263

Now we choose 8, 6, 3, 1. Since 8 and 1 are already in place, we must make sure that 6 and 3 share the same vertex as 8 and 1. We still have a third combination to choose: 6 does not occur in any other combination with 8, so it must go in an outer triangle, and 3 goes in an inner triangle. Finally we choose 8, 5, 3, 2; we place 5 in the remaining (outer) triangle, and 4 will go on the face apparently missing in the diagram, this being the face which is opposite 8 and which is represented by the large surrounding outside triangle (fig. 263).

We have left out the pair containing 8, 5, 4, 1, and we find that 4 appears on the opposite face to 8. If we leave out 8, 6, 3, 1, then 6 will appear on the opposite face to 8; and if we leave out 8, 7, 2, 1, then 7 will appear on the opposite face to 8. These numbers, 4, 6, and 7, are those which appear only once in combination with 8. The only combination we cannot leave out is 8, 5, 3, 2. If we did so, we should have to accommodate three combinations containing both 8 and 1, and no two numbers can share three vertices. Therefore we have only three distinct solutions to the problem; we can enter the numbers differently in the triangles, but these will not give significantly different solutions: each will appear as a mirror image or as a rotation of one of the three solutions we have already found.

A similar problem can be stated as follows. Just as we can never see more than three faces of a cube at any one time, so we can never see more than four faces of an octahedron at any one time. Can we write the numbers from 1 to 8 on an octahedral die so that from whatever angle we view the die, the four numbers we see always add up to the same total. The answer is "No". Why?

Neither of these problems can be solved for the numbers on a die in the shape of a cube. Why not?

Chapter 8

THE REGULAR DODECAHEDRON

[*Note*: This chapter contains frequent references to the "Golden Section" or "Golden Ratio", a number usually denoted by ø, the Greek letter *phi*. This number is calculated as ½(√5 + 1) and has an approximate value of 1.618. An account of the Golden Ratio and of its connection with the regular pentagon will be found in Appendix A, "The Regular Pentagon", pages 193 f.]

A regular dodecahedron (fig. 264), which we shall refer to from now on simply as a "dodecahedron", has twelve faces, each of which is a regular pentagon. A net for the regular dodecahedron appears in fig. 265. (We shall not investigate how many distinct ways there may be of joining twelve pentagons to form the net of a dodecahedron, but shall be content to use this one net only.)

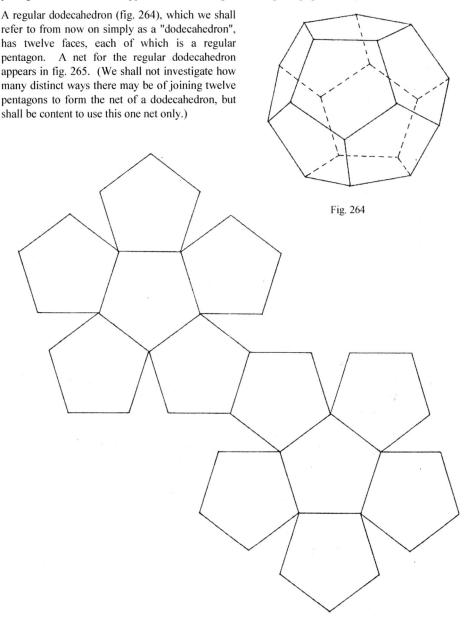

Fig. 264

Fig. 265

There is a short-cut method for drawing the net in fig. 265.

1. Draw a large pentagon with its five diagonals (see Appendix A "The Regular Pentagon", page 193 f., for instructions for drawing regular pentagons.) These five diagonals make a star with a small pentagon inside it.
2.. Draw the five diagonals of this smaller pentagon, producing them so that they meet the sides of the larger pentagon (fig. 266).

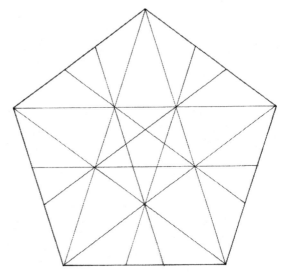

Fig. 266

The pattern in fig 266 contains six congruent regular pentagons (fig. 267). To obtain the full net of the dodecahedron shown in fig. 265, draw a second similar pattern of small pentagons, joined to the first in such a way that two small pentagons, one from each large pentagon, join side to side.

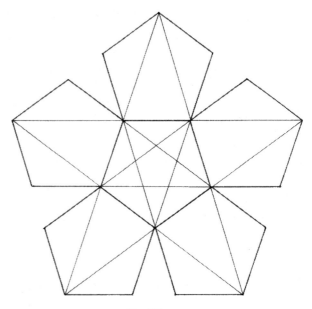

Fig. 267

It should be noted however that, no matter how carefully we follow the instructions given above, we may nevertheless run into difficulties. The small pentagons are unlikely to be perfectly congruent, since it is easy for small errors to creep in early and to be magnified later. For this reason it is better to mark at the start where we expect the extended diagonals of the inner pentagon in fig. 266 to meet the sides of the large pentagon. From fig. 503 on page 199 we see that if the large pentagon has sides 1 unit long, then the sides of the inner pentagon will be $2 - ø$ $(= 1/ø^2) \approx 0.38$ units long. The five small pentagons surrounding the inner pentagon (fig. 267) will also have sides $2 - ø$ units long, the gap between them being $1 - 2(2 - ø) = 2ø - 3$ $(= 1/ø^3) \approx 0.24$ units long.

Alternatively, if we are confident that we have drawn the large pentagon and its diagonals accurately, we can set compasses with the length a of one side of the inner pentagon as radius and draw arcs of this radius centred on each corner of the large pentagon to cut the two adjacent sides $2 - ø$ units along each one (fig. 268). Even so it is safer to check all distances by measuring.

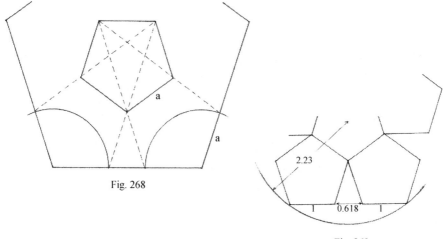

Fig. 268

Fig. 269

If we want the small pentagons to have sides one unit long, then the gap referred to above will be $(2ø - 3)/(2 - ø) = (1/ø^3)/(1/ø^2) = 1/ø \approx 0.618$ units long (fig. 269). The large pentagon will have sides $(ø + 1)$ units long, and its circumcircle will have a radius of $(ø + 1)/\sqrt{(3 - ø)} = ø^3/\sqrt{(ø + 2)} \approx 2.23$ units (see pages 194 and 200 for the calculations leading to this result).

These instructions should make it possible to draw accurately the full net of the dodecahedron as shown in fig. 265. Fig. 270 overleaf shows the net with flaps added; to construct the dodecahedron the flaps can be stuck in alphabetical order.

A "Self-Raising" Dodecahedron

It is possible to make a model of a dodecahedron which will in a sense create itself.

1. Draw and cut out in thin card two of the half-nets shown in fig. 267.
2. Score and fold the lines between the pentagons of each half-net.
3. Place the two half-nets together as in fig. 271 overleaf, with the scoring on the outside faces.
4. Wind a thin elastic band round the outside of the nets, alternately over and under the corners of the pentagons, to hold the nets together. Keep light pressure on the inside pentagon.
5. Release the pressure slowly. The tension of the elastic band will cause the nets to fold and rise into a dodecahedron.

An illustration of this process is given on pages 196 and 197 of Steinhaus, *Mathematical Snapshots*, figs. 245-247.

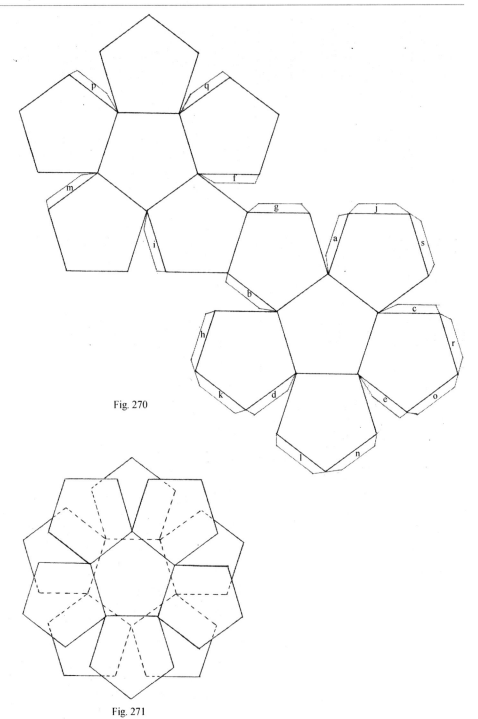

Fig. 270

Fig. 271

The Symmetry of the Regular Dodecahedron

The regular dodecahedron has twelve faces, each with five sides, so it must have (5 x 12) ÷ 2 = 30 edges. Three edges meet at each vertex but each edge joins 2 vertices, so the dodecahedron must have 30 ÷ 3 x 2 = 20 vertices. These numbers of faces, edges and vertices obey Euler's relation, F + V = E + 2: 12 + 20 = 30 + 2. Pairs of opposite faces lie on parallel planes, although the two faces are rotated in relation to each other through 36°, as can be seen in the plan view of the dodecahedron in fig. 272, where the hidden edges (and faces) are drawn as broken lines.

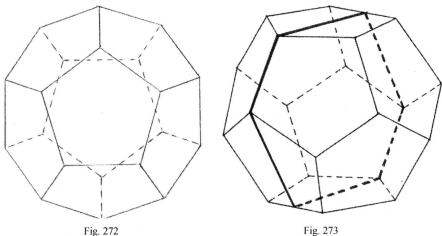

Fig. 272   Fig. 273

Each face of the dodecahedron has five lines of reflective symmetry, each line joining one corner of the face to the mid-point of the opposite side, and each lying on a plane of symmetry of the solid. Each plane of symmetry lies along two edges of the dodecahedron and also along a line of symmetry of four different faces (fig. 273). The number of planes of symmetry of a regular dodecagon can therefore be calculated either as 5 x 12 ÷ 4 = 15 (calculating from the number of faces) or as 30 ÷ 2 = 15 (calculating from the number of edges). The Petrie polygon (see page 76) of the dodecahedron has ten sides (fig. 272), and the rule that the number of planes of symmetry is 3/2 times the number of sides of the Petrie polygon holds here: 3/2 x 10 = 15.

The dodecahedron has thirty-one axes of rotational symmetry. Ten of these, each of order three, pass through opposite vertices; six others, each of order five, pass through the centres of opposite faces; and fifteen more, each of order two, pass through the mid-points of pairs of opposite edges. Once again we find that the number of axes of rotational symmetry, 10 + 6 + 15 = 31, is half the total number of faces, edges and vertices, 12 + 30 + 20 = 62; and is also one more than the number of edges, 30.

The dodecahedron has twenty vertices, and each vertex can be joined with straight lines to nineteen others. A study of a model of the dodecahedron will show that each vertex is joined to each of nine other vertices not by an internal diagonal but by a line which lies on the surface of the solid. Three of these lines are the three edges which meet at that vertex, while the other six lines lie along two diagonals of each of the three different faces to which the vertex belongs (fig. 274 overleaf).

This leaves ten other vertices of the solid remaining and the first vertex is joined to these by diagonals passing through the interior of the solid. Just one of these diagonals, that joining the vertex to the opposite vertex, is both a main (internal) diagonal of the solid and also an axis of rotational symmetry. The other nine are lesser diagonals and are not axes of symmetry. The total number of diagonals inside the solid is therefore 20 x 10 ÷ 2 = 100, of which only 20 ÷ 2 = 10 are main diagonals.

To check by counting that a dodecahedron has as many as 100 diagonals, we should need to build a strong skeleton model from wood or wire with threads showing the diagonals. Drinking straws would not be strong enough for such a model.

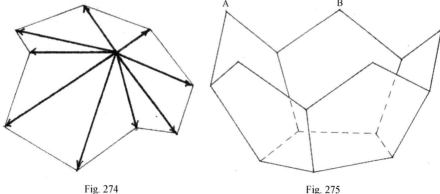

Fig. 274   Fig. 275

A less ambitious model of a half-dodecahedron with its diagonals can be made from thick card from the net in fig. 267. Fig. 275 shows this half-dodecahedron in the shape of a bowl. (The rim of the "bowl" comprises the ten sides of the Petrie polygon, referred to above, page 93.) We could use thread for diagonals between the vertices of the bowl, perhaps threading it through "eyes" from dressmakers' hooks and eyes, noting however that two adjoining "top" vertices, e.g., A and B in fig. 275, are corners of the same pentagonal face in the complete dodecahedron and so are not joined by internal diagonals. Fig. 276 shows the ten "top" vertices arranged as corners of a regular decagon, together with the (internal) diagonals joining them. Twenty-five of the hundred diagonals of the dodecahedron appear in this diagram, the five crossing at the centre of the decagon representing main diagonals of the solid.

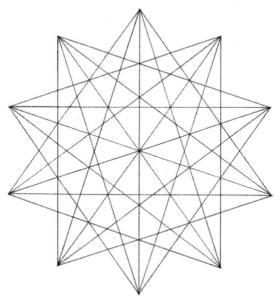

Fig. 276

The Trigonometry and Views of the Regular Dodecahedron.

To be able to draw accurate views of the dodecahedron, and to calculate distances within its interior, we need to know something about lengths on its surface. Detailed calculations of these lengths appear in Appendix A, but for ease of reference here, certain significant lengths are marked on the regular pentagons shown in figs. 277 and 278. In fig. 278, P is the centre of the circumcircle of the pentagon.

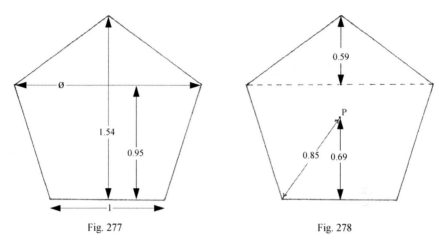

Fig. 277   Fig. 278

Views of the regular dodecahedron are not as easy to draw as are views of the simpler Platonic solids, and we give here three views only; a view looking directly at an edge, a plan view looking down directly on to a face, and a view looking directly at a vertex. In drawing these we are helped by the relationship which exists between the dodecahedron and an inscribed cube (see pages 150-1).

Fig. 279 is a sketch of the dodecahedron as it appears when we look directly at an edge AB. (See the note on page 29 for an explanation of the phrase "look directly at".) Four vertices, C, D, E and F, are at the corners of a square. This square is one face of a cube inscribed within the dodecahedron, each vertex of the cube coinciding with a vertex of the dodecahedron. Each side of the square CDEF is a diagonal of a pentagonal face of the dodecahedron, and as we see in fig. 277, the diagonal of a regular pentagon is ø times the length of its side. This means that each edge of the cube is ø times the length of an edge of the dodecahedron, which, if we take the edge of the dodecahedron to be 1 unit, is simply ø units. The internal diagonals of the cube are also main diagonals of the dodecahedron, and are each √3 x ø ≈ 2.8 units long. Instructions on how to draw the view in fig. 279 are given on page 98.

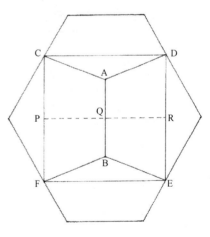

Fig. 279

From all the foregoing it follows that we may regard the dodecahedron simply as a cube with a "roof" placed on each square face. On page 151 we suggest a suitable net for building such a roof; but for the present we look only at the dimensions of the roof.

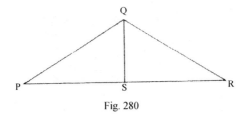

Fig. 280

In fig. 279 Q is the mid-point of AB. A cross-section of the roof through P, Q and R is shown in fig. 280. PR is ø units long, while PQ and QR, as we see from fig. 278, are both 0.95 units long. This latter length is exactly $\frac{1}{2}\sqrt{(ø + 2)}$ (see page 200). The angle QPR is $\cos^{-1} [\frac{1}{2}ø/\frac{1}{2}\sqrt{(ø + 2)}] = \cos^{-1} [ø/\sqrt{(ø + 2)}] = 31.72°$, while the angle PQR is $2(90 - 31.72)° = 116.57°$ and is the *dihedral* angle of the dodecahedron, the angle between two faces. (Cundy and Rollett, *op. cit.*, page 87, note that this is $\pi - \tan^{-1} 2$.) S is the mid-point of PR, and the height QS of the triangle is by Pythagoras $\sqrt{[\{\frac{1}{2}\sqrt{(ø + 2)}\}^2 - \{\frac{1}{2}ø\}^2]} = \sqrt{[\frac{1}{4}(ø + 2) - \frac{1}{4}ø^2]} = \sqrt{[\frac{1}{4}(ø + 2) - \frac{1}{4}(ø + 1)]} = \sqrt{\frac{1}{4}} = \frac{1}{2}$ (since $ø^2 = ø + 1$, see page 197). There is another identical "roof" on the far side of the dodecahedron, so that the perpendicular distance between opposite edges of the dodecahedron is exactly $ø + 1 \approx 2.618$ units.

Fig. 281 shows two opposite pentagonal faces of a dodecahedron whose edges are 1 unit long. Note that they are orientated differently, as we have seen earlier in fig. 272 on page 93. AB is the line joining two opposite vertices of the dodecahedron and is a main diagonal of the solid. As we have also seen earlier this diagonal is $ø\sqrt{3} \approx 2.8$ units long. PQ is the line joining the respective centres of the two pentagonal faces. This line is perpendicular to both faces. The two lines AB and PQ both pass through O, the centre of the dodecahedron, and bisect each other.

AP and QB are both radii of the circumcircles of the pentagons, and they are both $ø/\sqrt{(ø + 2)} \approx 0.85$ units long. By Pythagoras PO (= QO) ≈ 1.114 units; the perpendicular distance between faces is about 2.23 units. The exact distance is $2\sqrt{[(\sqrt{3}ø/2)^2 - \{ø/\sqrt{(ø + 2)}\}^2]} = 2\sqrt{\{ø^6/4(ø + 2)\}} = ø^3/\sqrt{(ø + 2)}$ units, which as we saw on page 91 (fig. 269) also happens to be the radius of the circumcircle of the large pentagon in fig. 266.

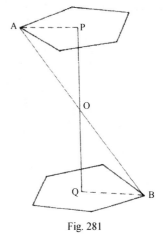

Fig. 281

Summary: Distances between opposite :

Vertices	$ø\sqrt{3}$	2.8 units
Edges	$ø + 1$	2.618 units
Faces	$ø^3/\sqrt{(ø + 2)}$	2.23 units

Drawing the Regular Dodecahedron

To draw the plan view of the dodecahedron shown in fig. 282 opposite, we begin by drawing a regular pentagon inside a regular decagon. We can draw both these polygons inside circles. Both circles have the same centre and are therefore *concentric*. We need to know what the radius of each circle must be.

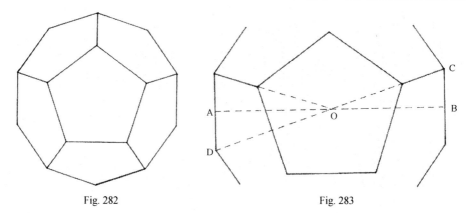

Fig. 282   Fig. 283

The radius of the circle containing a pentagon of side 1 unit we already know from fig. 278 on page 95 to be ø/√(ø + 2) ≈ 0.85 units. All we know for certain about the regular decagon is that the points A and B in fig. 283 are the mid-points of opposite edges of the dodecahedron, separated by a distance of ø + 1 = ø² units. (Note that although C and D are opposite vertices of the dodecahedron, the line CD is not parallel to the face represented by the inner pentagon, and so appears foreshortened in the plan view from its true length of 2.8 units.) The radius OC of the outer circle can be calculated as OB (= ½AB) divided by the cosine of <BOC (= 18°), which is ½√(ø + 2) (see page 199). OC is therefore ½ ø²/½√(ø + 2) = ø²/√(ø + 2) or about 1.376 units (making the apparent length of CD about 2.75 units). The two radii are in the ratio of ø²/√(ø + 2):ø/√(ø + 2) = ø:1.

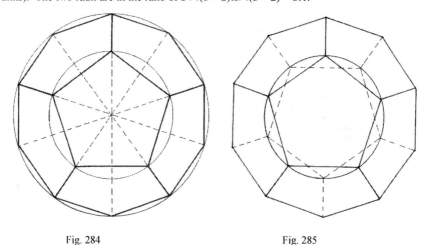

Fig. 284   Fig. 285

1. Draw two concentric circles whose radii are in the ratio of ø:1. Draw a regular pentagon inside the smaller circle.
2. Draw diameters of the larger circle to pass through the five vertices of the pentagon. The ends of these diameters will mark the vertices of the regular decagon to be drawn inside the larger circle (fig. 284).
3. Firm in or erase lines to give the diagram in fig. 282.

Fig. 285 includes fig. 282 and also indicates how points on the circumcircle of the pentagon may be used to show by broken lines the position of the hidden edges and faces of the dodecahedron. It also includes fig. 272 on page 93 and is a parallel projection of the solid, one which ignores perspective. In particular the decagon (the Petrie polygon of the dodecahedron) is a projection of the ten edges of the dodecahedron which form a zig-zag around the equatorial region of the solid.

Fig. 287 shows the view of the solid seen earlier in fig. 279 on page 95, a parallel projection viewed from the direction of an edge (GH). Both AB and CD are edges of the solid shown as their true lengths: we shall take each to be 1 unit long. Each of the other four sides of the bordering hexagon represents the height of a face. GH is one unit long and is placed centrally on the vertical axis of symmetry of the diagram. The height of the diagram is the perpendicular distance between two opposite edges, AB and CD. This distance is ø + 1 ≈ 2.62 units, and is equal to the width EF of the diagram, since both E and F also represent opposite edges; these edges, however, are perpendicular to the plane of the drawing, and so appear here end on.

1. Draw a square with sides 2.62 units long. Mark K, L, E and F, the mid-points of the sides, and join KL and EF to cross at M (fig. 286).
2. Mark A and B half a unit on either side of K, and C and D half a unit on either side of L. Join EA, EC, FB and FD.
3. Mark G and H respectively half a unit vertically above and below M.
4. Find the position of P on EA by using the fact that F, G and P all lie on the same straight line. Find the positions of Q, R and S in a similar way.
5. Join PG, QG, RH and SH and erase construction lines to give fig. 287.

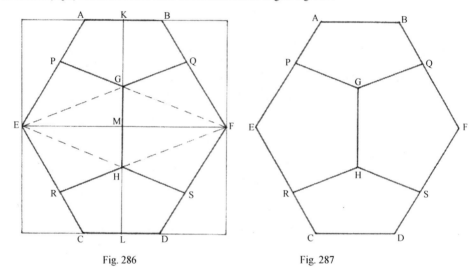

Fig. 286   Fig. 287

Each of EA, EC, FB and FD represents the height of a face of the dodecahedron and is ½ø/√(ø + 2) ≈ 1.54 units long. PQRS is a square of side ø units, and, as we have seen on page 95, is a face of the cube inscribed in the dodecahedron. Its corners divide the four long sides EA, etc. of the hexagon in the ratio of ø:1. The significance of all these lengths can be understood fully only if we have at hand a model of the solid and study it closely from this particular angle.

One interesting feature of this diagram is that there is no need to draw broken lines to show hidden edges, since all hidden edges are truly hidden behind the visible edges. (Compare fig. 287 with fig. 315 on page 111 with shows a corresponding view of the regular icosahedron.) It is not too difficult to work out exactly where the hidden edges are, and to check that the total of all edges, visible or hidden, is indeed 30. We can also see that both KL and EF lie on planes of symmetry of the dodecahedron. One plane of symmetry passes through the mid-points of each pair of opposite edges; the solid has fifteen planes of symmetry in all. This agrees with the conclusion we reached on page 93.

The third view (fig. 289) is a parallel projection of the dodecahedron in which a vertex (T) is facing us.

The view can be drawn within a rectangle (fig. 288) whose height is $ø^3/\sqrt{(ø + 2)}$ units, the distance between two opposite faces; and whose width is $ø + 1$ units, the distance between two opposite edges. All edges except the top edge HI are sloping away from us as we look at them, and this will affect their lengths in the projection, although it will not prevent us from drawing an accurate view of the solid.

1. Draw the rectangle ABCD 2.62 units wide and 2.23 units high. Mark E, the mid-point of AB, and F, the mid-point of DC. Join EF.
2. Mark the eight points from G to N inclusive so that AG = HE = EI = JB = DK = LF = FM = NC = ½ unit.
3. Mark the points P and Q on BC so that BP = QC and PQ = ½ unit. Mark R and S similarly on AD. Join pairs of points on opposite sides of the rectangle to give fig. 288.

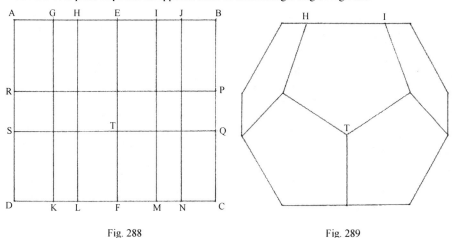

Fig. 288   Fig. 289

On this framework we can construct the view in fig. 289. Using the points where lines intersect in the same framework we can add broken lines to show the hidden edges of the dodecahedron (fig. 290). The hidden edges and faces appear as reflections of the visible edges and faces in the central horizontal line XY shown in fig. 291.

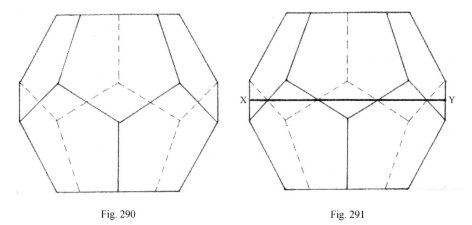

Fig. 290   Fig. 291

The line XY in fig. 291 passes through the mid-points of the zig-zag of edges around the middle of the dodecahedron (fig. 292). This line marks the position of a cut which will divide the dodecahedron into two congruent pieces, although the cut does not lie in a plane of symmetry of the solid. When the line is drawn on the surface of the dodecahedron, it takes the form of a regular decagon, and can be compared with the hexagons which, as we saw earlier, can be drawn by joining the mid-points of edges on the cube and the octahedron (pages 25 and 80). Six of these decagons can be drawn on the surface of the dodecahedron. Each decagon passes through the mid-points of two edges of each of ten pentagonal faces but it does not pass through the two faces which lie in the plane parallel to the decagon (see fig 458, page 178). The six intersecting decagons are the edges of an *icosidodecahedron*, which as we shall see (page 168) is the shape left when the dodecahedron is fully truncated.

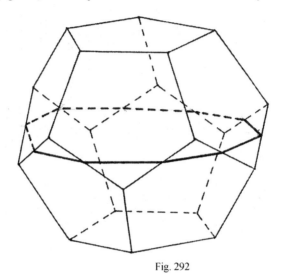

Fig. 292

Dissections of the Regular Dodecahedron

It is clear that we could build models showing how a regular dodecahedron can be dissected along its planes of symmetry into varying numbers of congruent parts. However such dissections are unlikely to tell us much more about the geometry of the dodecahedron than we already know, so we describe here only one dissection which might be instructive, a dissection of the dodecahedron into twelve congruent pyramids.

Twelve Pyramids Fold into a Regular Dodecahedron

A regular dodecahedron can be built from twelve pentagonal pyramids meeting at the centre of the dodecahedron. The slant edge of each pyramid will be half the length of a main diagonal of the dodecahedron, and this length we have already calculated (page 96) as $\varnothing\sqrt{3} \approx 2.8$ times the length of an edge of the dodecahedron. If the regular pentagon at the base of each pyramid has sides 1 unit long, then attached to each side will be an isosceles triangle whose other sides are 1.4 units long. The net for the pyramid is shown in fig. 293 opposite.

1. Draw a regular pentagon ABCDE with sides 1 unit long. On AB draw an isosceles triangle ABP with AP = BP = 1.4 units.
2. With centre P and radius AP draw a long arc of a circle through B.
3. With radius AB, step off four arcs round the long arc to fix the positions of F, G, H and I. Join each point to its neighbours and also to P. Draw flaps as shown. Stick flap *f* first.

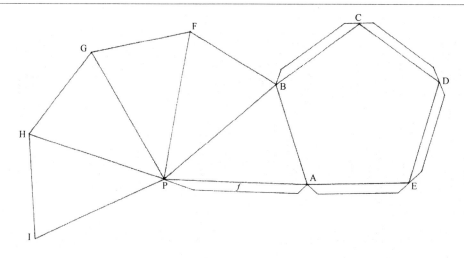

Fig. 293

Note that in this net the triangular faces are attached to one another rather than to the pentagon, an arrangement which makes it easier to stick the finished model together. Note also that P, A, and E do not all lie on the same straight line, and nor do P, B and C..

When twelve of these pyramids are fastened together so that their bases form the net of a dodecahedron, they will fold together to make the dodecahedron itself, with their apexes all meeting at the centre.

[*Note*: when we dissected the cube into six pyramids in a similar way (page 25), we found that the pyramids folded outwards to form a named solid, the *rhombic dodecahedron*. Unfortunately the twelve pyramids into which the regular dodecahedron can be dissected do not fold outwards to form a named solid. If however we fasten together twelve pyramids whose sloping edges are each $ø \approx 1.62$ times the length of the base, and wrap these round the faces of a regular dodecahedron, they will form the Kepler-Poinsot solid known as the *small stellated dodecahedron* (see page 188). The net of one of these pyramids will be very like the net in fig. 293; in this new net P, A, and E will all lie on the same straight line, as will P, B and C.]

The Volume of the Regular Dodecahedron

To find the volume of the whole dodecahedron, we find the volume of one of the pyramids described in the previous section and multiply this volume by 12. We assume that the length of each edge of the solid is a units. (We note also that areas are measured as square units and volumes as cubic units.)

1. The area of the pentagonal base is $5/4$ x a^2 x tan $54°$. Since tan $54° = ø^2/\sqrt{(ø + 2)}$ (see page 199), the area of the base is $5a^2ø^2/4\sqrt{(ø + 2)}$.
2. The height of the pyramid is half the distance between opposite faces of the dodecahedron. This height is $½$ x a x $ø^3/\sqrt{(ø + 2)}$ (see page 96).
3. The volume of one pyramid is $^1/_3$ x $[5a^2ø^2/4\sqrt{(ø + 2)}]$ x $[½\ aø^3/\sqrt{(ø + 2)}] = 5a^3ø^5/24(ø + 2)$.
4. The volume of the whole dodecahedron will be 12 times the volume of one pyramid, and is therefore 12 x $[5a^3ø^5/24(ø + 2)] = 5a^3ø^5/2(ø + 2)$. This gives the volume of a regular dodecahedron of edge a units as about $7.663a^3$ cubic units.

Journeys on the Surface of the Regular Dodecahedron

We considered earlier the problems of finding shortest paths across the surface of the cube and of the regular octahedron and we shall shortly do the same for the regular dodecahedron. First we discuss the problems of the shortest paths along the edges of the dodecahedron, taking an edge to be one unit long.

For this purpose we use the Schlegel diagram of the dodecahedron (fig. 294).

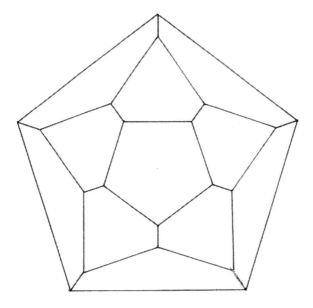

Fig. 294

1. Draw a regular pentagon, together with the regular pentagon enclosed by its diagonals (see fig. 503, page 199). [Note that these pentagons need not be regular for the Schlegel diagram to serve its purposes.]
2. Draw short lines, pointing inwards towards the centre from the corners of the outside pentagon and outwards away from the centre from the corners of the inside pentagon. Each of these lines should be about one-eighth the length of the sides of the outside pentagon.
3. Join the ends of these lines to obtain the diagram in fig. 294. This has ten other non-regular pentagons within the boundaries of the figure. The twelfth pentagon is as usual represented by the region outside the diagram.

Fig. 295 shows one route among many possible routes by which, travelling along the edges, we may visit each of the twenty vertices in turn and return to the starting point. The journey, starting at A and visiting the other vertices in alphabetical order, is twenty units long.

If we wish to travel along all edges at least once and return to the starting point, we have a problem. All the nodes in the Schlegel diagram are odd nodes, of order 3, and for such a journey to be possible, the whole network has to be made traversable. We must therefore do as we did on pages 35 and 64 with the cube and tetrahedron and make each node an even node by doubling up some of the arcs.

There are twenty nodes altogether in the network. One extra arc will make two of these nodes even, so we need to draw ten extra arcs to make all twenty nodes even. Fig. 296 shows one way of doing this. We have simply doubled up the arcs along which we did not travel in fig. 295. We now follow the same alphabetical route, but the first time we come to each double arc, we travel along one branch and return at once along the other; so our journey will begin as ABLBCJCDHDEFGQGHIPI... and finish as ...LMTMNRNOPQRSTA.

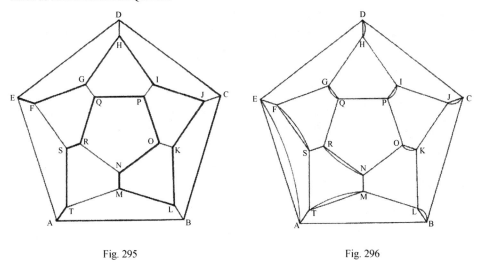

Fig. 295   Fig. 296

Any shortest journey along this amended network which passes along all edges at least once and returns to the starting point will be 30 + 10 = 40 units long in total, and this is the length of the shortest journey which satisfies these conditions.

Note that it is not just a matter of making the network traversable. Fig. 297 shows the Schlegel diagram transformed into a traversable network which retains the rotational symmetry of the original. However, since the added lines do not duplicate edges, we can travel along each edge at least once on this network only by taking short cuts across the faces of the dodecahedron, a stratagem not allowed us by the conditions of the problem!

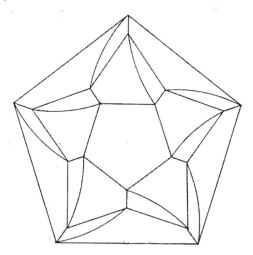

Fig. 297

Now we suppose that a spider sitting at one vertex of the dodecahedron knows that a fly is sitting at the opposite vertex. What is the shortest distance the spider needs to travel on the surface of the dodecahedron to get to the fly?

Looking at a model of the dodecahedron, we may well decide that the shortest path from one vertex to the opposite vertex lies across two faces and along an edge (see fig. 273, page 93). In fig. 298 this path is STF and if we take TF to be 1 unit long, then the length of this path is 2 x {½ ø√(ø + 2)} + 1 = {ø √(ø + 2)} + 1 ≈ 4.078 units. However a closer look at fig. 298 suggests that this is not the shortest route.

In fig. 298 three regular pentagons are laid out to represent three faces of the dodecahedron. S and F are opposite vertices. A straight line from S to F will cross all three faces, and this line will be shorter than the path across two faces from S to T and then along TF.

The angle STF is (108 + 54)° = 162°; by the cosine rule, SF² = ST² + TF² – 2.ST.TF.cos 162°. The cosine of 162° is –cos 18° = $^{-1}$⁄₂√(ø + 2) (see page 199). Still taking TF = 1 unit, we have:

$$SF² = [ø√(ø + 2)]² + 1 – [2 \times ø√(ø + 2) \times 1 \times ^{-1}⁄₂√(ø + 2)]$$
$$= ø²(ø + 2) + 1 + ø(ø + 2)$$
$$= ø³ + 2ø² + 1 + ø² + 2ø$$
$$= 7ø + 5 \text{ (see page 197)} ≈ 16.33, \text{ giving } SF ≈ 4.041 \text{ units.}$$

The route from S to T and on to F is 4.078 units long, so the direct route saves the spider 0.037 of a unit, or 0.9% of the journey!

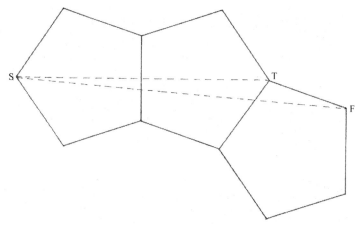

Fig. 298

Uses of the regular dodecahedron

Regular dodecahedra have in the past been used as dice, with a maximum possible score on two such dice thrown together of 24.

Cardboard calendar models in the form of regular dodecahedra have been obtainable commercially in the past, with each face containing the calendar for a particular month of the year. Such of course is the nature of the calendar that each model is of no further use once the year ends, until such time as January 1st falls again on the same day of the week. We could only overcome the problem by building up a collection to contain one for each day of the week on which January 1st falls, plus variants for leap years. How many models should we need to collect in all?

Chapter 9

THE REGULAR ICOSAHEDRON

The regular icosahedron (from now on referred to simply as the icosahedron) has twenty faces, each face being an equilateral triangle. Five faces meet at each vertex (fig. 299). It has $20 \times 3 \div 2 = 30$ edges and $20 \times 3 \div 5 = 12$ vertices. These numbers satisfy Euler's relationship, $F + V = E + 2$, since $20 + 12 = 30 + 2$.

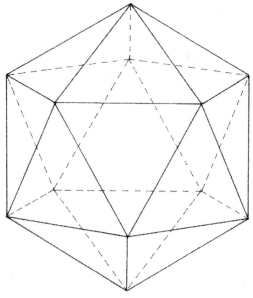

Fig. 299

The net of the icosahedron shown in fig. 300 is a standard net, suggested for example by Cundy and Rollett, *op. cit.* An alternative net with its flaps is shown in fig. 301 overleaf. This alternative net draws attention to the fact that the regular icosahedron can also be thought of as a pentagonal *antiprism* with two pentagonal pyramids as "caps" (fig. 302).

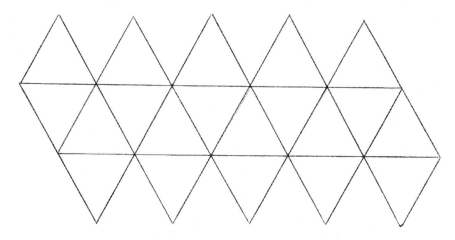

Fig. 300

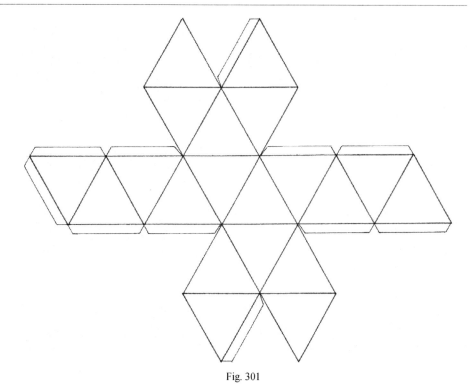

Fig. 301

The net for the antiprism on its own comprises the central strip of triangles shown in fig. 301, but with the five triangles at top and bottom replaced by two regular pentagons. Five triangles together with a regular pentagon make the net for each pyramidal "cap". (Drawings such as those in fig. 204, page 68, and in figs. 223 and 224 on page 74, together with the accompanying instructions, will help in drawing figs. 301 and 303.) Fig. 303 shows the net of a model of an icosahedron in which the pyramidal caps are attached to the antiprism and may be lifted to reveal the pentagonal faces of the antiprism. In this diagram, the broken lines must be scored on the reverse side and folded inwards instead of outwards. (For instructions on how to draw a regular pentagon, see pages 193-5.)

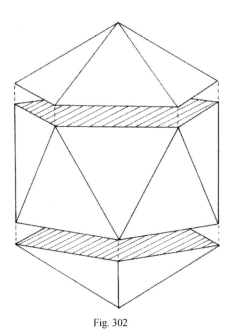

Fig. 302

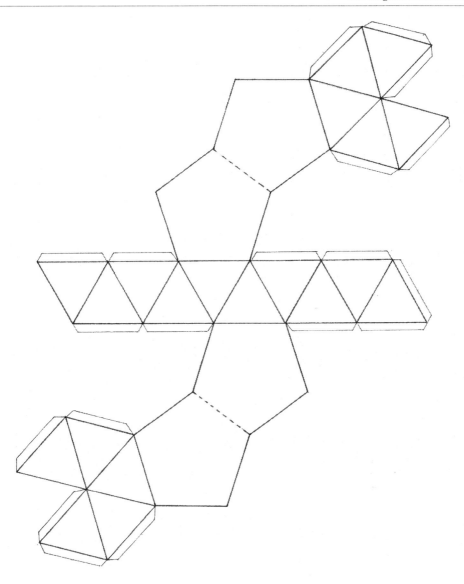

Fig. 303

The ten edges which join the two pentagonal faces of the antiprism form the zig-zag "Petrie polygon" of the icosahedron (see page 76). These ten edges give the decagon which forms the boundary of fig. 310, page 110.

The Trigonometry of the Regular Icosahedron.

The antiprism is of great help when we come to calculate distances and measurements inside the icosahedron. Fig. 304 overleaf is a general view of the antiprism, with the hidden edges shown as broken lines. For purposes of calculation, we take all edges to be 1 unit long.

AB is a diagonal of one pentagonal face of the antiprism while CD is a parallel diagonal of the other face. These diagonals are joined by AD and BC, which are parallel and opposite edges of the ring of triangles round the antiprism. ABCD is a rectangle, with AD = BC = 1 unit and AB = CD = ø units (see page 197). AD and BC are also opposite edges of the icosahedron, and from this we conclude that the perpendicular distance between any two opposite edges of the icosahedron is ø times the length of an edge. Likewise A and C are opposite vertices not only of the antiprism but also of the icosahedron itself, and by Pythagoras the distance between them is $\sqrt{(ø^2 + 1)} = \sqrt{(ø + 1 + 1)} = \sqrt{(ø + 2)}$ ≈ 1.902 units. (Here and below we make use of the equivalences $ø^2 = ø + 1$ and $ø^3 = 2ø + 1$, explained in Appendix A, page 197.)

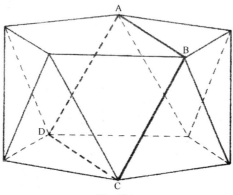

Fig. 304

In fig. 305 we see two opposite faces of the icosahedron, whose distance apart we now calculate. The triangles have sides of unit length, and in the diagram two of their vertices are joined by a line AB representing a main diagonal of the icosahedron (e.g., AC in fig. 304) whose length is $\sqrt{(ø + 2)}$ units. P and Q are the centres of the two triangles, and so PQ is the distance we have to find. The centre P of the top triangle is vertically above the centre Q of the bottom triangle, but the triangles are reversed relative to each other. The distance AP is the same as the distance QB and is $^2/_3 \times \sqrt{3}/2 = \sqrt{3}/3$ units. The lines AB and PQ bisect each other at O, the centre of the icosahedron. If we translate the line AB until A coincides with P, then B will move to B' by $\sqrt{3}/3$ units, and the line QB' will be $2\sqrt{3}/3 = 2/\sqrt{3}$ units long. In fig. 306 we have the triangle PQB' and we use Pythagoras to calculate the distance PQ. $(PQ)^2 = (PB')^2 - (QB')^2 = \{[\sqrt{(ø + 2)}]^2 - (2/\sqrt{3})^2\} = ø + 2 - ^4/_3 = ø + ^2/_3 = (3ø + 2)/3 = (ø^4/3)$ (see page 197), and PQ, the distance between opposite faces of the icosahedron, is $\sqrt{(ø^4/3)} = ø^2/\sqrt{3}$ ≈ 1.5115 units.

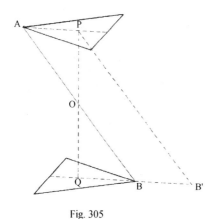

Fig. 305

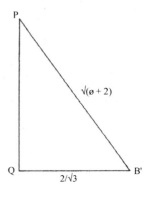

Fig. 306

Fig. 307 shows two triangular faces of the "cap" of the icosahedron (fig. 302, page 106), fixed to its pentagonal base, with B the mid-point of DE. Fig. 308 shows the isosceles triangle ABC from fig 307. If we take the sides of the faces to be 1 unit long, then AC = ø units. The cosine of angle BAC is ½ø/½√3 = ø/√3 ≈ 0.934, and the angle itself is about 20.9°. The dihedral angle between faces is (180 – [2 x 20.9])° = 138.2°, or as Cundy and Rollett state, *op. cit.*, page 88, $\pi - \sin^{-1} {}^2/_3$.

The vertical height of the "cap" is EF (fig. 309), where F is the centre of the pentagonal face. AF is the radius of the circumcircle of the pentagon = ø/√(ø + 2) ≈ 0.85 units (page 200), so by Pythagoras the height EF is √(1 – [ø²/{ø + 2}]) = √([{ø + 2} – {ø + 1}]/{ø + 2}) = 1/√(ø + 2) ≈ 0.5257 units. As we have seen on page 108, the distance between opposite vertices of the icosahedron (its "height"), is √{ø + 2} ≈ 1.902 units. The "height" of the antiprism, that is, the vertical distance between its pentagonal faces, is √(ø + 2) – 2/√(ø + 2) = (ø + 2 – 2)/√(ø + 2) = ø/√(ø + 2), or 1.902 – (2 x 0.5257) ≈ 0.85 units which is exactly the same as the radius of the circumcircle of the pentagon (see page 194).

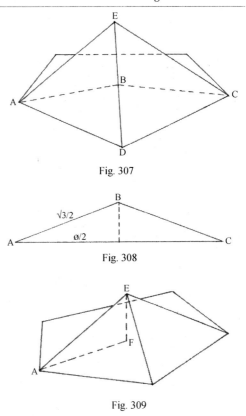

Fig. 307

Fig. 308

Fig. 309

Drawing the Regular Icosahedron

We now have enough information to enable us to draw various views of the regular icosahedron. The key dimensions, taking the length of an edge to be 1 unit, are set out below.

Summary: Distances between opposite:

Vertices	√(ø + 2)	1.902 units
Edges	ø	1.618 units
Faces	ø²/√3	1.5115 units

Fig. 310 overleaf shows a plan view of the icosahedron when it stands with one vertex vertically above the opposite vertex. Fig. 311 is the same view with hidden edges shown as broken lines, which gives an indication of how we may draw fig. 310.

1. Draw a circle and inside it draw a regular pentagon (see page 193).
2. Draw the five diameters of the circle which meet the corners of the pentagon. Join the ends of these diameters to obtain the outside decagon.
3. Either erase the lines which are not wanted (fig. 310), or draw broken lines to show the hidden edges (fig. 311).

If the side of one pentagon is 1 unit long, then the radius of the (common) circumcircle of the two pentagons in fig. 311 is 0.85 units. The outer decagon is the Petrie polygon of the icosahedron, mentioned on page 107, and in figs. 310 and 311 each of its sides is 1/√(ø + 2) ≈ 0.5257 units long.

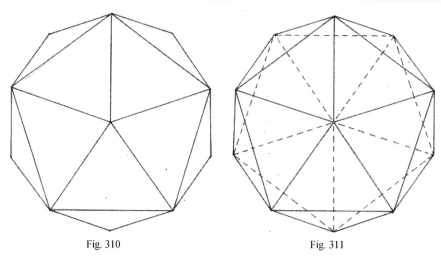

Fig. 310   Fig. 311

Fig. 312 shows a front elevation of the icosahedron, again standing on one vertex, B. The edge TU has a true length of 1 unit; PT = UQ. (Note that TUV is not an equilateral triangle.) The distance from A to B is the "height" of the icosahedron, 1.902 units, while the distance PQ is the distance between the opposite edges PR and QS, which is ø (≈ 1.618) units. PR and QS, which represent edges sloping away from the vertical, measure the "height" of the antiprism, 0.85 units.

1. Draw a rectangle PQRS with PQ = 1.62 units and PR = 0.85 units.
2. Mark the points T and U on PQ such that TU = 1 unit long and TU lies centrally on PQ (i.e., PT = UQ = 0.31 units).
3. Mark V as the midpoint of RS. Join TR, TV, UV and US.
4. Draw a line to pass through V and also through the mid-point of PQ to find A and B, each 0.53 units respectively above and below the rectangle PQRS. Join AP, AT, AU, AQ, BR, BV and BS.

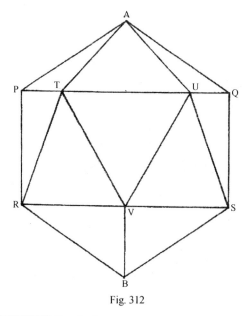

Fig. 312

The view shown in fig. 314 is very like that shown in fig. 312, but is more fully symmetrical, with rotational symmetry of order 3. This is a plan view of the icosahedron when it is resting on a face. The central triangle KLM is equilateral and has sides 1 unit long. The distance from P to Q, which are mid-points of opposite edges, is ø units and so the radius of the circle containing the outside regular hexagon is $\frac{1}{2}ø/\cos 30° = \frac{1}{2}ø/\frac{1}{2}\sqrt{3} = ø/\sqrt{3} \approx 0.934$ units. This makes the distance AD about 1.87 units, a little less than the distance between opposite vertices, since in moving the large triangle from its off-centre position in fig. 312 to a central position, we have caused the vertical axis of the icosahedron to lean towards us. Fig. 299 (page 105) is a copy of fig. 314 with the hidden edges shown as broken lines and with similar symmetry.

1. Draw a circle with radius 0.93 units. Inside the circle draw a regular hexagon ABCDEF.
2. With the same centre draw a circle with radius $1/\sqrt{3} \approx 0.58$ units. Join opposite corners of the hexagon to find the positions on the inner circle of K, L and M (fig. 313).
3. Join K, L and M to obtain an equilateral triangle whose sides should be exactly 1 unit long.
4. Join each of K, L and M to three corners of the hexagon to obtain fig. 314. (Note that the ratio of the two radii is $ø/\sqrt{3}:1/\sqrt{3} = ø:1$.)

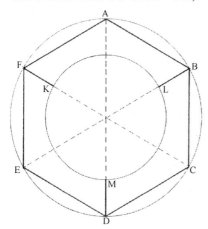

Fig. 313

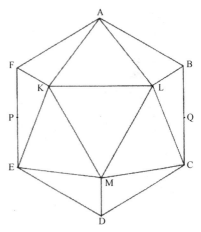

Fig. 314

Fig. 315 shows a view of the icosahedron looking directly at an edge GH. The view is drawn inside the square PQRS whose sides are ø units long. This is the distance between opposite edges AB and CD of the icosahedron, and also the distance between those edges of the icosahedron seen end-on at E and F, which are mid-points of the sides of the square. AB and CD are each 1 unit long, and are placed centrally along the sides of the square. The straight lines AF and BE cross at G, while ED and CF cross at H, GH being the edge of unit length at which we are looking directly. Note that all hidden edges of the solid lie behind the visible edges, so no broken lines appear in the diagram. (Compare fig. 315 with fig. 287 on page 98, which shows a corresponding view of the regular dodecahedron.)

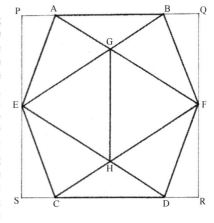

Fig. 315

Fig. 316 shows the same view as fig. 315 but with the front edge GH horizontal, while fig. 317 shows the same view with A vertically above D, these being opposite vertices of the icosahedron. This asymmetrical view is the view we see when we rotate the icosahedron through 36° on its AB axis from its position in fig. 312.

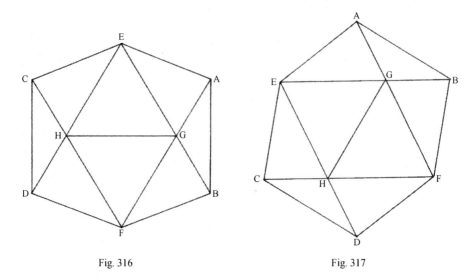

Fig. 316   Fig. 317

The Symmetry of the Regular Icosahedron

The regular icosahedron has 15 axes of rotational symmetry each of order 2 passing through the mid-points of opposite edges, 10 axes of symmetry of order 3 passing through the centres of opposite faces, and 6 axes of symmetry of order 5 passing through opposite vertices, a total of 31 in all. This is the same number of axes of rotational symmetry that we counted in the regular dodecahedron (page 93), and, as was the case with that solid, is half the sum of the numbers of its faces (20), edges (30) and vertices (12); or alternatively the number of its edges plus one.

The regular icosahedron also has fifteen planes of symmetry. A close study of diagrams such as figs. 299 and 312, and of the solid itself, should convince us that one plane of symmetry of the regular icosahedron passes through each pair of opposite edges, both of which themselves lie on the plane of symmetry; and also through the mid-points of a second pair of opposite edges. Fig. 318 shows one such plane of symmetry. Since the solid has thirty edges, it has fifteen pairs of opposite edges and hence fifteen planes of symmetry. This is confirmed by the fact that the Petrie polygon has ten sides and that 10 x 3/2 = 15 (see page 76).

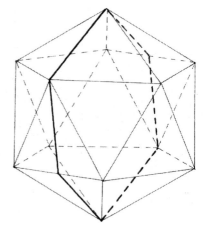

Fig. 318

Dissecting the Icosahedron

Dissecting the icosahedron into congruent parts is not really a practicable task, and the following remarks are merely theoretical.

The symmetry of fig. 315 (page 111) suggests that cuts through the icosahedron along the three planes of symmetry which contain (a) the pairs of opposite edges AB and CD, (b) those edges seen end-on at E and F, and (c) GH and its corresponding edge at the far side of the icosahedron, will dissect the solid into eight congruent parts.

The five main diagonals of the decagon shown in fig. 311 (page 110) mark five planes of symmetry of the icosahedron, and cuts vertically downwards through all five diagonals will dissect the icosahedron into ten congruent parts. A cut downwards through each edge shown meeting at the central vertex in fig. 310 (page 110) will give five congruent parts. Fig. 319 shows these five lines rotated together through the same angle to a new position, which gives a further way of obtaining five congruent parts. Since there is an infinite number of such positions available for these five lines, there is an infinite number of ways of dissecting the icosahedron in this manner into five congruent parts.

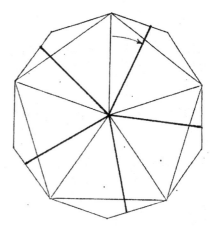

Fig. 319

Fig. 320 shows the line of a cut AB made half-way between two opposite vertices of the icosahedron and perpendicular to the line through these vertices. The cut passes through the mid-points of ten edges and the line of the cut on the surface of the icosahedron will be a regular decagon. Although the cut is not made along a plane of symmetry, the two parts so obtained are congruent, and each part can itself be cut into five or ten congruent pieces in the manner described above. In fig. 321, which is a "plan" view of one of these two parts, the hidden edges of the decagon are shown as broken lines.

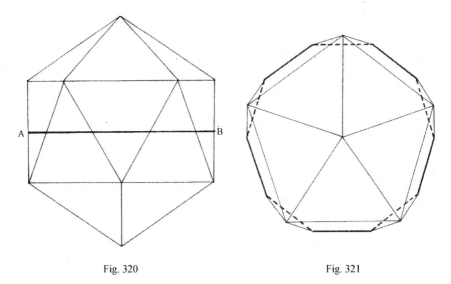

Fig. 320   Fig. 321

Six such cuts, each made half-way between pairs of opposite vertices and each passing through the mid-points of ten edges, can be made on the icosahedron. Fig. 322 shows how two of these cuts encircle the icosahedron and intersect at two points. When all six decagons are drawn on the icosahedron, they divide each face into four congruent equilateral triangles (fig. 323) and form the edge pattern of the *icosidodecahedron*, which, as we shall see on page 169, is the solid left when the icosahedron is fully *truncated*.

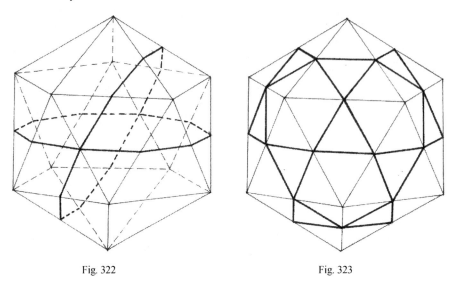

Fig. 322   Fig. 323

Finally, like all other regular solids, the icosahedron can be dissected into congruent pyramids, each with one face of the solid as its base and with the apexes meeting at the centre of the solid. Twenty of these triangular pyramids make up the regular icosahedron, and we use this fact to help us work out the volume of the solid.

The Volume of a Regular Icosahedron

For a general result, we take each edge of the icosahedron, and hence each side of the triangular bases of the pyramids described above, to be *a* units long.

Each pyramid will have a vertical height of half the distance between opposite faces, that is, half $ø^2/\sqrt 3$ x $a = \frac{1}{2}ø^2 a/\sqrt 3 \approx 0.756a$ units (see page 109).
The area of the base of the pyramid will be $\frac{1}{2}$ a^2 sin 60° = $\frac{1}{2}$ a^2 x $\sqrt 3/2$ = $\sqrt 3 a^2/4 \approx$ 0.433a^2 square units.
The volume of one pyramid will be $(\frac{1}{2}$ $ø^2 a/\sqrt 3$ x $\sqrt 3 a^2/4)/3 = ø^2 a^3/24 \approx 0.109a^3$ cubic units.
The volume of the whole icosahedron will be twenty times this, or $5ø^2 a^3/6 \approx 2.182a^3$ cubic units.

The length of the slant edge of each pyramid will be half the distance between two opposite vertices, which is half $\sqrt{(ø + 2)}a \approx \frac{1}{2}$ x 1.902a = 0.951a units. If twenty such pyramids were joined with their bases forming the net of an icosahedron, and if they were then wrapped round an icosahedron, with one pyramid projecting from each face of the icosahedron, the resulting solid would hold little of mathematical interest. On the other hand, it is easy to build pyramids which, when fixed to the faces of the icosahedron, will form the *great stellated dodecahedron*, referred to in more detail on page 190.

Journeys on the Surface of the Regular Icosahedron

We pose once more the question we have considered earlier with the other regular solids, namely, what is the shortest distance we have to travel, first if we wish to visit each vertex of the icosahedron in turn, returning to the starting point; and secondly if we wish to travel along all edges of the solid at least once before returning to the starting point? Again we turn for help to a Schlegel diagram.

1. Draw a regular hexagon together with its main diagonals in a circle of radius, say, 2 cm.
2. Join three corners of the hexagon to obtain an equilateral triangle, and inside this triangle draw another equilateral triangle (fig 324).
3. Firm in part of each main diagonal as in fig. 325. Draw extensions of the diagonals outside the hexagon in the directions of A, B and C (fig 326). These extensions should be about 4 cm long, or double the length of the sides of the hexagon.
4. This fixes the positions of A, B and C in fig. 327. Join AB, BC and AC. Two more lines from each of A, B and C to the nearest corners of the hexagon complete the Schlegel diagram for the regular icosahedron.

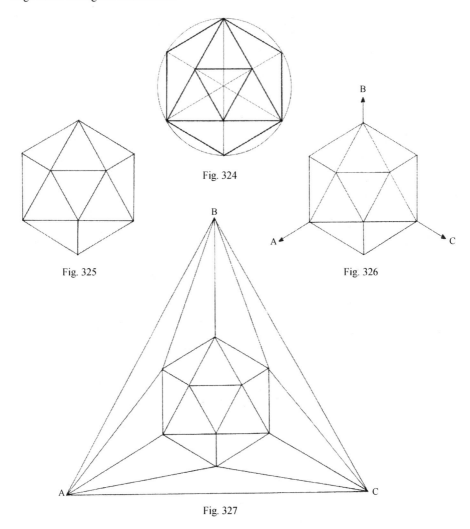

Fig. 324

Fig. 325

Fig. 326

Fig. 327

Fig. 328 shows one route among many possible routes by which, travelling along the edges, we may visit each of the twelve vertices in turn and return to the starting point. The journey, starting and finishing at A and visiting the other vertices in alphabetical order, is twelve units long, and no other journey which fulfils the conditions of the problem is shorter than this.

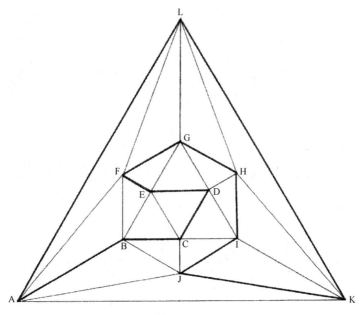

Fig. 328

If we wish to travel along all the edges of the solid at least once and return to the starting point, we meet with a difficulty. The Schlegel diagram is not traversable. All its nodes are odd nodes, of order 5, and for such a journey to be possible, we must make each node an even node. We did this with the cube and the dodecahedron by doubling up some of the arcs, so making the network traversable, and we do the same here.

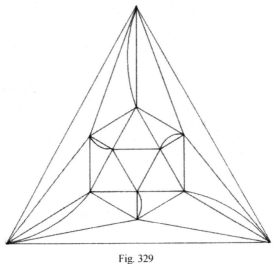

Fig. 329

There are twelve nodes in the network altogether. We can make each node an order 6 node by joining nodes in pairs. We need half twelve, that is six, extra arcs to make each node even. Fig. 329 shows one way of doing this. Here we have doubled up arcs symmetrically; each node is now a 6-node, and there should be no difficulty in finding a route among the many routes possible which passes along all edges at least once and returns to the starting point. The route passes along each doubled-up edge twice, once in each direction, so the route will be 30 + 6 = 36 units long.

Next we suppose that a spider sitting at one vertex S of the icosahedron knows that a fly is sitting at the opposite vertex F. What is the shortest distance the spider needs to travel over the surface of the icosahedron to get to the fly?

If we look at a model of the icosahedron, or at fig. 330, we may well conclude that the shortest route from S to F lies across two faces and along an edge. If however we study fig. 331, we may possibly have doubts about this.

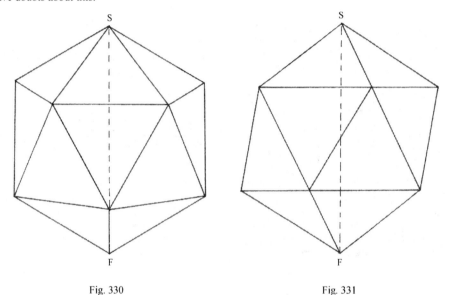

Fig. 330   Fig. 331

To find the shortest route we draw four connected triangles to represent the four faces across which the spider's route must presumably lie. The shortest distance between two points either on the plane or on the surface of the icosahedron lies along a straight line, shown clearly as SF in fig. 332. A journey from S to F across two faces and along an edge (fig. 330) will be ($\sqrt{3} + 1$) ≈ 2.732 units long, whereas by Pythagoras the straight-line distance is $\sqrt{(2.5^2 + [\sqrt{3}/2]^2)} = \sqrt{7} ≈ 2.646$ units, a saving of 0.086 units or just over 3%.

[In which direction must the spider head when he starts out from vertex S towards F? It is clear that B is the midpoint of RQ, but where is A? Consideration of the similar triangles SAQ and SCT tells us that CT = 2AQ and by symmetry RC = AQ, so RC is one-third of RT and again by symmetry AQ is one-third of PQ.]

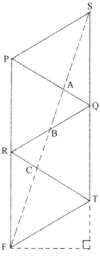

Fig. 332

Other Models of a Regular Icosahedron

In fig. 197 on page 154 of *Mathematical Models*, Cundy and Rollett show a fairly complicated strip of equilateral triangles which can be plaited to make a regular icosahedron.

A rigid skeleton model of the icosahedron can be made using 30 lengths of drinking straw, threaded with shirring elastic.

On page 105 we looked at the rectangle (ABCD in fig. 304) bounded by two opposite edges of the icosahedron and two diagonals of the pentagonal faces of the antiprism. This rectangle was a Golden Rectangle, with sides in the ratio of ø:1 (see page 196). Within the antiprism we can draw a second congruent rectangle which passes symmetrically through this first rectangle at right angles to it (EFGH in fig. 333). But this is not the whole story. A third congruent golden rectangle, perpendicular to both the other two, has for two of its sides two other opposite edges of the icosahedron. These edges are not part of the antiprism, but I and J are opposite corners of this rectangle, the other corners being the two vertices of the icosahedron which are the apexes of the "caps". Thus the twelve corners of the three rectangles are the twelve vertices of the icosahedron (fig. 334). (The heavy lines in fig. 334 show three edges of the solid which are mutually perpendicular, each edge belonging to one of the three rectangles.)

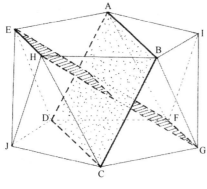

Fig. 333

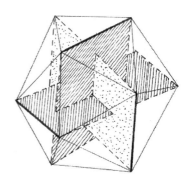

Fig. 334

This model can readily be made from card.

1. Cut three golden rectangles from card, drawing them perhaps using one of the methods described on page 204.
2. In each card cut a slot the length of a short side and placed symmetrically midway between the long sides (fig. 335).
3. On one card extend the cut to one edge of the card.
4. Slot the three cards together (fig. 336). Stick sellotape or paper along the cut which reaches the edge of the third card.

If we wish we can make a cap (without its pentagonal base) of five equilateral triangles, adapting fig. 337 overleaf, to see how the faces of the icosahedron fit over these rectangles; or we may join the corners of the rectangles with cocktail sticks or matchsticks fixed with glue or plasticine to show the thirty edges and twenty faces of the icosahedron.

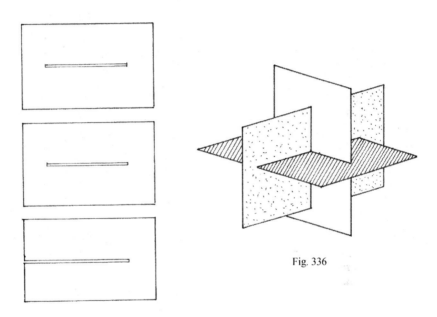

Fig. 336

Fig. 335

Uses of the Regular Icosahedron.

The regular icosahedron has an attractive shape and its decorative potential has been considerably exploited commercially. The shape has been used for lamp-bases and for lamp-shades, with a face or an edge uppermost rather than a vertex, while a rotating regular icosahedron was formerly the logo of Grundy Television.

Postscript: A Decahedron

The two "caps" of the icosahedron shown in fig. 301 on page 108 will, when placed together base to base, form a *decahedron*, with ten faces, each face being an equilateral triangle. This decahedron can be made from the net in fig. 337, which is part of the net shown in fig. 224, page 74, and which can be drawn following the same instructions. When completed, the model can be held between finger and thumb at its top and bottom vertices (fig. 338), and can be made to rotate by blowing against one side. When it is rotating fast enough it can be released, when it float to the floor, in more or less close imitation possibly of a "flying saucer".

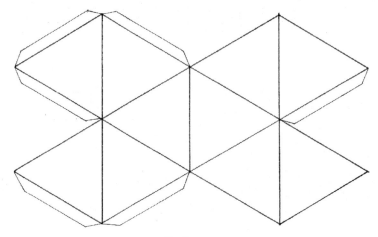

Fig. 337

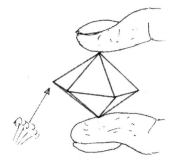

Fig. 338

Chapter 10

DUAL SOLIDS

We have used the terms "dual" and "dual solid" once or twice already. We now look at the concept of "duality" in some detail.

If we take any solid and join the centres of adjacent faces with straight lines, these lines will form the edges of a *dual* solid contained within the first solid. The dual solid has a vertex positioned on each face of the first solid; each face on the dual solid corresponds to a vertex of the first solid; and both solids have the same number of edges. In fig. 339 we see for example that the solid dual to a cube is a regular octahedron.

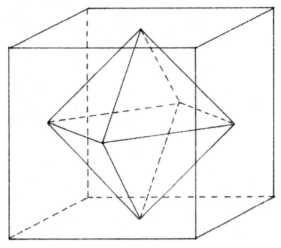

Fig. 339

The dual of every Platonic solid is another Platonic solid. Just as the regular octahedron is dual to the cube, so the cube is dual to the regular octahedron; the regular dodecahedron is dual to the regular icosahedron, and vice versa; while the dual of the regular tetrahedron is another regular tetrahedron. The table below shows the relationship between the numbers of faces, vertices and edges of dual solids:

Solid	Faces	Vertices	Edges
Tetrahedron	4	4	6
Cube	6	8	12
Octahedron	8	6	12
Dodecahedron	12	20	30
Icosahedron	20	12	30

The Regular Octahedron is Dual to the Cube

We can build a model in two pieces to show how the dual octahedron fits into the cube. The net for each piece of this model is shown in fig. 341 overleaf.

1. Draw a square ABCD with sides double the length of the edges of the complete cube. By measuring, mark points which divide each side of the square into four equal parts.

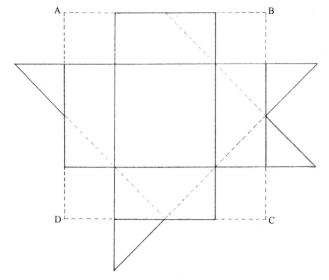

Fig. 340

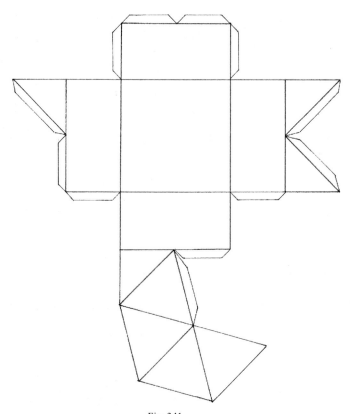

Fig. 341

2. By joining appropriate pairs of points on opposite sides of ABCD, extending some of the lines, and drawing right-angled isosceles triangles, construct the diagram shown in fig. 340. Broken lines are construction lines showing how the triangles can be drawn.
3. Add four equilateral triangles to the hypotenuse of one isosceles triangle (see e.g. page 15), and draw flaps as shown to obtain the complete net (fig. 341).

To make the first piece, fold the net into a half-cube and fold the equilateral triangles into a pyramidal depression (fig. 342) These triangles may be stuck first to form the depression, with edges creased to fold inwards instead of outwards.

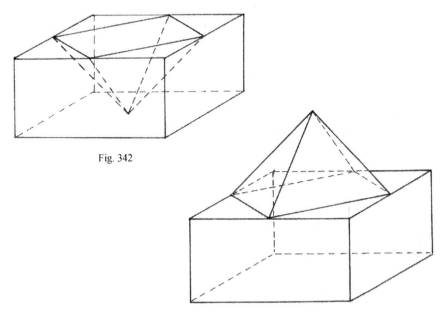

Fig. 342

Fig. 343

The second piece forms the rest of the cube. The equilateral triangles are now stuck together to form, instead of a depression, a pyramid which will fit into the depression in the other piece (fig. 343). (The edges of the equilateral triangles which make this new pyramid should be drawn a millimetre or two shorter to ensure a good fit.) The two pieces together make a whole cube. They will separate to show as it were the octahedron inside. It should be noted that the vertices of the octahedron meet the centres of the faces of the cube.

Alternatively, we may make two pieces, each with a depression as in fig. 342, and a regular octahedron to fit inside, again with its edges slightly shorter to ensure a good fit.

This last model will help us to calculate the symmetry number of the octahedron, as discussed on page 76. Each of the six vertices of the octahedron may be placed in the depression in turn, each time in four different orientations, giving a symmetry number of 6 x 4 = 24.

The volume of the dual octahedron is exactly one-sixth the volume of the cube. The equatorial square of the octahedron joins the mid-points of the square cross-section of the cube, and so has half the area of the cross-section. We can regard the octahedron as being made from two pyramids, one above and one below this square base. The height of each pyramid is half the height of the cube. The volume of the octahedron is therefore $2 \times \frac{1}{3} \times \frac{1}{2} \times \frac{1}{2} = \frac{1}{6}$ the volume of the cube.

We can dissect the model shown in fig. 342 into four congruent pieces, eight of which together with the dual octahedron will make a cube. Each of the eight pieces will itself be a smaller cube with one corner completely removed, leaving it with three faces which are square, three which are right-angled isosceles triangles, and one face which is an equilateral triangle (fig. 344). The net for one such piece is shown in fig. 345.

1. Draw a line ABCDE four units long and draw its mediator to cross AE at C. On the mediator mark F one unit below C, and G and H respectively one and two units above C.
2. Mark B so that AB = BC and D so that CD = DE. Complete the squares BCGL, CDKG, and CDJF, and then join AL and HE to obtain three right-angled triangles.
3. Draw the equilateral triangle KEM on KE, and draw flaps as shown. Stick flap *f* first.

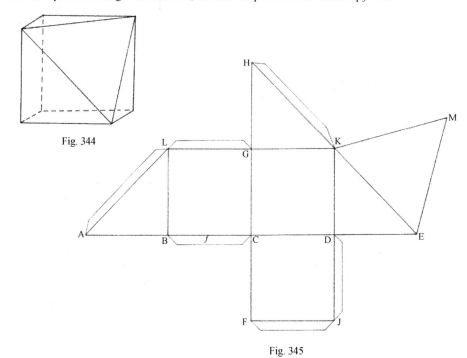

Fig. 344

Fig. 345

Eight of these pieces will fit together to form a cube with an octahedron-shaped hole inside, into which a dual octahedron will fit. However if we reassemble the eight pieces so that all the vertices marked C in fig. 345 meet at a point in the centre with the equilateral triangular faces all facing outwards, we obtain a *cuboctahedron* with fourteen faces, six of which are squares and eight of which are equilateral triangles (fig. 346). Details of this solid, which is one of the *Archimedean* or *semi-regular* solids and which we study in depth in chapter 15, can be found in Cundy and Rollett, *op. cit.*, page 102. It should be clear that this solid in combination with the regular octahedron will fill space.

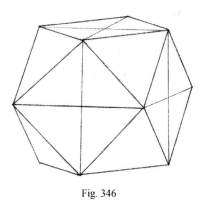

Fig. 346

The Cube is Dual to the Regular Octahedron

Fig. 347 shows the dual cube within a regular octahedron.

In fig. 251 on page 83 we showed the net of a detachable section of a regular octahedron, and looked ahead to making a model to show a dual cube enclosed in the octahedron, using an adaptation of this net. The adapted net appears in fig. 348.

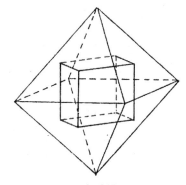

Fig. 347

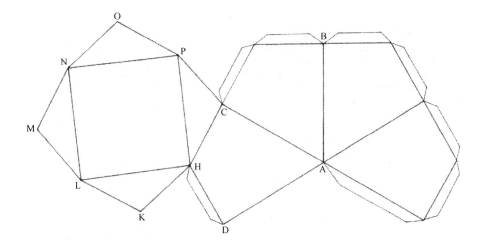

Fig. 348

The four kites are drawn following the instructions given on page 82 and illustrated in figs. 250 and 251 on page 83. P is placed at the intersection of two arcs of appropriate radius centred on C and H. If AB = 1 unit, then CH = CP = tan 30° = √3/3 ≈ 0.577 units long and PH = 2√2/3 ≈ 0.94 units long. PHLN is a square, and the four isosceles triangles on its sides are all congruent.

These four triangles have sides in the ratio of 1:1:(2√2)/√3 (= √3:√3:√8). They are of particular interest because each is made from two smaller congruent right-angled triangles whose sides are in the ratio of √3:√2:1, or alternatively of 1:√(2/3):√(1/3) (fig 349 overleaf). One of these smaller triangles appears in fig. 63 on page 24 where its sides are respectively an edge of the cube (1 unit), a diagonal of a face (√2 units), and an interior diagonal of the cube (√3 units). When the two smaller triangles are joined along the sides which are √2 units long, they form the isosceles triangle which appears in fig. 355 on page 128 as CLE, whose sides are in the ratio then of 2:√3:√3. The angle PCH in fig. 348 is 2 tan⁻¹ √2 (= tan⁻¹ ⁻2√2) = 109.47° and is the dihedral angle of the octahedron (see page 77) as well as being the *Maraldi* angle mentioned on page 32.

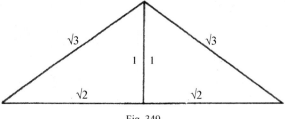

Fig. 349

Six models made from the net in fig. 348, mounted one on each face of a cube, will together make a regular octahedron containing its dual cube. Fig. 350 shows the net of a model of this octahedron when just one vertex section (corner) is removed. This net is an adaptation of the net shown in fig. 225 on page 74. The point O is the centre of the face of an equilateral triangle. The four triangles OPQ, etc., are all congruent to the triangle PHC in fig. 348 (shown also in fig. 349). If the length of the side, e.g. AB, of one of the equilateral triangles is taken to be 2 units, then OP will be the same length as PH in fig. 348, that is, $2\sqrt{2}/3 \approx 0.94$ units.

When it is made up the model contains a square hole. Fig. 351 shows the net of an open cube which is to be stuck into this hole to contain the dual cube. This open cube must be stuck to the flaps marked h in fig. 350. If we make a "dual" cube to fit into the open cube, using any of the nets shown on pages 39 and 40, then the edges of this cube must be a little shorter than the edges of the hole if the dual cube is to fit into it easily. This model shows how the vertices of the dual cube touch the centres of the faces of the octahedron.

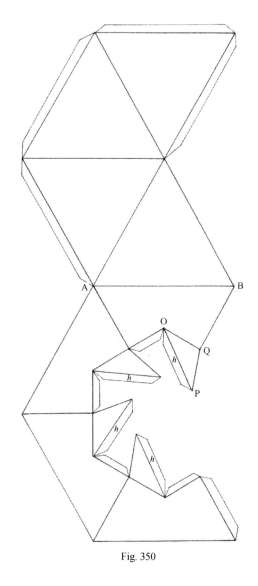

Fig. 350

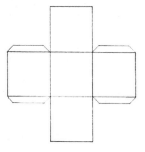

Fig. 351

Fig. 353 is a plan view of the octahedron with the dual cube shown inside it.

1. Draw a square ABCD with its diagonals. Mark the mid-points of its sides E, F, G, H.
2. Join each of these mid-points to the others to find the mid-points K, L, M, N of the half-diagonals (fig. 352).
3. Join AL and BK to find P, the centre of the triangle ABO (fig. 353). Find Q, R and S in a similar way. The triangle ABO represents a face of the octahedron, and P is the position of one vertex of the dual cube, with three other vertices of the cube at Q, R and S.

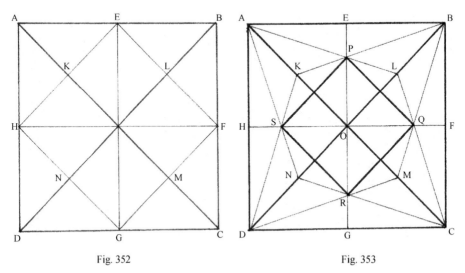

Fig. 352   Fig. 353

The construction lines not only find for us the centres of the faces of the octahedron and hence the positions of the vertices of the cube: they also help us to calculate by similar triangles (contained for instance within the triangle ALC) that the length of the edge PQ of the dual cube is one-third the length of the diagonal AC of the equatorial square of the octahedron, or √2/3 times the length of its edge AB. (Note that LQ = ½QC – why?). If the edge of the octahedron is 1 unit long, then its volume is √2/3 cubic units (see page 73); the volume of the dual cube is (√2/3)³ cubic units; and the cube will therefore occupy [(√2/3)³]/[(√2/3)] = (√2/3)² = 2/9 (≈ 0.222) of the volume of the octahedron.

We can imagine a dual octahedron inside a cube, whose volume is 1/6 that of the cube (see page 123), and a dual cube inside this dual octahedron, and so on, in an infinity of nesting. The volume of the second cube as a fraction of the volume of the first, (and also the volume of the next dual octahedron in the series as a fraction of that of the first) will be 1/6 x 2/9 = 1/27 (see also page 150).

The Regular Tetrahedron is Dual to another Regular Tetrahedron.

Fig. 354 shows how the dual solid within a regular tetrahedron is another regular tetrahedron.

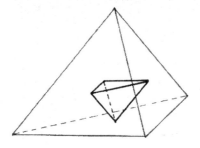

Fig. 354

In fig. 187 on page 62 we showed the net of a detachable vertex section or corner of a regular tetrahedron, and looked ahead to making a model, using an adaptation of this net, to show the dual tetrahedron enclosed within the first one. This adapted net is shown in fig. 355. The corners of the isosceles triangle CEL correspond to the points C, E and L in fig. 186, and the triangle has sides in the ratio of 2:√3:√3. The triangle LEN is equilateral, and the triangles EMN and LNO are congruent to the triangle CEL.

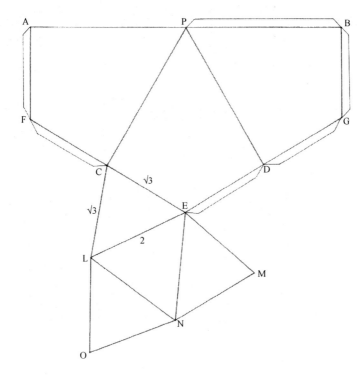

Fig. 355

Fig. 356 is an adaptation of the net of a regular tetrahedron shown in fig. 125 on page 43, and shows the net (on a smaller scale) of the other portion of the tetrahedron. The model will contain a depression to take the dual tetrahedron. In fig. 356 P is the mid-point of AD, Q is the mid-point of AF, and R is the centre of the triangle ADF. Fig. 357 shows where flaps are to be placed on this net. The depression is best made separately, using the net shown in fig. 358, which combines a line of three equilateral triangles, ACD, ABD and BDE, with three isosceles triangles. Each isosceles triangle is congruent to the triangle CEL in fig. 355, and has sides in the ratio 2:√3:√3, the sides AH, BH, etc., being equal in length to AF, the altitude of the equilateral triangle ABD.

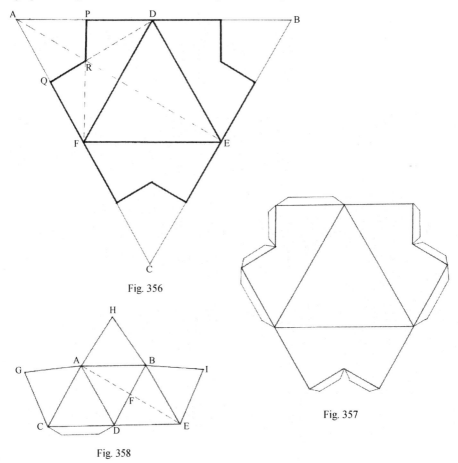

Fig. 356

Fig. 357

Fig. 358

Stick the flap on CD in fig. 358 to form an open tetrahedron with three triangles attached, and then push down the whole piece into the space in the model made from the net in figs. 356 and 357, sticking the isosceles triangles on to glued flaps. A tetrahedron made with slightly shorter edges will fit into the depression to show the dual tetrahedron touching the centres of all four faces of the large tetrahedron.

The volume of the dual tetrahedron is much smaller than that of the large tetrahedron. Fig. 359 is a plan view of the regular tetrahedron with the dual tetrahedron inside it. ABC is an equilateral triangle with centre O. The points D, E and F are the midpoints of OA, OB and OC respectively. If the edges of the larger tetrahedron are 1 unit long, those of the dual tetrahedron (by similar triangles, e.g., CDB and PDQ) are only 1/3 unit long, and if the large tetrahedron has a volume of 1 cubic unit, then the dual tetrahedron has a volume of $(1/3)^3$ = 1/27 cubic units, which is about 3.7% of the volume of the large tetrahedron.

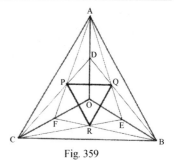

Fig. 359

We note that this fraction, 1/27, is the same as the proportion of the volume of successive similar solids in the series of dual cubes and octahedra we referred to on page 127. This correspondence reflects the fact that all these solids are related to one another in a manner which we examine in detail in chapter 13, page 150.

The Regular Dodecahedron is Dual to the Regular Icosahedron, and Vice Versa.

It is not easy to make models which show the dual relationship between the regular dodecahedron and the regular icosahedron. Photographs of such models appear in figures 252 and 253 on pages 200 and 201 of Steinhaus, *Mathematical Snapshots*, in a chapter which also contains photographs of the other duals we have discussed earlier. Martin Gardner on pages 61 and 62 of *More Mathematical Puzzles and Diversions* describes and illustrates how the corners of the three Golden Rectangles which define the vertices of a regular icosahedron (see fig. 334, page 118 above) also coincide with the centres of the faces of a regular dodecahedron, in consequence of the reciprocal duality of the two solids.

Here we do no more than calculate the relative volumes of the two dual solids. The regular dodecahedron with edge *a* units has a volume of $5\o^5a^3/2(\o + 2)$ cubic units (see page 101). The corresponding formula for the volume of the regular icosahedron is $5\o^2a^3/6$ cubic units (see page 114).

It is helpful to make a table showing the lengths of edges and the distances between opposite vertices and opposite faces of the two solids, bearing in mind that a dual solid will have a distance between opposite *vertices* (DV) equal to the distance between opposite *faces* (DF) of the first solid. We take the figures in the table below from pages 96 and 109 of the earlier chapters on the dodecahedron and the icosahedron.

Solid	Edge	DV	DF
Dodecahedron	1	$\o\sqrt3$	$\o^3/\sqrt(\o + 2)$
Icosahedron	1	$\sqrt(\o + 2)$	$\o^2/\sqrt3$

We begin by calculating the volume of the dual icosahedron contained within a regular dodecahedron. For this purpose we keep the dimensions of the dodecahedron unchanged and adjust the dimensions of the icosahedron so that DV in the latter is equal to DF $[\o^3/\sqrt(\o + 2)]$ in the former. The scale factor for making this change is $[\o^3/\sqrt(\o + 2)] \div [\sqrt(\o + 2)]$, which simplifies to $\o^3/(\o + 2) = \o^3/(\o^2 + 1)$ $= \o^2/(\o + 1/\o) = \o^2/(\o + \o - 1) = \o^2/(2\o - 1) = \o^2/\sqrt5$, and this will be the length of edge of the dual icosahedron.

Solid	Edge	DV	DF
Dodecahedron	1	$\o\sqrt3$	$\o^3/\sqrt(\o + 2)$
Dual Icosahedron	$\o^2/\sqrt5$	$\o^3/\sqrt(\o + 2)$	$\o^4/\sqrt15$

The volume of the dual icosahedron will therefore be $5\o^2(\o^2/\sqrt5)^3/6 = \o^8/6\sqrt5 \approx 3.5$ cubic units. As a fraction of the volume of the dodecahedron, which is $5\o^5/2(\o + 2) \approx 7.66$ cubic units, this will be $[\o^8/6\sqrt5] \div [5\o^5/2(\o + 2)] = \o^3(\o + 2)/15\sqrt5 \approx 0.457$, or somewhat under half the volume.

We follow the same line of argument when calculating the volume of the dual dodecahedron as a fraction of the volume of the enclosing icosahedron.

Solid	Edge	DV	DF
Icosahedron	1	$\sqrt{(\text{ø}+2)}$	$\text{ø}^2/\sqrt{3}$
Dodecahedron	1	$\text{ø}\sqrt{3}$	$\text{ø}^3/\sqrt{(\text{ø}+2)}$

Here we keep the dimensions of the icosahedron unchanged and adjust the dimensions of the dual dodecahedron, so that DV in the latter is equal to DF ($\text{ø}^2/\sqrt{3}$) in the former. The scale factor for making this change is ($\text{ø}^2/\sqrt{3}$) ÷ ($\text{ø}\sqrt{3}$), which simplifies to ø/3, and this will be the length of edge of the dual dodecahedron.

Solid	Edge	DV	DF
Icosahedron	1	$\sqrt{(\text{ø}+2)}$	$\text{ø}^2/\sqrt{3}$
Dual Dodecahedron	ø/3	$\text{ø}^2/\sqrt{3}$	$\text{ø}^4/3\sqrt{(\text{ø}+2)}$

The volume of the dual dodecahedron will be $5\text{ø}^5(\text{ø}/3)^3/2(\text{ø}+2)$ = $5\text{ø}^8/54(\text{ø}+2) \approx 1.202$ cubic units. As a fraction of the volume of the icosahedron (2.18 cubic units) this will be $[5\text{ø}^8/54(\text{ø}+2)] \div [5\text{ø}^2/6]$ = $\text{ø}^6/9(\text{ø}+2) \approx 0.552$, or somewhat over half the volume.

We can imagine a dual icosahedron inside a dodecahedron, and a dual dodecahedron inside this dual icosahedron, and so on, in an infinity of nesting. The ratio of the volume of any solid to the volume of the next similar solid down will be the reciprocal of the product of the two volume ratios we have just found, namely 1/(0.457 x 0.552) which is about 3.965. It is tempting to see this optimistically as an approximation to a true figure of exactly 4, but sadly the true figure is $1/\{[\text{ø}^3(\text{ø}+2)/15\sqrt{5}]$ x $[\text{ø}^6/9(\text{ø}+2)]\} = 135\sqrt{5}/\text{ø}^9 \approx 3.97$, or just under 4. Mathematics is not always quite as neat as we may have come to expect it to be. However we may say that as we take successive duals in a series of nested dodecahedra and icosahedra, the volume of any one solid is about half the volume of the one next outside it and double the volume of the one next inside it.

Circum-spheres and In-spheres

While we are looking at the volumes of the regular dodecahedron and the regular icosahedron, it may be worth checking a statement made by David Wells, *op. cit.*, page 58, to the effect that if a regular dodecahedron and a regular icosahedron are both inscribed in a sphere (the *circum-sphere*) which touches all the vertices of both solids, the dodecahedron will occupy a greater fraction of the volume of the sphere than will the icosahedron. This is in spite of the fact that common sense may suggest that the triangular faces of the icosahedron, being smaller and more numerous, must be closer to the surface of the sphere than the pentagonal faces of the dodecahedron.

If we take the radius of the circum-sphere to be one unit, then for both solids the distance between opposite vertices must be 2 units. We adjust all dimensions accordingly and in proportion.

Solid	Edge	DV	DF
[Dodecahedron	1	$\text{ø}\sqrt{3}$	$\text{ø}^3/\sqrt{(\text{ø}+2)}]$
[Icosahedron	1	$\sqrt{(\text{ø}+2)}$	$\text{ø}^2/\sqrt{3}]$
Dodecahedron	$2/\text{ø}\sqrt{3}$	2	$2\text{ø}^2/\sqrt{\{3(\text{ø}+2)\}}$
Icosahedron	$2/\sqrt{(\text{ø}+2)}$	2	$2\text{ø}^2/\sqrt{\{3(\text{ø}+2)\}}$

Note that the factor by which we multiply distances on the dodecahedron is $2/\text{ø}\sqrt{3}$, while the factor for the icosahedron is $2/\sqrt{(\text{ø}+2)}$.

The volume of the regular dodecahedron with edge $2/\text{ø}\sqrt{3}$ units will be $5\text{ø}^5(2/\text{ø}\sqrt{3})^3/2(\text{ø}+2)$ = $20\text{ø}^2/[3\sqrt{3}(\text{ø}+2)] \approx 2.785$ cubic units, while the volume of the regular icosahedron with edge

$2/\sqrt{(\o + 2)}$ units will be $(5\o^2/6) \times [2/\sqrt{(\o + 2)}]^3 = 20\o^2/[3\sqrt{(\o + 2)^3}] \approx 2.536$ cubic units. The volume of the circum-sphere of radius 1 unit is $4\pi/3 \approx 4.19$ cubic units. In terms of percentage, the dodecahedron occupies about 66.5% of the interior of the sphere, while the icosahedron occupies only about 60.5% of it.

One interesting point to note in the last table on the previous page is that the values of DF as well as the values of DV are the same for both solids. This means that not only do the two solids have their vertices touching the same circum-sphere, but they also have their faces touching a smaller inner sphere (the *in-sphere*), of radius $\frac{1}{2} \times 2\o^2/\sqrt{\{3(\o + 2)\}} \approx 0.795$ units and whose volume is about 2.1 cubic units, or just over half the volume of the larger sphere.

The fact that the distances between opposite faces as well as those between opposite vertices on the two solids are equal is true not for these two solids alone. If we do the same calculations for the cube and the regular octahedron, which are dual to each other, we find the following:

Solid	Edge	DV	DF
[Cube	*1*	$\sqrt{3}$	$\sqrt{2}]$
[Octahedron	*1*	$\sqrt{2}$	$2/\sqrt{6}]$
Cube	$2/\sqrt{3}$	2	$2/\sqrt{3}$
Octahedron	$2/\sqrt{2}$	2	$2/\sqrt{3}$

Again it turns out that when the vertices of these two solids touch the same circum-sphere, their faces touch the same smaller in-sphere. The cube occupies nearly 37% of the volume of the circum-sphere, while the octahedron occupies only about 32% of it. If the radius of the circum-sphere (the *circum-radius*) is 1 unit, then the radius of the in-sphere (the *in-radius*) is $1/\sqrt{3}$ units. Compared with the volume of the circum-sphere, the volume of the in-sphere is $(1/\sqrt{3})^3 \approx 0.192$ or just under 1/5 that of the circum-sphere.

Rouse Ball (*op. cit.*, page 133) observes that "The ratio of circum-radius R to in-radius r is exactly the same for the cube as for the octahedron, and for the dodecahedron as for the icosahedron" and goes on to confirm that "the relative size of two reciprocal (i.e. dual) polyhedra may be adjusted so as to make them have the same circum-sphere and the same in-sphere. (In general, their corresponding edges will no longer intersect.)" (Solids which are dual to each other can be combined so that their edges do intersect, as in the combination of the cube and the octahedron shown in fig. 435, page 167 and reproduced below in fig. 360. See also Cundy and Rollett, *op. cit.*, pages 78-79.)

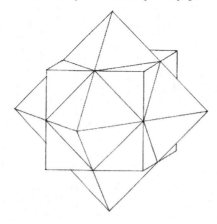

Fig. 360

In fig 361 we reproduce fig 339 from page 121 and in fig 362 we show the cross-section through ABCD of the cube and EFGH of the dual octahedron. ABCD is a rectangle with sides in the ratio of √2:1; EFGH is the same section as the rhombus DJLK in fig. 232, page 77. O is the centre of both solids. OP is the distance from the centre of the octahedron to the centre of a face. Note that EC and OB intersect at right angles; this is a property of the rectangle ABCD, related to the fact that the rectangles AEGD and EBCG are congruent to each other and both are similar to ABCD. (Note also that ABCD could represent a sheet of, say, A4 paper, divided by a cut along EG into two A5 sheets of paper.) The triangles EOP and EOB are similar, so the ratios OE:OP and OB:OE, the ratios referred to by Rouse Ball (above), are the same.

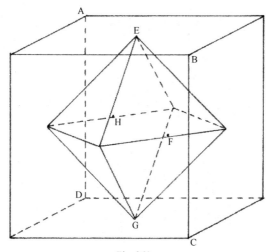

Fig. 361

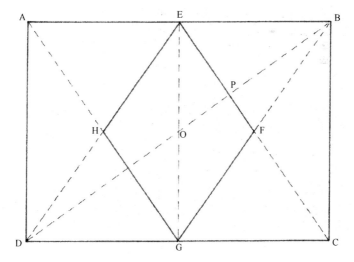

Fig. 362

In fig. 363 we see the circles which are cross-sections of the circum-sphere and the in-sphere of the cube. We see also that if we enlarge the cross-section of the (dual) octahedron from EGFH to E'F'G'H' so that E' now lies on the circum-sphere, E'F' will be a tangent to the in-sphere, touching at P', the image of P under the enlargement; and that both circles now represent cross-sections of the circum-sphere and the in-sphere of the octahedron as well as that of the cube.

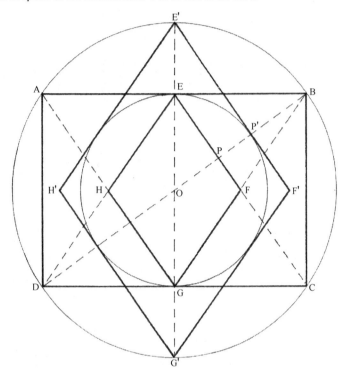

Fig. 363

Chapter 11

THE RHOMBOID AND ITS PARTS

Fig. 75 on page 28 shows a "skeleton" model of a cube made from lengths of drinking straw threaded together with shirring elastic. Fig. 364, which reproduces fig. 77 on the same page, shows that if we pull apart two opposite vertices of this model a little, each face changes from a square to a rhombus and the model becomes that of a *rhombic hexahedron*.

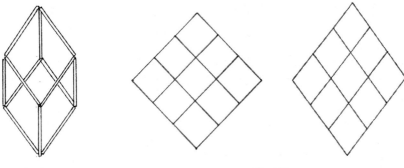

Fig. 364   Fig. 365

Fig. 365 reminds us that a tessellation of squares will still fill the plane if we distort each square into a rhombus by "pulling" opposite corners. We know also that the cube will "tessellate" to fill space. If we arrange cubes face to face in a three-dimensional tessellation, and then distort them so that they all become congruent rhombic hexahedra, then these hexahedra will themselves "tessellate" to fill space, in much the same way as the rhombuses in fig. 365 still fill the plane. We shall, as it were, have "pulled" cube-filled space so that it becomes space filled with rhombic hexahedra.

In this chapter we look specifically at the rhombic hexahedron whose face angles are 60° and 120°, and each of whose faces is therefore made up of two equilateral triangles. We shall refer to this particular hexahedron as a "rhomboid". Fig. 366 shows one net of such a rhomboid drawn on a network of intersecting circles, with flaps to be drawn on the sides marked F. [Fig. 366 is a modification of the net of a cube shown in fig. 122(j) on page 40. It is a good exercise in reasoning and visualisation for pupil and teacher alike to try to make such a net by modifying any one of the eleven distinct nets of the cube (see pages 39-41) and then checking that it folds to make a rhomboid.]

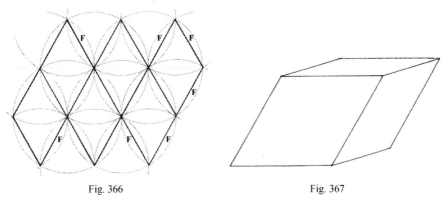

Fig. 366   Fig. 367

Fig. 367 shows an oblique view of the rhomboid. The front face is a 60°/120° rhombus. The other faces may be drawn in much the same way as those of the cube were drawn in the oblique view of that solid shown in figs. 84-86 on page 30.

One fact of particular interest about the 60°/120° rhomboid is that it can be dissected in a number of different ways into other regular or semi-regular solids, from which it follows that these other solids when taken together will also fill space. For example we can dissect the rhomboid into a regular octahedron and two regular tetrahedra (fig. 368). Neither of these regular solids will fill space on its own, but the fact that they combine to make a rhomboid means that they will also combine to fill space.

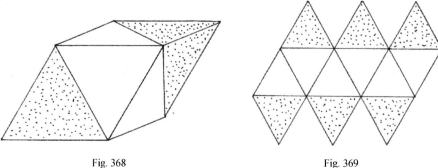

Fig. 368   Fig. 369

The two tetrahedra fit on to opposite faces of the octahedron to form the rhomboid. Half of each face of the rhomboid belongs to a tetrahedron and half to the octahedron. The net of the rhomboid can be coloured in such a way (fig. 369) that the finished model appears to be made from the three component solids.

We can make a model of a cube coloured in a similar way, to show which parts of the cube "pull" into the two tetrahedra and which part becomes the octahedron (fig. 370). A net for this cube is shown in fig. 371. Each face of the cube is divided in two by a diagonal. Cuts made along the planes of these diagonals dissect the cube into three parts. Two parts are pyramids with one face an equilateral triangle and with three faces right-angled isosceles triangles. The third "central" part is a triangular "anti-prism", with two opposite faces equilateral triangles, joined by six right-angled isosceles triangles.

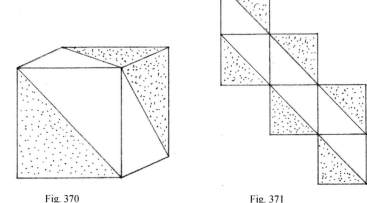

Fig. 370   Fig. 371

The process of "pulling" the cube in fig. 370 into a rhomboid does not alter the ratio of the volumes of the three parts. If we stand one of the triangular pyramids on a right-angled triangular face, we can calculate its volume to be $\frac{1}{3} \times \frac{1}{2} s^2 \times s = \frac{1}{6} s^3$ cubic units, where s is the length of an edge of the cube. The volume of each pyramid is one-sixth the volume of the cube and the ratio of the volumes of the three parts is therefore 1:4:1. The volumes of the three parts of the rhomboid stand in the same ratio, which means that the volume of a regular octahedron is four times that of a regular tetrahedron with the same length of edge.

We imagine now that a number of congruent rhomboids are fitted together so that they all point as it were in the same direction with each face of any rhomboid fitting the face of another rhomboid. We also imagine that each rhomboid is dissected as in fig. 368 into an octahedron and two tetrahedra. Each octahedron will then be surrounded by eight tetrahedra and each tetrahedron will be surrounded by four octahedra. However the ratio of tetrahedra to octahedra in this arrangement will still be 2:1. We shall see in the next chapter (page 143) that this combination of octahedra and tetrahedra can be further dissected to make congruent *rhombic dodecahedra*, which themselves tessellate to fill space.

On pages 25 and 26 we saw how a cut passing through the mid-points of six edges of a cube will divide the cube into two congruent parts, each with a hexagonal face. Fig. 372 shows a similar cut passing through the mid-points of six edges of the rhomboid. (Note that a similar cut also divides the regular octahedron into two congruent parts, as we saw on page 80, fig. 241.) Two more cuts, each made through the mid-points of the three edges which meet at each "pointed" or "sharp" vertex of the rhomboid, will produce two regular tetrahedra, smaller however than the tetrahedra shown in fig. 368. These three cuts will dissect the rhomboid into four pieces (fig. 373), all of which are solids with special names. In addition to the two regular tetrahedra there are two *truncated tetrahedra*, which are regular tetrahedra whose corners have been cut off by cuts made one-third and two-thirds of the way along their edges (see chapter 14, page 153).

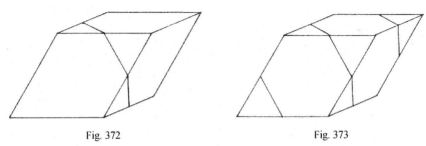

Fig. 372   Fig. 373

The net of a truncated tetrahedron can be drawn on a grid of triangles, these triangles being contained within an equilateral triangle whose sides are divided into six equal parts (fig. 374). The net with flaps appears in fig. 375.

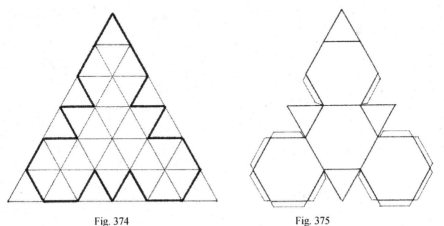

Fig. 374   Fig. 375

Since two truncated tetrahedra and two regular tetrahedra fit together to form the rhomboid, it follows that these two solids will also combine to fill space. In such a three-dimensional tessellation, it is clear that tetrahedra and truncated tetrahedra occur in equal proportions: how is each type of solid then surrounded?

Fig. 376 shows how the rhomboid may be dissected into six pieces by the cuts shown separately in figs. 368 and 373. The two central pieces fit together to make a regular octahedron, and are separated by the cut made on the octahedron seen in fig. 241 on page 80. The net for each of these pieces is shown in fig. 243 on the same page. The outermost two pieces seen in fig. 376 are the small tetrahedra seen in fig. 373; and the other two pieces are tetrahedra truncated to half their height from one vertex only (fig. 377). The net for one of these pieces is given in fig. 378; it is based on a equilateral triangle with its sides divided into four equal parts.

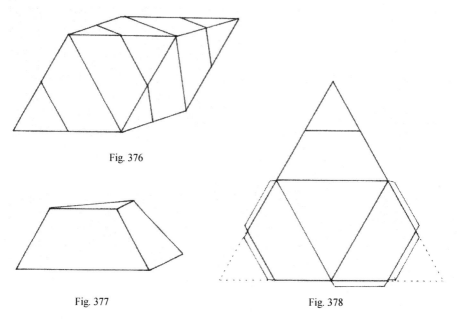

Fig. 376

Fig. 377   Fig. 378

These partially-truncated tetrahedra combine with the small tetrahedra to give the two large tetrahedra of fig 368. They also combine with the half-octahedra to give the two truncated tetrahedra seen in fig. 373. The six pieces taken together can be regarded as components of a puzzle all of whose parts combine to make a rhomboid, and from a selection of whose parts we can make two larger tetrahedra, or an octahedron, or two truncated tetrahedra, as we wish.

It is not difficult to work out the relative volumes of the six pieces. We have seen above (page 136) that the volume of a regular octahedron is four times that of a regular tetrahedron with the same length of edge, and that the dissection shown in fig. 368 divides the rhomboid in the ratio by volume of 1:4:1. Each small tetrahedron in fig. 373 has an edge half the length of the tetrahedron seen in fig. 368, so the volumes of the small and large tetrahedra are in the ratio of $(\frac{1}{2})^3$:1 or 1:8, while the ratio of the volume of the small tetrahedron to that of the partially-truncated tetrahedron of fig. 377 is 1:7. From this we can work out that the ratios of the volumes of the parts of fig. 376 taken in order are 1:7:16:16:7:1.

Chapter 12

THE RHOMBIC DODECAHEDRON

This polyhedron is not one of the Platonic solids, but its close association particularly with the cube means that we cannot ignore it entirely.

We have seen earlier (fig. 67, page 25) how a cube can be dissected into six congruent pyramids whose bases are the six faces of the cube and whose apexes all meet at its centre. There it was mentioned that these same six pyramids when deployed outwards and wrapped around a second congruent cube will form a *rhombic dodecahedron*, a solid with twelve faces each of which is a rhombus (fig. 379). (In chapter 11 we investigated the properties of the rhomboid, a *rhombic hexahedron* with six faces, each a rhombus. We should note that although the faces of the rhombic dodecahedron are also rhombuses, these latter rhombuses are of a different shape from those which form the faces of the rhomboid, having angles, as we shall see below, which are not 60° and 120°.)

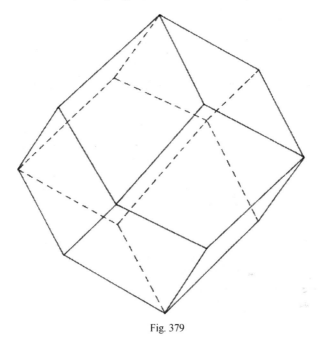

Fig. 379

The rhombic dodecahedron, like the cube, will "tessellate" to fill space. It is worth making several of these solids to see how they fit together to do this, and instructions for making a rhombic dodecahedron appear below. First, however, we look at the trigonometry of the rhombuses and at the way in which they fit together to make the solid.

The Composition and Symmetry of the Rhombic Dodecahedron

Each of the twelve faces of the solid has four sides, so that the solid has 12 x 4 ÷ 2 = 24 edges. According to Euler's theorem it must have 24 − 12 + 2 = 14 vertices. At six of these vertices four rhombuses (and also four edges) meet: at eight vertices three rhombuses (and also three edges) meet. The six 4-vertices lie outside the six faces of the enclosed cube, whose twelve edges lie along the shorter diagonals of the dodecahedron's faces. The eight 3-vertices lie outside the eight faces of an enclosed regular octahedron, whose twelve edges lie along the longer diagonals of the dodecahedron's faces (see below, page 143). The long and the short diagonals all lie along the edges of the solid which is formed when a cube and a regular octahedron are combined, (see fig. 360, page 132), and the fourteen vertices of the dodecahedron are also the vertices of this (enclosed) combined solid.

Fig. 380 shows the twelve rhombic faces separated and joined at only four of the 4-vertices. It should be clear from this diagram how four of the faces meet at a "top" vertex, while four others meet at a "bottom" vertex, and the other four form a "girdle" around the "waist" of the solid. It should also be clear how the long diagonals come together to form the edges of the enclosed regular octahedron referred to above, and perhaps a little less clear how the short diagonals come together to form the edges of the enclosed cube.

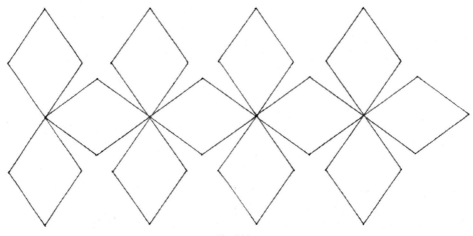

Fig. 380

The rhombic dodecahedron has thirteen axes of rotational symmetry. Seven of these pass through opposite vertices and six pass through the centres of opposite faces. None passes through the mid-points of opposite edges. The solid has nine planes of symmetry, passing through the diagonals of the faces. Of these nine, six pass through opposite edges of the enclosed cube and three pass through the "equatorial" edges of the enclosed octahedron.

The Trigonometry of the Rhombic Dodecahedron

If we refer back to page 24 and to the six pyramids into which we dissected the cube (of unit edge), we see that the length of each edge of the rhombic dodecahedron is half the length of the interior diagonal of the cube, that is, half $\sqrt{3}$ units. The short diagonal of each face of the solid, being an edge of the cube, is 1 unit long. By Pythagoras the long diagonal of each face (fig. 381) is twice $\frac{1}{2}\sqrt{2}$ or just $\sqrt{2}$ units long. The angles of the face are twice $\cos^{-1} 1/\sqrt{3}$ (= $\tan^{-1} \sqrt{2}$) $\approx 2 \times 54.736° \approx 109.47°$ and $(180 - 109.47)° \approx 70.53°$, and therefore differ somewhat in size from the 60° and 120° angles of the faces of the rhomboid. R. Thatcher (see below) mentions that 109.47° is the *Maraldi angle*, important in natural structure, which as we have seen (fig. 97, page 32) is the angle at which two interior diagonals of the cube cross, and also the angle AHB in fig. 176, page 58, the angle at which pairs of lines meet which join the vertices of a regular tetrahedron to its centre.

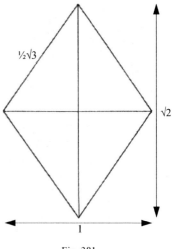

Fig. 381

To draw a face of the rhombic dodecahedron:

1. Draw a line AB 3 units long. With its mid-point C as centre, draw a circle of radius CA (fig. 382).
2. Mark D on AB 2 units from A, and draw the mediator of AD to meet the circle at E and F. Join A, E, D and F to obtain the rhombus which is a face of the dodecahedron.

AD is 2 units long, EF is 2√2 units long and ED is √3 units long. If we take ED to be 1 unit long as the edge of the dodecahedron, then the ratios of AD, EF and ED become 2/√3:2√2/√3:1.

[Note that the triangle AEF is also the isosceles triangle shown in fig. 349, page 126. Is this to be expected?]

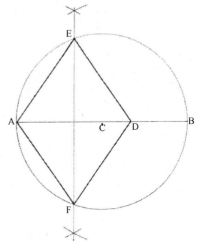

Fig. 382

Three of these rhombuses fitted together in the plane (fig. 383) leave a gap with an angle of (360 − {3 x 109.47})° ≈ 31.59°. Half this angle is 15.79° = tan⁻¹ √2/5 = sin⁻¹ √(2/3)/3. Taking AD to be 1 unit long, the length of AB is 2 x sin 15.79° x 1 = 2 x √(2/3)/3 = 2√2/3√3, which is one-third the length of the long diagonal EF of a face. The "length" CD of the gap is 5/3√3 units.

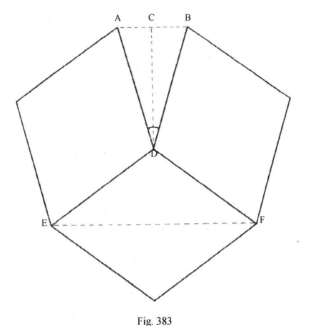

Fig. 383

A Net of the Rhombic Dodecahedron

It would be difficult to improve upon the net of the rhombic dodecahedron shown on page 120 of Cundy and Rollett's *Mathematical Models*, but the length of the net means that in drawing it we have plenty of room for error. This same net is reproduced in fig. 384, together with suggested construction lines which will reduce the likelihood of such error.

Along both the lines marked P and S, the gaps between the rhombuses are one-third the length of the long diagonals. P and S are $1/\sqrt{3} + 5/3\sqrt{3} = 8/3\sqrt{3}$ units apart. The lines Q and R divide this distance in the ratio of $1/\sqrt{3}:2/3\sqrt{3}:1/\sqrt{3}$ or 3:2:3. Points along Q and R are placed symmetrically in fairly clear relation to the points along P.

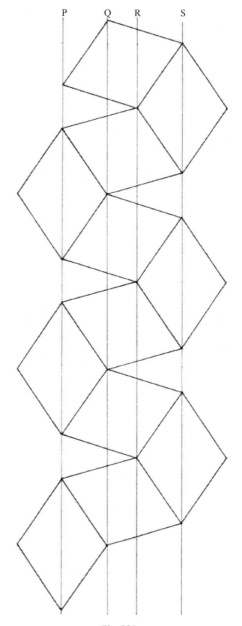

Fig. 384

The Rhombic Dodecahedron, the Cube and the Regular Octagon

We began this chapter with a reminder that the rhombic dodecahedron can be obtained by taking the six square-based pyramids into which a cube can be dissected and wrapping them around a cube of the same size, or alternatively by simply fixing one such pyramid to each face of a cube. A model of the rhombic dodecahedron made in this way will show clearly how the short diagonals of its faces coincide with the edges of an enclosed cube. We can demonstrate in a similar way how a rhombic dodecahedron can be made from a regular octagon and eight triangular-based pyramids.

The net of one such pyramid is shown in fig. 177 on page 58. If we fix one of these pyramids to each face of a regular octahedron, we obtain a rhombic dodecahedron, but it is possible to make a model which demonstrates this in a slightly more dramatic fashion.

Fig. 145 on page 49 shows how four of these pyramids fit together to make a regular tetrahedron. Fig. 385 shows a model in which the four pyramids are attached by their edges and are ready to be folded up into a tetrahedron.

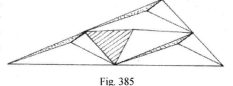

Fig. 385

1. Make two of the tetrahedron models shown in fig. 385, and a regular octahedron with the same length of edge as one pyramid.
2. Stick the middle pyramid of one tetrahedron model to any face of the octahedron, and stick the middle pyramid of the other tetrahedron model to the opposite face of the octahedron. When the pyramids are folded up to make the two tetrahedra, the resulting solid will be the rhomboid shown in fig. 368 on page 136.
3. When the pyramids are deployed outwards so that each meets a face of the octahedron, the resulting solid will be a rhombic dodecahedron.

This model shows clearly how the long diagonals of the rhombic dodecahedron coincide with the edges of an enclosed regular octahedron.

If in the model of the rhombic dodecahedron described above we replace the pyramid attached to each face of the octahedron with a *regular tetrahedron*, the resulting solid is a *stella octangula*, shown in fig. 397 on page 147. The stella octangula therefore contains a rhombic dodecahedron, and lines joining the centres of the tetrahedra to the nearest vertices of the octahedron will be half-edges of the enclosed rhombic dodecahedron.

Views of the Rhombic Dodecahedron

Figs. 386 and 387 show views of the solid looking directly along axes of symmetry at the two different types of vertex, with the outlines being respectively a square and a regular hexagon. The two distances AB are equal. Fig. 388 shows a view looking directly at a face, and is also the plan view when the solid is resting on a face. The rhombus in fig. 388 is a face drawn to scale. The four parallelograms are oblique views of four other faces. The length CD is equal to the shorter diagonal of the rhombus, and EF is double this length.

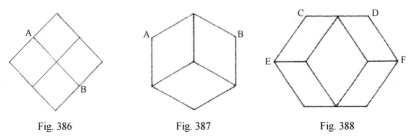

Fig. 386   Fig. 387   Fig. 388

The oblique view of the solid shown in fig. 391 below can be drawn by developing the oblique view of the cube shown in fig. 86, page 30. Eight of the vertices of the dodecahedron are the vertices of the cube.   The other six vertices are the apexes of the pyramids added to the cube to make the dodecahedron. The height of each pyramid is half the length of an edge of the cube, or the distance from the centre of the cube to the centre of a face.

1. Draw an oblique view of a cube.
2. By joining two or more pairs of opposite vertices, find the centre A of the cube (fig. 389).
3. Through A draw three lines, each parallel to one set of edges of the cube, each double the length of the corresponding edge of the cube, and each with its mid-point at A (fig. 390).
4. Join each of the six end-points of these lines to the corners of the nearest face of the cube to obtain an oblique view of the dodecahedron (fig. 391).

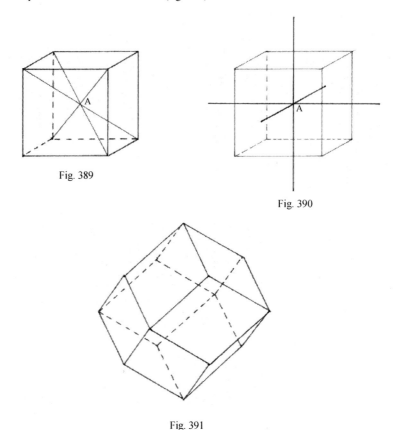

Fig. 389

Fig. 390

Fig. 391

Dissections of the Rhombic Dodecahedron

In an article in *Mathematics Teaching*, no. 44, Autumn 1968, page 4, R. Thatcher of Stockwell College discusses several aspects and features of the rhombic dodecahedron, and describes models made both in card and from drinking straws.

The rhombic dodecahedron, like other solids, can be made from pyramids whose bases are the faces of the solid. The net for such a pyramid is shown in Cundy and Rollett, *op. cit.*, fig. 189, page 149, and, with alterations to the position of its flaps, is also shown below in fig. 392.

1. Draw AB twice the (unit) length of the shorter diagonal of a face.
2. Draw the mediator of AB to pass through the mid-point C.
3. Draw an arc with centre C and radius AC to cut the mediator at D.
4. With radius AD (= $\sqrt{2}$ units) and centre C, draw an arc to cut CD produced at E. Join EA and EB ($\sqrt{3}$ units each).
5. Draw two arcs of length CE with centres at A and B to cut two other arcs with radius AC centred on E to give the positions of F and G.
6. Join FG, FC and GC to give the finished net. Draw flaps where shown and stick flap *f* first. The sides of the rhombus HEIC will be $\sqrt{3}/2$ units long.

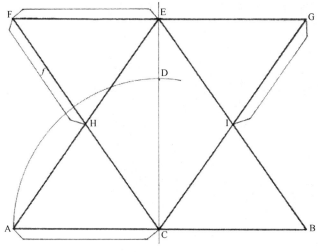

Fig. 392

Thatcher suggests that each of these rhombic pyramids can be thought of as being half of two particular congruent square pyramids placed base to base, the dissecting plane lying along four of their edges and diagonally across the square bases. We can see this clearly if we fit two rhombic pyramids together with their rhombic faces coinciding.

These pyramids will fill space just as the cube and the rhombic dodecahedron will fill space, and it is interesting and instructive to find out in how many ways four or five pyramids can be fitted together, and what shapes they will make. Twelve of them together will make the rhombic dodecahedron itself, while a further twelve added one to each face of the dodecahedron will make the *first stellation of the rhombic dodecahedron*, and more will make the second and third stellations. These stellations are explained and illustrated on pages 150-152 of Cundy and Rollett, *op. cit.* Tarquin under the title of "Rhombic Star" offer a set of six identical pieces which fit together to make the first stellation of the rhombic dodecahedron.

There is a connection between the rhombic dodecahedron and the close packing of spheres, mentioned by Cundy and Rollett, *op. cit.*, page 196, and discussed in more detail by Rouse Ball, *op. cit.*, pages 148-151, and by Steinhaus in *Mathematical Snapshots*, page 206. (In close packing, a sphere will be surrounded by twelve other touching spheres.   In a three-dimensional tessellation of rhombic dodecahedra, each face of any dodecahedron will meet a face of one of the twelve surrounding dodecahedra.)

Steinhaus also illustrates on page 186 the space-filling property of the rhombic dodecahedron, and goes on to illustrate how the hexagonal cells of a honeycomb are shaped at their bases as part rhombic dodecahedra (fig. 393). A model of a cell can be made quite easily.   The net of the hexagonal part, to which three rhombuses (fig. 383, page 141) must be attached to close the upper end, is shown in fig. 394.   The length AB is three times the length BC.

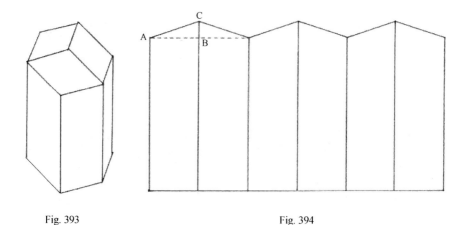

Fig. 393   Fig. 394

Chapter 13

RELATIONS BETWEEN THE SOLIDS

The Regular Tetrahedron and the Regular Octahedron

If we take a regular tetrahedron of edge 2*a* units, draw lines on each of its faces which join the mid-points of its edges (fig. 395), and then cut through the tetrahedron along these lines, we shall have dissected the solid into four smaller regular tetrahedra, each of edge *a* units, together with a regular octahedron also of edge *a* units (fig. 396). Note that the three lines drawn on each of the four faces of the original tetrahedron together mark the twelve edges of the octahedron. This means that when we reassemble the pieces, four faces of the octahedron appear as equilateral triangles in the middle of each face of the original tetrahedron, the other four faces now being hidden by the small tetrahedra.

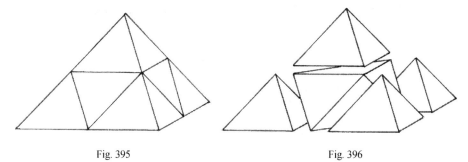

| Fig. 395 | Fig. 396 |

The best way of building a model to demonstrate this dissection is to work in reverse.

1. Make separately a regular octahedron and four regular tetrahedra, all with edges the same length.
2. Attach the tetrahedra one to each of four alternate faces of the octahedron, to make a regular tetrahedron whose edges are twice the length of the edges of its component pieces.

We know that if the lengths of the edges of two similar solids are in the ratio of 2:1, then their volumes will be in the ratio of 8:1. The large tetrahedron therefore has a volume eight times that of each small tetrahedron. The four small tetrahedra together make up half this volume; the octahedron must account for the other half, so a regular octahedron must have a volume four times that of a regular tetrahedron with the same length of edge. This confirms the calculations we made on pages 73 and 136 on the comparative volumes of the two solids.

The Stella Octangula

Eight congruent regular tetrahedra fitted one to each of the eight faces of an regular octahedron with the same length of edge make a *stella octangula* (fig. 397). We can think of this solid in at least two different ways. First, it is the only possible *stellation* of the regular octahedron, formed by extending faces of the octahedron until they meet (see page 187). Secondly, we can see it as two intersecting congruent regular tetrahedra, each penetrating the other symmetrically to form a *regular compound*.

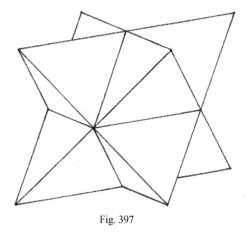

Fig. 397

147

A net for making the stella octangula is given on page 129 of Cundy and Rollett, *op. cit.* Alternatively, and more easily, we may make a stella octangula by fixing a tetrahedron to each face of an octahedron; or we may first make a large tetrahedron and then fix a small tetrahedron of the appropriate size centrally to each of its four faces. The net for one such small tetrahedron is shown in fig. 398. Three of its flaps stick directly on to the face of the octahedron or of the large tetrahedron.

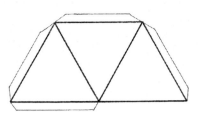

Fig. 398

The Regular Tetrahedron and the Cube.

Fig. 399 shows three diagonals AB, BC and CA drawn on adjacent faces of a cube to form an equilateral triangle ABC. If we draw diagonals from each of the corners of this triangle to the hidden vertex Z of the cube, opposite to D, the six diagonals will mark the six edges of a regular tetrahedron ABCZ contained within the cube (fig. 400).

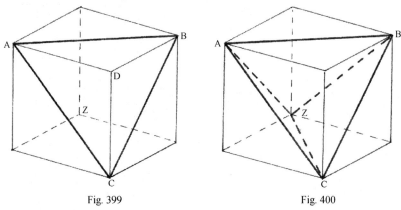

Fig. 399   Fig. 400

If the edges of the cube are 1 unit long, the tetrahedron will have edges √2 units long. A model showing this tetrahedron fitting inside the cube is easy to make. However, if the cube has edges of unit length, then the edges of the tetrahedron must be made a little less than √2 units long if it is to fit inside. If, for example, we make the cube with edges 10 cm long, the tetrahedron should have edges no more than 14 cm long. (The cube must of course have an open top or a lid if the tetrahedron is to be fitted inside it.)

When the tetrahedron is inside the cube, there will be four spaces left inside, each of which can be filled with a (non-regular) tetrahedron. One face of this tetrahedron will be an equilateral triangle and three faces will be right-angled isosceles triangles. The net of one of these tetrahedra is shown in fig. 401. Again, the tetrahedra must have edges a little less than either 1 or √2 units in length if they are to fit snugly. When all five tetrahedra are laid out together alongside the cube, it may seem unlikely that they will all fit inside, but they will of course do so.

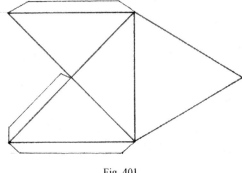

Fig. 401

The volume of each non-regular tetrahedron is $\frac{1}{3}$ x Ah = $\frac{1}{3}$ x ½ x 1 = $\frac{1}{6}$ cubic units. These four tetrahedra occupy four-sixths or two-thirds of the volume of the cube, so the regular tetrahedron occupies the remaining one-third.

In place of a single regular tetrahedron to fit inside the cube, we can build a regular tetrahedron of the same size from a regular octahedron and four regular tetrahedra, as explained above on page 147, and fit this dissected tetrahedron into the cube instead. We can then see clearly that the octahedron is the dual of the cube (see page 121), with its vertices touching the centres of the faces of the cube. (It may be necessary to cheat a little and stick the small tetrahedra to the faces of the octahedron in order to fit the whole assembly into the cube easily and correctly!)

If we now add four additional small regular tetrahedra to the large tetrahedron to convert it into a stella octangula, then this solid will also fit inside the cube, twelve of its edges coinciding with the twelve diagonals of the cube's faces (fig. 402). It is as if we have fitted into the cube in fig. 400 a second tetrahedron to intersect the first, whose edges lie along the diagonals not drawn in that diagram.

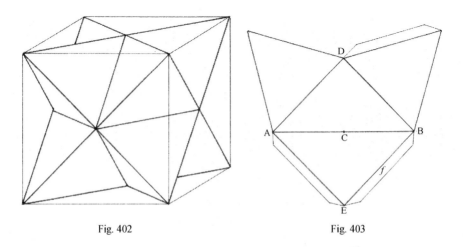

Fig. 402   Fig. 403

The four additional tetrahedra have a volume $\frac{4}{8}$ = ½ that of the large tetrahedron, so the volume of the stella octangula is $\frac{3}{2}$ x $\frac{1}{3}$ = ½ that of the cube (see above).

When the stella octangula is fitted into the cube, twelve small spaces remain inside the cube. Each can be filled by a tetrahedron with equilateral triangles for two of its faces and right-angled isosceles triangles for its other two faces. The volume of this tetrahedron, whose net appears in fig. 403, is one-twenty-fourth that of the cube.

1. Draw AB, the length of an edge of the cube.
2. Draw the mediator of AB. This cuts AB at its mid-point C.
3. With centre C draw a circle with radius CA to cut the mediator at D and E. ADBE is a square with diagonal AB.
4. Draw equilateral triangles on AD and on BD. (The diagonal AB, being an edge of the tetrahedron, must be scored and folded.) Draw flaps where shown and stick flap f first.

We now have the components of a puzzle in which twelve of these non-regular tetrahedra, eight regular tetrahedra and a regular octahedron all have to be fitted inside a cube.

In fig. 404, showing the dissected tetrahedron inside the cube, the point marked S is of particular interest.

1. It is the central point of the triangle ABC, which is one face of the regular tetrahedron ABCZ fitted into the cube.

2. DEF is a face of the regular octahedron which is dual to the cube and is also part of the tetrahedron ABCZ. S is also the centre of the face DEF of the octahedron and is therefore at one vertex of the cube which is dual to the octahedron.

3. But S is the centre of the face ABC of the tetrahedron ABCZ, and hence is a vertex also of the small tetrahedron which is dual to ABCZ.

Just as the tetrahedron ABCZ fits into the original cube, so this dual tetrahedron fits into the cube which is dual to the octahedron which in turn is dual to the original cube. We therefore have two similar configurations, each of a tetrahedron fitting into a cube. This confirms our earlier conclusion (page 129) that the ratio of the volumes of the cube and the dual cube (and, by extension, of the octahedron and the dual octahedron) must be the same as the ratio of the volumes of the tetrahedron and the dual tetrahedron, namely, 27:1.

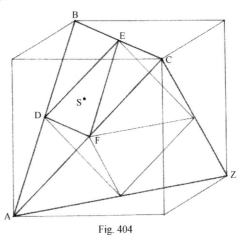

Fig. 404

The Cube and the Regular Dodecahedron

We mentioned earlier (page 95 f.) that a cube can be inscribed inside a regular dodecahedron, and we used this fact to investigate the trigonometry of the dodecahedron.

Cundy and Rollett on page 122 of *Mathematical Models* show the net of a "roof", six of which placed one on each face of a cube will make the dodecahedron. Fig. 408 opposite shows the same net, together with flaps. Cundy and Rollett *op. cit.* show in fig. 166(a) on page 134 how these "roofs" are placed. A triangle on one roof has to combine with a trapezium on an adjoining roof to make a pentagon: each roof contains the elements of two whole pentagons. Fig 405 shows how six such "roofs" can be attached to a net of six squares which can then be wrapped round a cube to form a regular dodecahedron, in the same way that six pyramids were joined together in fig. 67 on page 25 so that when wrapped round a cube they formed a rhombic dodecahedron.

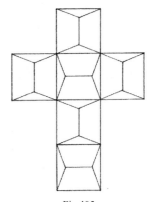

Fig 405

To draw the net in fig. 408.

1. Using any of the methods described in Appendix A, page 193 f., draw a regular pentagon ABCDE with its sides 0.62 times the length of the edges of the cube.
2. Draw the diagonals AC, AD, BE and CE of the pentagon (fig. 406). These will be equal in length to the edges of the cube. Let AC and BE intersect at F and let AD and CE intersect at G. Check that FG = AF.
3. With radius AF and centre C, draw an arc to cut CB at H and CD at J (fig. 407).
4. Join FG, FH, GJ and HJ. Check that HJ = AE. This diagram contains the net shown with its flaps in fig. 408.

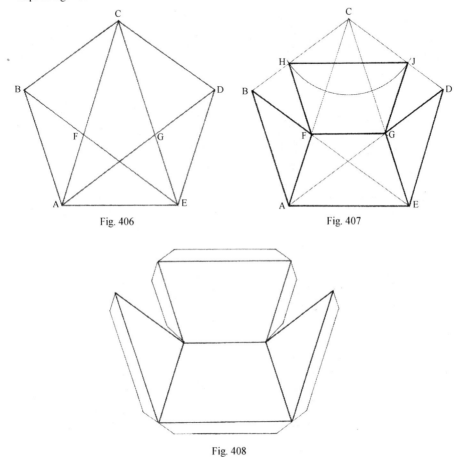

Fig. 406   Fig. 407

Fig. 408

The cube has twelve edges and the dodecahedron has twelve faces, and each face of the dodecahedron has an edge of the cube as one of its diagonals. Since each pentagonal face has five diagonals, it follows that five separate cubes can be inscribed in a dodecahedron. But there is more to it even than this. On page 134 of *Mathematical Models*, Cundy and Rollett remark that "...each cube can be replaced by two tetrahedra as in a stella octangula; five of these ten tetrahedra can then be chosen so as to have one vertex at each dodecahedral vertex." On the following page they illustrate the compound solid "Five cubes in a dodecahedron", and on the next page explain how to construct the model. On page 139 f. they illustrate "Five tetrahedra in a dodecahedron" and "Ten tetrahedra in a dodecahedron", with suggestions on how to construct these models.

The Regular Octahedron and the Regular Icosahedron.

On page 69 we saw how the regular octahedron has its vertices at the corners of three mutually perpendicular squares; and on page 118 we saw how the regular icosahedron has its vertices at the corners of three mutually perpendicular golden rectangles. We can draw a golden rectangle on each square inside the octahedron (see fig. 512, page 204), and the corners of these rectangles are then the vertices of an icosahedron contained within the octahedron. Fig. 409 shows how the vertices of the icosahedron lie at points which divide the sides of the squares (and therefore the edges of the octahedron) in the ratio of the Golden Section, ø:1. The broken lines are sides of the golden rectangles and are also edges of the icosahedron.

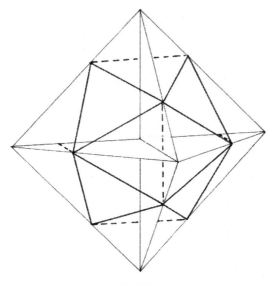

Fig. 409

We may make a model of this icosahedron by joining the Golden Ratio points on the three squares with thread or with thin sticks, or by doing the same on an octahedral framework of drinking straws or of rods. A point to note is that if we choose to join the points with thread, then, since four threads meet at any one point, our journey will take us along a three-dimensional traversable network with all its nodes even, and we shall be able to use one length of thread only, travelling from point to point until we arrive back at the start.

Regular Compounds.

Cundy and Rollett, *op. cit.*, page 129, explain how "if a regular polyhedron and its dual are placed together with their edges bisecting each other at right angles, ...a regular compound is formed". We have already met the simplest of these compounds, the stella octangula, which is a regular tetrahedron plus the dual regular tetrahedron enlarged appropriately. Cundy and Rollett illustrate the compound of the cube and the regular octahedron (see fig. 360, page 132, and fig. 436, page 167 below), whose edges lie on the diagonals of the faces of an enclosing rhombic dodecahedron. This fact follows from what we discovered about the rhombic dodecahedron in chapter 12. The solid common to the cube and the octahedron is the cuboctahedron which we shall study in chapter 15. Cundy and Rollett also illustrate the dodecahedron plus icosahedron, the solid common to these two being the icosidodecahedron, which we shall also study in chapter 15. Cundy and Rollett give full instructions for building models of these compounds.

Chapter 14

TRUNCATED SOLIDS

A *truncated* body is one which has lost its arms and legs. A truncated *polyhedron* is one from which the "corners" have been cut off, a "corner" being a portion or section adjacent to a vertex. It should be noted however that the truncated polyhedron has the advantage over the truncated body in that, while they are both diminished by truncation, the process provides the polyhedron with new and more numerous vertices. In the course of truncation the faces of the polyhedron change shape, and it is these changes in shape which give an interest to the whole process.

The Truncated Tetrahedron

We have already met the truncated tetrahedron in chapter 11, and we now look closely at the process by which a regular tetrahedron becomes truncated. We cut successive slices of equal size from each corner of the tetrahedron by cuts made perpendicular to the axis of symmetry which passes through the vertex at that corner. These cuts create new faces in the shape of equilateral triangles, while each of the four original triangular faces of the tetrahedron becomes a hexagon (fig. 410). When the amount cut from each corner is enough to change the original faces to *regular* hexagons (fig. 411), the solid is then a "truncated tetrahedron", a *semi-regular Archimedean solid*. The length of each edge of this solid is one-third the length of the edge of the original tetrahedron. If we then continue removing more and more of the solid, each hexagonal face in the end reduces to an equilateral triangle again and the solid which remains is a regular octahedron, whose edges are half as long as those of the original tetrahedron (see fig. 396, page 147). (Note that the total length of the edges of the solid remains constant throughout this process, whether these edges be the six edges of the original tetrahedron, the eighteen edges of the truncated tetrahedron, or the twelve edges of the final octahedron.)

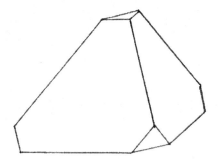

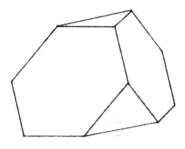

Fig. 410	Fig. 411

We have seen also on page 147 that the volume of this regular octahedron is one-half that of the original tetrahedron. The volume of the truncated tetrahedron in fig. 411 will be the volume of the original tetrahedron less the total volume of the four small tetrahedra removed from its corners. Each of these small tetrahedra has edges one-third the length of the edges of the original tetrahedron and so will have $(^1/_3)^3 = 1/27$ of its volume. The volume of the truncated tetrahedron will therefore be $1 - 4/27 = 23/27$ of the volume of the original.

If we take the length of edge of the truncated tetrahedron to be 1 unit, then the original tetrahedron would have edges 3 units long and its volume (see page 50) would be $\sqrt{2}/12 \times 3^3 = 9\sqrt{2}/4$ cubic units. The volume of the truncated tetrahedron is therefore $23/27 \times 9\sqrt{2}/4 = 23\sqrt{2}/12$ cubic units. We can confirm this result by considering that the volume lost from each corner is $\sqrt{2}/12$ cubic units and the truncated tetrahedron contains the equivalent of 23 of these. In general terms the volume of a truncated tetrahedron of edge a units is $23\sqrt{2}a^3/12$ cubic units.

A net for making the truncated tetrahedron appears in fig. 375, page 137, and two plan views are shown in figs. 412 and 413. The view in fig. 412 shows all the construction lines needed for both views. For each plan view, the first looking down on a hexagonal face, and the other looking down on a triangular face, we draw the outer hexagon first.

1. Draw a circle and a regular hexagon ABCDEF within the circle (see page 11).
2. Find the mid-points of the sides of ABCDEF and join these to form a smaller inner hexagon. This smaller hexagon is a face of the truncated tetrahedron.
3. Draw diagonals of this inner hexagon to locate the three corners of an equilateral triangle which is a face of the truncated tetrahedron.

In each view the equilateral triangle has sides the same length as those of the inner hexagon.

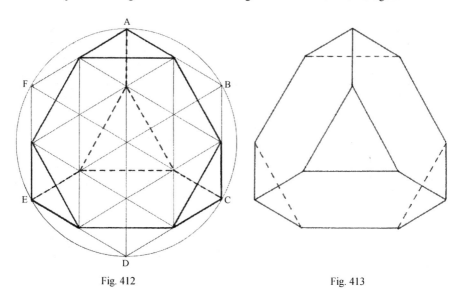

Fig. 412   Fig. 413

Truncation in Two Dimensions

It may be helpful at this point to look at what happens to shapes in two dimensions when we remove part or all of their corners. Fig. 414 shows how a tessellation of equilateral triangles is transformed stage by stage first into a tessellation of regular hexagons and finally into one of equilateral triangles together with regular hexagons, these hexagons being made from the "lost" parts of the original triangles. Fig. 415 on page 156 shows how a tessellation of squares is transformed stage by stage through a tessellation of squares and octagons to one of squares again, some of these squares being made from the "lost" parts of the original squares.

Regular pentagons do not tessellate in the plane, although they fit neatly together in space to form a regular dodecahedron. However, as we see in fig. 416 on page 156, truncating a single regular pentagon transforms it from a pentagon through a regular decagon into a smaller regular pentagon again at the end.

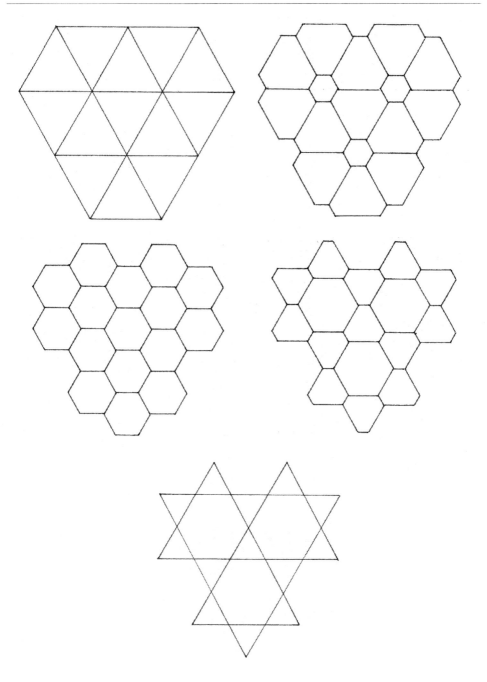

Fig. 414

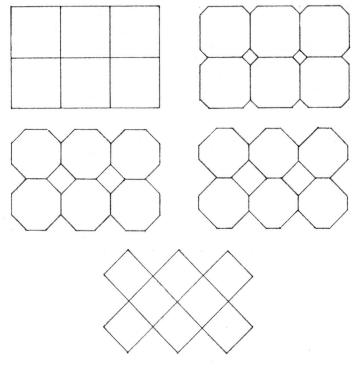

Fig. 415

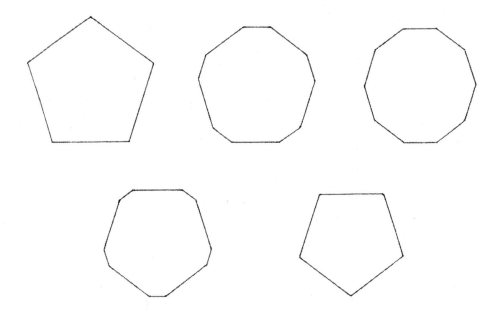

Fig. 416

The Truncated Cube

The polygonal faces of regular solids not surprisingly undergo the same transformations during truncation as do plane polygons. The *truncated cube* (fig. 417), with equilateral triangles and regular octagons for its faces in place of squares, is from one point of view (and an important point of view) merely an intermediate stage in the cube's journey to becoming in the limit a cuboctahedron, with its square faces square once more (fig. 418).

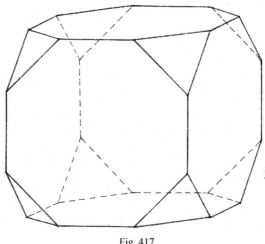

Fig. 417

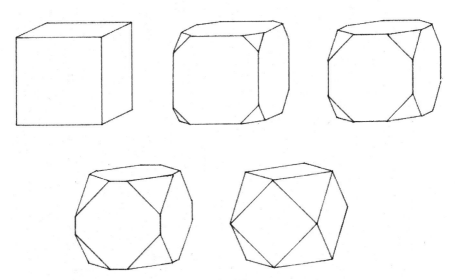

Fig. 418

At every stage of this journey we see removed from each corner of the cube a tetrahedron, growing in size all the time, with an equilateral triangle as its base and with isosceles right-angled triangles as the other three faces. The new faces on the solid revealed by these cut-off corners are equilateral triangles.

To make a truncated cube, we need to know how to draw a regular octagon. In fig. 419, which shows the regular octagon drawn within a square, we have labelled the lines whose lengths we need to know as a and b. By symmetry AQ = RB = BS = a units, and QR = RS = b units. We take AB to be 1 unit long, so that 2a + b = 1, and by Pythagoras RS² = b² = a² + a² = 2a².

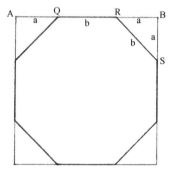

Fig. 419

We now solve the two simultaneous equations $2a + b = 1$ [I] and $b^2 = 2a^2$ [II].

Transforming [I]: $2a + b = 1 \Rightarrow b = 1 - 2a \Rightarrow b^2 = (1 - 2a)^2 = 1 - 4a + 4a^2$
$\Rightarrow b^2 = 4a^2 - 4a + 1$
But $b^2 = 2a^2$ [II]
so $4a^2 - 4a + 1 = 2a^2 \Rightarrow 2a^2 - 4a + 1 = 0$
Using the quadratic formula: $a = [4 \pm \sqrt{(16 - 8)}]/4 = [4 \pm \sqrt{8}]/4 = 1 \pm \tfrac{1}{2}\sqrt{2}$
But a < 1 so $a = 1 - \tfrac{1}{2}\sqrt{2} \approx 0.29$
Since $b = (1 - 2a)$, then $b = 1 - 2(1 - \tfrac{1}{2}\sqrt{2}) = 1 - 2 + \sqrt{2} = \sqrt{2} - 1 \approx 0.41$,
and so Q and R divide AB approximately in the ratio of 3:4:3.

The important result here however is that $AQ = a = 1 - \tfrac{1}{2}\sqrt{2}$, which means that $QB = \tfrac{1}{2}\sqrt{2}$, and this leads to a method of constructing the octagon.

In fig. 420 ABCD is a square, centre P. AB = BC = 1, so by Pythagoras $AC = \sqrt{2}$ and $BP = AP = \tfrac{1}{2}\sqrt{2}$, which is the required length of QB. To fix the position of Q:

1. Place the compass point on B and the pencil on P.
2. Draw an arc to cut AB at Q and BC at T.
3. With the compass point placed on each corner of the square in turn, draw similar arcs to cut each side of the square in two points.
4. Join each of these points to its neighbours to obtain a regular octagon (fig. 421).

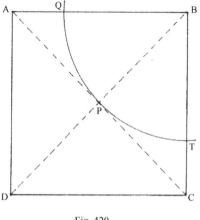

Fig. 420

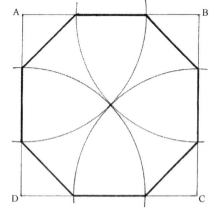

Fig. 421

Now that we know how to draw a regular octagon in a square, we are ready to draw the net of a truncated cube.

1. Choose any one of the eleven available nets for a cube and in each of the six squares of the net draw a regular octagon. [Cundy and Rollett (*op. cit.*, page 103) show one particular net; we have chosen here the net shown in fig. 422, with an octagon drawn in each square.]

2. Erase the corners of the squares and replace them with equilateral triangles as in fig. 423 overleaf. Draw flaps where shown.

3. Cut out, score and fold the net, and stick flap *f* first to side *s*.

Once flap *f* has been stuck, it should be clear which flap is to be stuck next, and so on until the solid has been completed. It is better to stick down the triangles as the construction proceeds rather than leave them all to be stuck down at the end.

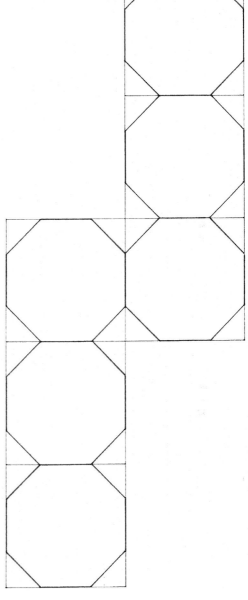

Fig. 422

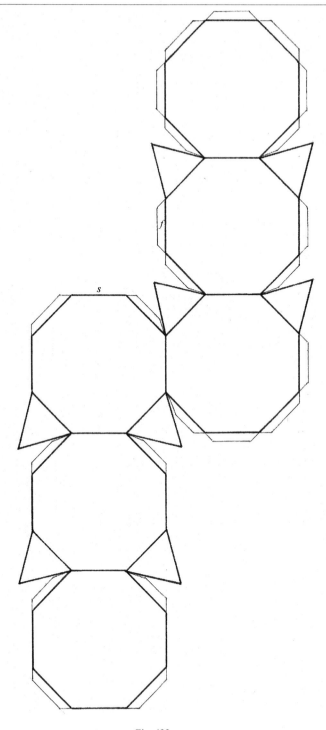

Fig. 423

Filling Space

The truncated cube combines with regular octahedra to fill space. If a tessellation of cubes in space is so arranged that eight cubes meet each with a vertex at the same point, which we may call a *node* of the tessellation, and if each cube is then truncated, the eight truncated corners situated at each node will combine to form a regular octahedron. These eight truncated corners are the triangular pyramids mentioned on page 78, and their nets are given both in fig. 209 on page 70 and in fig. 234 on page 78. [Note that the "truncated" cubes will combine to fill space with regular octahedra of appropriate size at any stage of their progressive truncation. Since the cube reduces to a cuboctahedron when fully truncated, it follows that cuboctahedra and regular octahedra will also combine to fill space (see page 177).]

The Volume of the Truncated Cube

The volume of the truncated cube is the volume of the original cube less the total volume of the eight pyramids lost at its corners. If the original cube had edges one unit long, so that its volume was 1 cubic unit, then each of these pyramids will have a volume of $(1 - \frac{1}{2}\sqrt{2})^3 \times \frac{1}{2} \times \frac{1}{3} = (10 - 7\sqrt{2})/24$ cubic units (see fig. 419, page 158). Eight such pyramids will have a total volume of $(10 - 7\sqrt{2})/3$ cubic units, or about 3.35% the volume of the original cube, and the volume remaining will be $7(\sqrt{2} - 1)/3 \approx 0.966$ cubic units.

If instead we take the edge of the *truncated* cube to be 1 unit long, then the edge of the original cube becomes $\sqrt{2} + 1$ units long, and its volume will be $(\sqrt{2} + 1)^3 = 7 + 5\sqrt{2} \approx 14.07$ cubic units. The truncated cube will have a volume of $(7 + 5\sqrt{2}) \times (7\{\sqrt{2} - 1\}/3) = 7(3 + 2\sqrt{2})/3 \approx 13.6$ cubic units.

When the cube is fully truncated and becomes a cuboctahedron, the pyramids lost at its corners will each have a volume of $(\frac{1}{2})^3 \times \frac{1}{2} \times \frac{1}{3} = 1/48$ of the volume of the cube. Eight of these pyramids together will have a volume 1/6 that of the cube and the cuboctahedron will therefore have a volume 5/6 that of the cube..

The truncated cube is not particularly attractive to look at when placed on an octagonal face but when set on a triangular face it looks a little more interesting. If its other triangular faces are removed so that they become "windows" (fig. 424), the truncated cube could then perhaps be used as a standing or hanging decoration with a light inside.

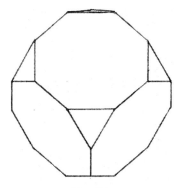

Fig. 424

The Truncated Octahedron

When we truncate a regular octahedron, it passes through the stage of being a semi-regular *truncated octahedron* {fig. 425(c)}, with the triangles of its eight faces reduced to regular hexagons and with its lost corners revealing new square faces; and reaches its limit when the triangular faces are once again triangular {fig. 425(e)}. It has now become, as did the fully-truncated cube earlier, a cuboctahedron.

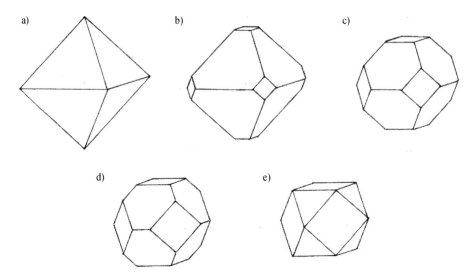

Fig. 425

The Volume of the Truncated Octahedron

The "lost" corners of the octahedron at any stage of its truncation are square-based pyramids, each with four equilateral-triangular faces. Pairs of these pyramids will themselves fit together base to base to form regular octahedra. For the *truncated octahedron* each of these smaller octahedra will have edges one-third the length of the edges of the original octahedron, and so will have 1/27 of its volume. The six lost corners together will make three such octahedra, so the truncated octahedron has $(1 - 3/27) = 24/27 = 8/9$ of the volume of the original. For the *cuboctahedron*, each of these three lost octahedra will have edges one-half the length of the edges of the original octahedron, and so will have 1/8 of its volume, which means that the cuboctahedron has $(1 - 3/8) = 5/8$ or $62\frac{1}{2}$% of the volume of the original octahedron. Compared with the cube under truncation, the octahedron fares relatively badly. As we have seen, the eight lost corners of the cube when it reduces to a cuboctahedron account for only 1/6 of its volume, and the cuboctahedron has 5/6 or $83\frac{1}{3}$% of the volume of the original cube.

Filling Space

We saw earlier that four congruent cubes, each dissected by a cut to reveal a regular hexagonal face, can be reassembled to make a truncated octahedron (fig. 74, page 27). We also noted on page 27 that the truncated octahedron is one of the few regular or semi-regular solids which will "tessellate" on its own to fill space, and this is something which regular octahedra by themselves will not do. By truncating regular octahedra, we remove as it were the obstructions that prevent the octahedra from fitting snugly together. For an illustration of how truncated octahedra fit together to fill space, see Steinhaus, *op. cit.*, page 188, figs. 231 and 232.

Steinhaus comments that this "tessellation" of truncated octahedra, moreover, is the "simplest decomposition of space into congruent parts". When fitted together, only four of these solids meet at a node, and the number of (theoretical) cuts needed to separate them is a minimum, if we cut out each solid one at a time. (We may compare the economical "tessellation" of truncated octahedra in space with the economical tessellation of regular hexagons in the plane, where only three hexagons meet at each node.)

Again it is worth making several congruent truncated octahedra to see for ourselves how they fit together to fill space.

Views of the Truncated Octahedron

Figs. 427 and 428 show two plan views of the truncated octahedron, according to which shape of face the solid is standing on, hexagonal and square respectively. Fig. 426 shows the construction lines for fig 427, drawn inside a regular hexagon.

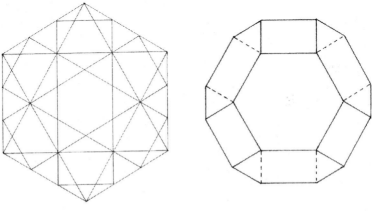

Fig. 426   Fig. 427

The view in fig. 427 is based on the plan of the octahedron shown in fig. 216, page 72. The construction lines in fig. 426 divide each of the sides of the surrounding hexagon into three equal parts, reflecting the fact that we make the truncated octahedron by dividing each edge of the regular octahedron into three equal parts before cutting off the corners. The surrounding dodecagon in fig. 427 is not regular, and its alternating short and long sides are in the ratio of 1:√3.

The view in fig. 428 is drawn inside a square. It is based on the plan of the octahedron shown in fig. 210, page 70, with the corners of the square cut off. This plan view of the truncated octahedron is drawn by dividing each side of the containing square into three equal parts, for the reason given in the previous paragraph. The surrounding octagon in the plan view is therefore not a *regular* octagon.

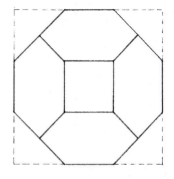

Cundy and Rollett, *op. cit.*, fig. 114, page 104, show both these plan views of the truncated octahedron. In fig. 427 the broken lines indicate six of the hidden edges of the solid. All other hidden edges in both plan views are covered by visible edges.

Fig. 428

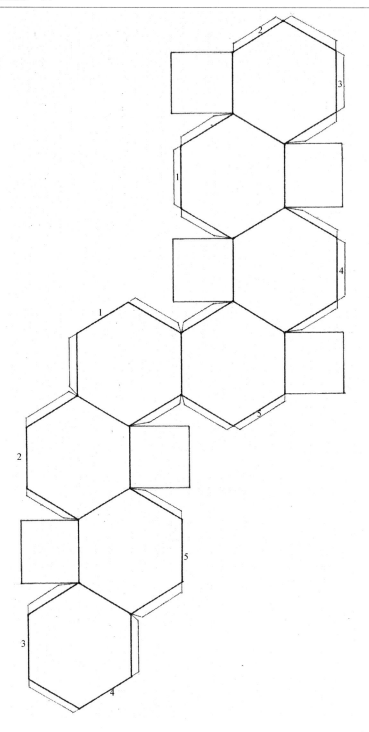

Fig. 429

Models of the Truncated Octahedron

A model of the truncated octahedron may be made in at least two different ways.

1. Fig. 429 opposite shows a full net of the solid. It is not easy to draw accurately and the drawing shown here is offered as a full-sized template for copying. The numbered flaps are stuck to the numbered sides in the order shown and the squares are stuck down last of all.

2. Wenninger (*op. cit.*, page 21) offers the net of half the solid (fig. 430) which has the advantage that it can be drawn inside a single equilateral triangle with a high degree of accuracy. The basic construction of the net is identical to that of the net of the truncated tetrahedron (fig. 375, page 137), with the difference that the small triangles in that net are replaced with squares (with one triangle lost). Two edges of each square are easily drawn, being extensions of lines joining corners of the hexagons (e.g., AB in fig. 430). On the other hand, sticking the two halves together is not easy. One half-net will need flaps on all its outside edges, while the other will need flaps only for sticking the squares on to the neighbouring hexagons. The best strategy is first to assemble the half with flaps on and then stick the other half on to it, one hexagon at a time, leaving the squares to be stuck down last of all.

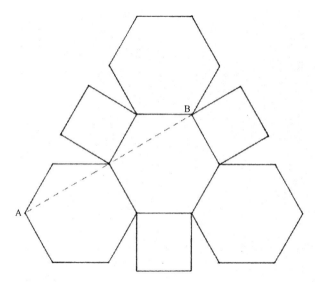

Fig. 430

If we draw the full net of the truncated octahedron but without its squares (fig. 431), we can assemble this as a rigid model with eight hexagonal faces and six square windows (fig. 432). Stick flap *f* first.

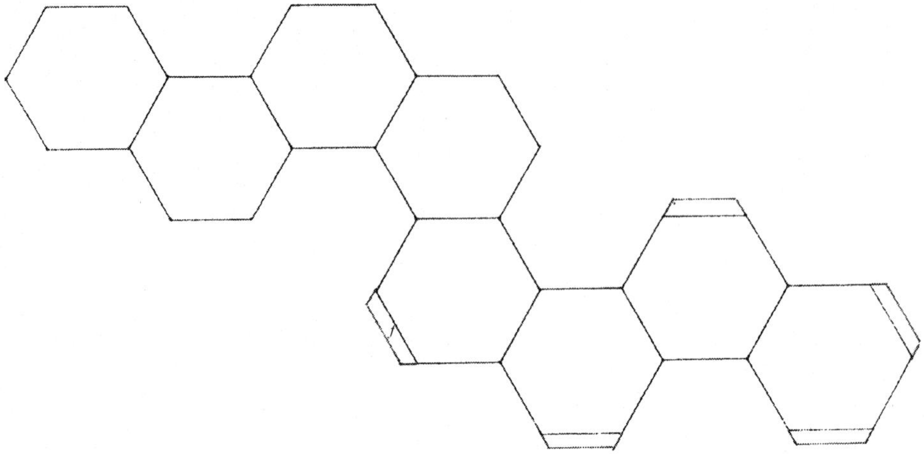

Fig. 431

The model can be used as a hanging or standing decoration. With one window closed by a square, we may hang or stand the model so that the closed square is its base and (taking appropriate fire precautions) may then use it as a Chinese lantern, with a candle or small electric lamp standing on this base.

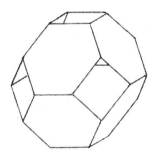

Fig. 432

Cundy and Rollett (*op. cit.*, page 104) give a third net for the truncated octahedron, which is based on their net for the regular octahedron (*op. cit.*, page 86) and is easy to draw and to assemble. Each triangle in the original net has lost its three corners and has become a regular hexagon, and squares have been drawn in six of the gaps. We may in fact choose any of the eleven distinct nets of the octahedron as a base for a net of the truncated octahedron, removing corners and inserting squares where they are needed.

Once again it is worth making several congruent models of the truncated octahedron to see how they fit together to fill space. Steinhaus (*op. cit.* page 190) shows a photograph of a number of models made in clear plastic and joined together, but it is better to make one's own models and to study directly in three dimensions the geometry of exactly how they do fit together.

We have seen that under truncation the cube and the octahedron both reduce at the limit to the cuboctahedron. The cuboctahedron is of sufficient interest to be studied separately, and we shall look at it in detail in the next chapter. However it is appropriate to mention here that if we take from the truncated cube and the truncated octahedron all their lost corners, whose nets are shown in figs. 433 and 434 respectively, and replace them on the cuboctahedron (fig. 435), we shall have the compound solid which is illustrated in fig. 159 on page 130 of Cundy and Rollett, *op. cit.*, under the title "Cube plus Octahedron". A note under this drawing points out that the solid common to both is a cuboctahedron, and that the vertices of the combined solid are also the vertices of a rhombic dodecahedron, the diagonals of whose faces are the edges of the combined solid.

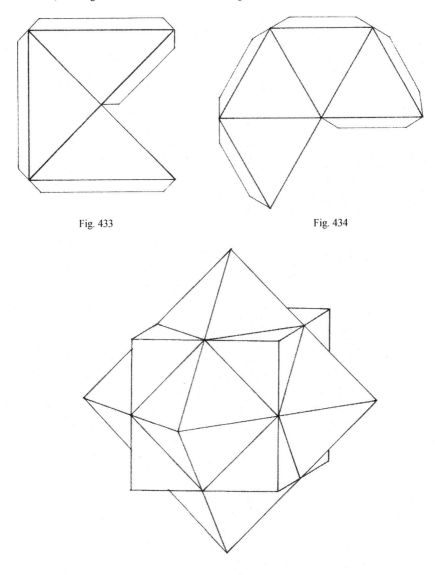

Fig. 433   Fig. 434

Fig. 435

We may also build the "Cube plus Octahedron" by fixing the lost corners of a truncated cube to the faces of a regular octahedron, or alternatively by fixing the lost corners of a truncated octahedron to the faces of a cube. Note that if we do this, the lengths of the edges of the original cube and octahedron must be in the ratio of 1:√2 if the edges are to bisect each other and so represent the diagonals of the rhombic dodecahedron which contains the combined solid (see fig. 381, page 140).

Jenkins and Wild, in *Mathematical Curiosities 3*, give a net in two pieces which will fold into the compound of the cube and the regular octahedron.

A group project might be to construct a set of models as described in the above paragraphs, to illustrate the successive stages of a transformation in which a cube is truncated into a cuboctahedron, which in its turn has its other lost corners restored to give a regular octahedron, and *vice versa* (fig. 436). Those readers with the necessary skills may be able to write a program to display on a computer screen a seemingly continuous three-dimensional transformation from one solid into the other.

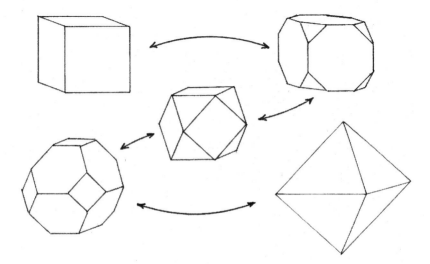

Fig. 436

The Truncated Dodecahedron

If we truncate a regular dodecahedron, we find that equilateral triangles appear at the cut-off corners, while the pentagonal faces become decagons. When these decagons are *regular* decagons, the solid is the *truncated dodecahedron* with twelve faces which are regular decagons and twenty faces which are equilateral triangles (fig. 437).   As we cut away more and more material, the pentagonal faces eventually become regular pentagons again and the solid is then a semi-regular Archimedean *icosidodecahedron*, with twelve pentagonal faces and twenty triangular faces (fig. 438).

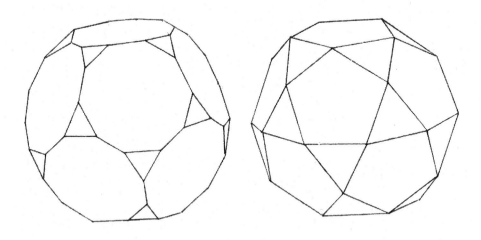

Fig. 437   Fig. 438

The Truncated Icosahedron

If we truncate a regular icosahedron, we see regular pentagons appearing at the cut-off corners, while the triangular faces become hexagons.   When these hexagons are regular hexagons, the solid is a *truncated icosahedron*, with twenty faces which are regular hexagons and twelve faces which are regular pentagons (fig. 439). This pattern of faces is familiar as the pattern of panels on a football, and is also the pattern whose sixty vertices are the positions taken up by the sixty carbon atoms in the molecule C_{60}, known as *buckminsterfullerene*, after Richard Buckminster Fuller (1895-1983), whose pioneering work on geodesic domes led to his name being linked with all such and similar structures. (The football with this pattern is sometimes known as a "Bucky-ball".   For a reference to more information on this subject see chapter 16, page 192.)

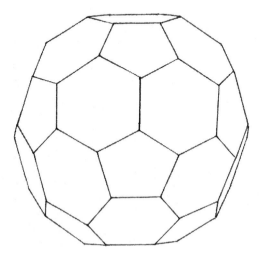

Fig. 439

If we continue to cut away the corners of the icosahedron, all the hexagonal faces will eventually reduce to triangles again, and we shall have once more the icosidodecahedron. If we place on this icosidodecahedron the lost corners of both the dodecahedron and the icosahedron, we shall have the compound solid shown on page 131 of Cundy and Rollett, *op. cit.* This same compound can be made by attaching the lost corners of the truncated dodecahedron to the faces of the regular icosahedron, or alternatively by attaching the lost corners of the truncated icosahedron to the faces of the regular dodecahedron.

The icosidodecahedron has a particular beauty of its own. We shall look at the structure of this solid in more detail at the end of the next chapter, and consider its affinities with the cuboctahedron.

Chapter 15

THE CUBOCTAHEDRON

The cuboctahedron is:

a) a solid which combines the six square faces of the cube with the eight triangular faces of the regular octahedron (see page 174 below);

b) the solid shared by the cube and the regular octahedron when they are joined as a compound body (see page 167);

c) the shape taken by both the cube and the regular octahedron when each is fully truncated (see pages 157 and 162);

d) the solid whose edges are the four regular hexagons which can be drawn on the surface of both the cube and the regular octahedron, by joining the midpoints of adjacent edges (see pages 27 and 81).

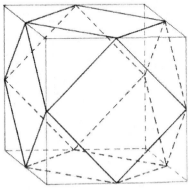
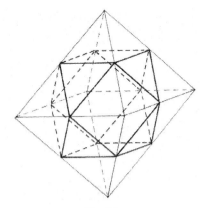

Fig. 440   Fig. 441

Fig. 440 shows the four hexagons mentioned in (d) above drawn on the faces of the cube. We may trace the path of each hexagon without difficulty as long as we remember that whenever the path comes to an edge, it must continue on to a new face. Each hexagon will cross each of the six faces of the cube. Fig. 441 shows these same four hexagons drawn on the faces of the regular octahedron. It should be clear that in both diagrams these are the same four hexagons. However, each hexagon drawn on the octahedron crosses only six of the eight faces of the solid, the remaining two faces being parallel to the plane of that hexagon (see fig. 246, page 81).

The four hexagons can be seen reasonably clearly in the oblique view of the cuboctahedron shown in fig. 442. They can also be seen more clearly in the plan view shown in fig. 443 overleaf, with the solid placed on a triangular face. One (regular) hexagon forms the boundary of the figure. In both these views the broken lines indicate the position of hidden edges. The plan view of the same solid placed on a square face, shown in fig. 444 overleaf and whose boundary is a square, appears not to show the four hexagons. Where have they gone?

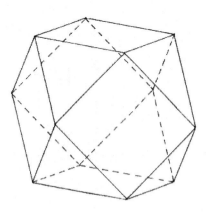

Fig. 442

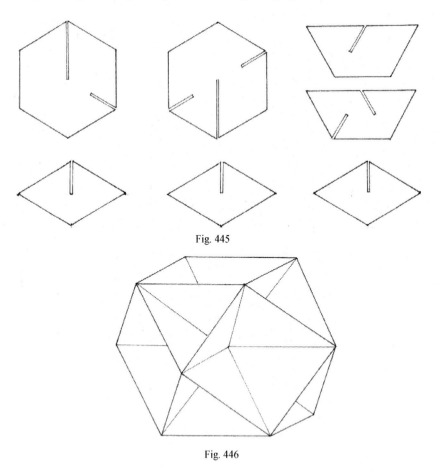

Fig. 443   Fig 444

Fig. 445 shows how to cut shapes from card which, when slotted together, will make a model displaying the "diametral" (or "equatorial") planes of the four hexagons within the cuboctahedron. This model (fig. 446) is similar in conception to the model of the regular octahedron displaying its three square "equatorial" planes of symmetry and shown in fig. 208, page 70.

Fig. 445

Fig. 446

To make the model:
1. Cut four regular hexagons, all the same size, from card.
2. Cut slots in two hexagons as shown. One slot in each hexagon extends to the centre, the other slots extend halfway to the centre.
3. Cut the third hexagon in half, with slots as shown, each slot extending to a point halfway between a corner and the centre.
4. Cut the fourth hexagon into three rhombuses, each with a slot as shown from a corner to the centre.
5. Slot together the two hexagons.
6. Slot the half-hexagons into the hexagons to make the third hexagonal plane.
7. Slot each rhombus into place to make the fourth plane.

Although it is possible to slot together the pieces as shown, it is not easy to do so. The best way of making the model is to slot together the two hexagonal pieces and then to cut any necessary slots in the other pieces to make them fit in. Some thought and experimentation is needed as to where the slots on the first pieces must come to accommodate those pieces fitted later. The finished model can be secured with adhesive tape, so that all pieces fit together with no gaps.

A "Solid" Model.

A net for making the cuboctahedron from squares and equilateral triangles is shown in fig. 447. It is the same net as that shown by Cundy and Rollett, *op.cit.,* fig. 107, page 102.

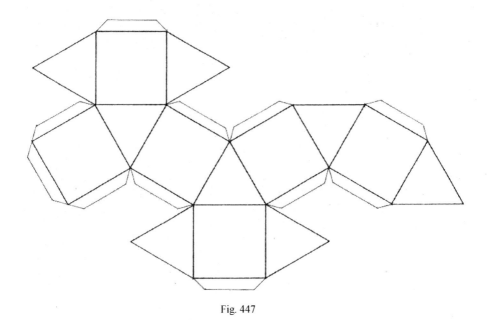

Fig. 447

Fig. 448 overleaf shows the net of half a cuboctahedron. The two halves can be made separately, one half with flaps where shown, and the other half with only those flaps needed for sticking down the triangular faces, that is, without the flaps shown with broken lines. These two halves can then be joined together to make the complete solid, using much the same method as was used to join the two halves of the truncated octahedron whose half-net was shown in fig. 430, page 165. Alternatively the two halves may be stuck one on each side of a shared base in the shape of a regular hexagon; or they may be stuck on separate bases, and then held together to show a complete solid. If one half of this solid is then rotated so as to bring together the squares and the triangles on both halves, the resulting solid will be what Cundy and Rollett (*op. cit.,* page 115) refer to as an "isomeric" form of the cuboctahedron, with the same number of faces of each type, squares and equilateral triangles, but with the faces arranged differently. (Note that in this "isomeric" form, the planes of the hexagons are planes of symmetry of the solid, whereas in the "pure" form of the cuboctahedron the four hexagons do not lie on planes of symmetry.)

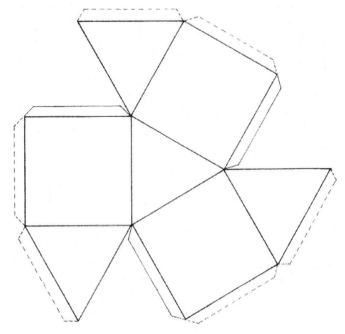

Fig. 448

A skeleton model of a cuboctahedron can be made from twenty-four short lengths of drinking straw, six each of four different colours, joined to make four connecting and intersecting hexagons (fig. 449). Although eight of the spaces enclosed will be triangles, six spaces will be squares, and the presence of the squares means that the model is not intrinsically rigid. It can be made rigid by inserting short pieces of pipe-cleaner at the vertices, bent to an appropriate angle.

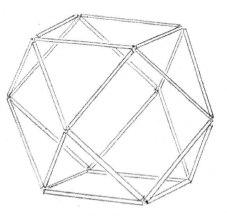

Fig. 449

The name "cuboctahedron" is given to the solid in recognition of the fact that it may be built by combining the six faces of a cube and the eight faces of a regular octahedron. If the six faces of a cube are each rotated through 45°, and are then made to touch at their corners instead of along their sides, they will enclose eight triangular spaces (fig. 450). If the eight faces of a regular octahedron are each rotated through 60°, and are then made to touch at their corners, they will enclose six square spaces (fig. 451). These two configurations of squares and triangles combine to make the cuboctahedron.

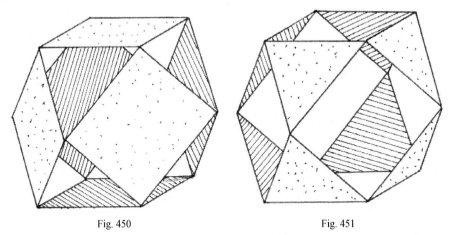

Fig. 450   Fig. 451

These models with spaces for faces can be made by first building a framework of sticks or of drinking straws, such as that shown in fig. 449, and then fixing squares and triangles to the framework where appropriate, since it is not easy to attach polygons at their corners only without the help of such a framework.

Instead of an open framework as a basis for these models we may use the open card model shown in fig. 446, page 172. The four hexagonal planes on their own give a *solid of zero volume* (see page 182), consisting of six empty square-based pyramids and eight empty regular tetrahedra, all meeting at the centre of the (non-)solid. Six square faces and eight triangular faces stuck on to this framework will of course give the complete cuboctahedron.

"Faceted" Cuboctahedra.

If the triangular faces alone were stuck on to the open card model (fig. 446. page 172), they would give a "faceted" solid, what Wenninger (*op. cit.*) calls an *octahemioctahedron* (fig. 452), with eight triangular faces surrounding six square-based pyramidal depressions. This model can also be made from the net shown in fig. 453 overleaf.

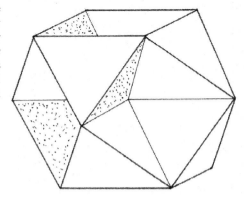

Fig. 452

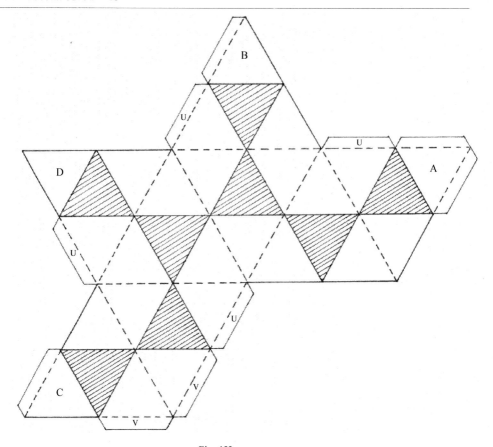

Fig. 453

The broken lines in fig. 453 mark very nearly the net of a regular octahedron, each of whose faces has been divided by the solid lines into four smaller triangles. The triangles shown shaded are the eight faces of the faceted solid; the other triangles are the surfaces of the pyramidal depressions. The solid lines are scored and folded as usual, but the broken lines have to be scored on the back and folded forwards, in the opposite direction to the other folds. Once the flaps marked U have been stuck to the underside of the correct triangles to form four depressions, it should be clear which flaps must be stuck next to form a fifth depression (those marked V). Finally the triangles A, B, C and D are stuck in succession to form the sixth depression, with triangle D being stuck down last of all.

The faceted solid with square faces and triangular depressions (fig. 454) cannot be made from a single net, since the angles of faces which meet at a vertex add up to more than 360°. The following instructions are for a model made in two halves, each half itself being made from two separate pieces.

1. Draw the net of squares and equilateral triangles shown in fig. 455.
2. Cut away the central shaded triangle, leaving three flaps.
3. The solid lines are to be scored and folded as usual, but the broken lines must be scored on the back and the triangles folded forwards, in the opposite direction to the other folds.

4. Fold the outside triangles and stick the flaps marked U underneath to provide three tetrahedral depressions.

5. Cut out a "base" hexagon on which to stick the half-model. The half-model should be stuck to the base not only by the flaps on the sides of the squares but also by the base points of the tetrahedral depressions, which should meet exactly at the centre of the hexagon. Check that these do meet by looking through the hole in the middle of the model.

6. Fill this hole with a hollow tetrahedron made by folding and sticking the half-hexagon of three triangles whose net is shown in fig. 456. Glue the flaps and push the tetrahedron down into the hole, where it should fit exactly.

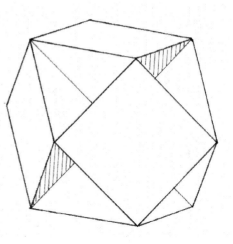

Fig. 454

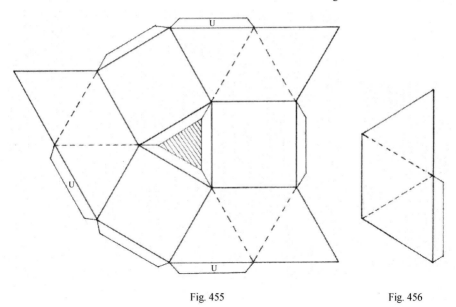

Fig. 455   Fig. 456

We look at other "faceted" models of polyhedra in the next chapter.

Lastly, we remind ourselves that we mentioned the cuboctahedron earlier when we were looking at dual solids. If we remove the dual regular octahedron from the interior of a cube, we can dissect what remains of the cube into eight pieces which can be reassembled to make a cuboctahedron, as in fig. 346, page 124. From this it follows, as we have mentioned before, that cuboctahedra and regular octahedra together will "tessellate" to fill space.

Postscript: The Icosidodecahedron

If the twelve pentagonal faces of a regular dodecahedron are each rotated through 36°, and are then made to touch at their corners rather than along their sides, they will enclose spaces in the shape of equilateral triangles. If the twenty triangular faces of a regular icosahedron are each rotated through 60°, and are then made to touch at their corners rather than along their sides, they will then enclose spaces in the shape of regular pentagons. These two configurations will combine to form the *icosidodecahedron* (fig. 457).

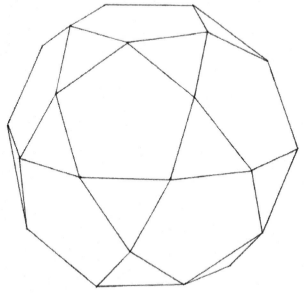

Fig. 457

This solid has certain properties which bring to mind the cuboctahedron. Its edges are six regular decagons, which we can draw on the surface both of the regular dodecahedron and of the regular icosahedron by joining the mid-points of adjacent edges. Figs. 458 and 459 show parts of three such decagons drawn on the two solids. (See also fig. 292, page 100, and figs. 322 & 323, page 114.)

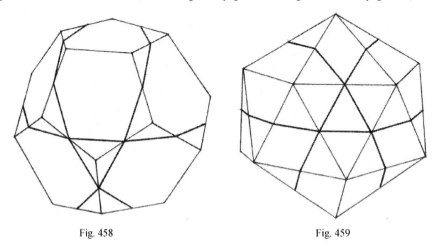

Fig. 458   Fig. 459

Each face of the dodecahedron is crossed by five of the decagons, and is parallel to the plane of the sixth. Each face of the icosahedron is crossed by three decagons and although not parallel to the plane of any of the other three decagons, lies away from them. The six decagons can easily be traced in the plan view of the icosidodecahedron in fig. 460, seen resting on a pentagonal face. One (regular) decagon forms the boundary of the figure

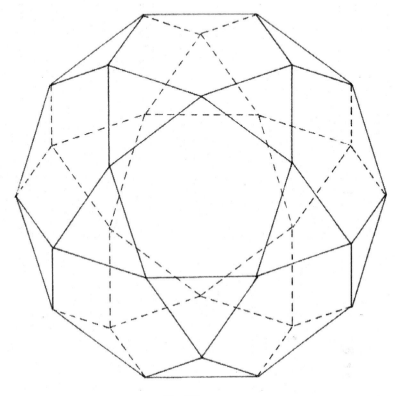

Fig. 460

If we replace all the "lost" corners of the truncated dodecahedron and the truncated icosahedron on the faces of the icosidodecahedron, we shall have the compound illustrated in fig. 161, page 131, of Cundy and Rollett, *op. cit.,* the "dodecahedron plus icosahedron".

A half-net for the icosidodecahedron is shown overleaf in fig. 461. Extra flaps may be added to the edges along the outer rim of the net to allow two half-icosidodecahedra to be stuck together to form a complete solid. Alternatively each half could be stuck one on either side of a shared base in the shape of a regular decagon, in much the same way as we suggested on pages 173 and 174 that two halves of a cuboctahedron could be stuck one on either side of a shared base in the shape of a regular hexagon.

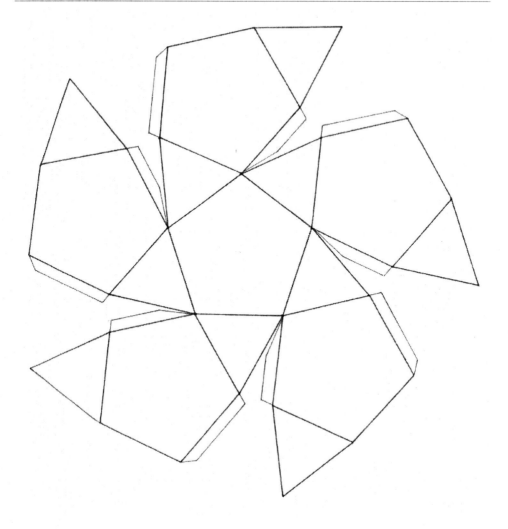

Fig. 461

Chapter 16

FURTHER DEVELOPMENTS

Faceted Models

It is sometimes helpful to think of polyhedra as being made up of "cells". For example fig. 233 on page 78 shows half an octahedron divided into four triangular pyramids. We can regard these pyramids as cells, eight of which make up the regular octahedron. The "faceted" octahedron, to which we refer below, is the solid left when four of these eight cells are removed.

Cells which make up a particular solid need not be all of the same shape. In the last chapter we looked at two "faceted" models of the cuboctahedron, that is, cuboctahedra from which some cells had been removed, these cells being either regular tetrahedra or square-based pyramids. The original faces remaining on the models were either all squares or all equilateral triangles, and the removal of the other faces and of the pyramids of which they were the base exposed (in part) as new faces the four intersecting hexagonal "diametral" or "equatorial" planes of the cuboctahedron.

One-sided Surfaces

One of these faceted cuboctahedra, that with square faces remaining, is of particular interest, since it is a *one-sided surface*. An ordinary piece of paper or card has two sides, and we can travel from one side to the other only by what we may call "doubling back" across an edge. A cube also has two sides, the outside and the inside, and no matter how far we travel on the inside or on the outside of a cube, our journey will never take us to the other side. The familiar Moebius strip (fig. 462) is however "one-sided". It is a twisted band of paper or other material and from any point on its surface we may travel to any other point, including the point on the "other" side of the point from which we started, without the need to "double back" over an edge.

To justify our calling the faceted cuboctahedron "one-sided" we must, when moving on the hexagonal faces, be allowed to pass through any "wall" we may meet on the way. Passing through this wall takes us either out of sight into the "interior" or back into view again and thus we are able to make our way to a spot on the "other side" of the point from which we started.

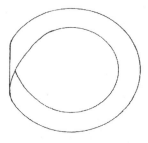
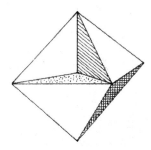

Fig. 462   Fig. 463

Two other one-sided "closed" surfaces, with no edges, also exist. They are the "Klein Bottle" and the "Steiner Surface". Cundy and Rollett, *op. cit.*, pages 191-195, describe and illustrate both these surfaces and link them to the two varieties of faceted cuboctahedra and also to the faceted octahedron (fig. 463), into which the Steiner Surface can be continuously deformed.

The net of the faceted octahedron, shown in fig. 464 overleaf, consists of quarter-squares and equilateral triangles. The broken lines have to be folded in the opposite direction to the solid lines. It is best to stick the quarter-squares together first to give the four depressions, before sticking down the equilateral triangular faces, although one triangular face has a flap on to which a quarter-square has to be stuck.

The finished model shows four alternate faces of the octahedron, together with (part of) its three equatorial ("diametral") squares, and hence is a *heptahedron*, with seven faces. We may travel to any point on the surface of the model, inside or out, from any other point, as long as we are allowed to pass through the "walls" erected on the square faces.

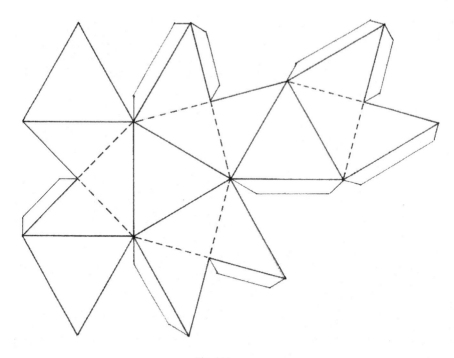

Fig. 464

An alternative net for the faceted octahedron appears in Jenkins and Wild, *Make Shapes 1*, under the name of *tetrahemihexahedron*. A net for the faceted cuboctahedron with its triangular faces in place also appears in *Make Shapes 1*, under the name of *octahemioctahedron*.

Cundy and Rollett, *op. cit.*, page 195, point out that whereas the faceted cuboctahedron which retains its square faces is one-sided, the faceted cuboctahedron with its triangular faces retained is two-sided, although touching triangles belong to different sides. They go on to say that "in the case of the icosidodecahedron, either the triangular or the pentagonal faces may be removed and replaced by the diametral decagons; in either case a one-sided surface results..."

Solids with Zero Volume

If the remaining four triangular faces of the faceted octahedron are removed, only the three equatorial squares remain (see fig. 208, page 70). The edges and vertices of the octahedron survive at the sides and corners of these squares, but the solid is no longer a solid, or is at best a *solid of zero volume*. (Note that, rather than by drawing and folding its net, we may construct the faceted octahedron simply by adding triangular faces to this framework of squares.)

We can make similar "frameworks" by removing the faces from the other regular polyhedra, but each of these frameworks consists only of triangles joining the edges to the centre of the solid, and these triangles do not combine to form planes as they do in the octahedron. Gerald Edgcombe, in *Mathematics Teaching*, no. 34, Spring 1966, page 54, wrote about "Solids of Zero Volume", with coloured illustrations of the five solids showing their faces removed and with only the internal structure remaining. One way of making these models is to make open pyramids without bases, and then fit them together with their apexes meeting at the centre of the "solid".

The regular tetrahedron of zero volume needs four pyramids, whose nets are identical with the net shown in fig. 177, page 58, with the equilateral triangle removed. Fig. 145 on page 49 shows the edges of this "framework".

The cube needs six pyramids, each made from the net shown in fig. 465, whose four triangles are those shown in fig. 66, page 25. We can join these six pyramids so that they fit together either inwards to make an empty cube or outwards to make a rhombic dodecahedron (see page 25). If we place any three of these pyramids together with their apexes meeting, we shall see clearly that the triangular faces do not meet to form a plane. Instead we see that opposite edges of the "empty" cube are joined by a "double" triangle (fig. 466).

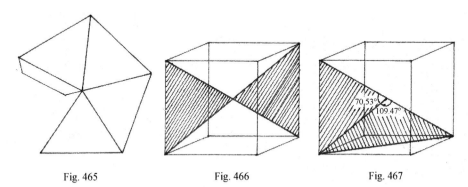

Fig. 465   Fig. 466   Fig. 467

Mr. Edgcombe shows how a triangle from a tetrahedron pyramid fits together with a triangle from a cube pyramid to form a right-angled triangle (fig. 467). This follows from the fact that the angles made by the lines joining the vertices of the two solids to their centres are supplementary, being approximately 109.47° and 70.53° respectively. One of his illustrations shows the tetrahedral framework contained within the cube framework (fig. 468), reflecting the fact that a tetrahedron can be inscribed in a cube. If we were to insert a second tetrahedron framework into the cube, we should then have the framework of a stella octangula, and the resulting model would comprise the six rectangles joining opposite pairs of edges of the cube (fig. 469).

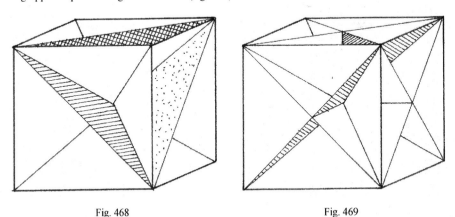

Fig. 468   Fig. 469

We have referred earlier to the pentagonal pyramids into which the regular dodecahedron can be dissected, and have shown the net of one of these pyramids in fig. 293, page 101. Twelve of these pyramids without their bases (faces) will make the empty framework of the dodecahedron. Twenty triangular pyramids without their bases, and each with slant edges 0.951 times the length of the base edge (see page 114), will fit together to form the empty framework of the regular icosahedron.

Stellation

We shall shortly be looking at *stellated polyhedra*. Stellation can thought of as being the opposite of faceting since, whereas faceting removes cells from a polyhedron, stellation adds new cells, whose shapes however may differ from those of existing cells. First however we look at the effect that *stellation* has upon some regular polygons.

A stellated polygon is one in which the sides of the original polygon have been extended until they meet to form a new polygon (or combination of polygons). The sides of an equilateral triangle or a square will not meet no matter how far they are extended. Fig. 470 shows that the sides of a regular pentagon however will meet and will then form a *pentagram*, a polygon with five *intersecting* sides.

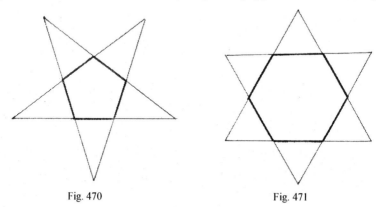

Fig. 470   Fig. 471

The sides of a regular hexagon will also meet when they are extended and will then form a star, the "Star of David" (fig. 471). However, this is not itself a polygon but is a combination of two separate polygons, each of them an equilateral triangle.

When the seven sides of a regular *heptagon* are extended, they meet first to form a seven-sided *heptagram* (fig. 472), in much the same way as the pentagon gave birth to the pentagram. However, we can extend the (intersecting) sides of this heptagram further, and other pairs of sides will then meet to form a second heptagram (fig. 473). The regular heptagon is the simplest regular polygon to have two stellated forms. Note that the first heptagram is included in the second. Any new stellation generally will contain all previous stellations as well as the original polygon.

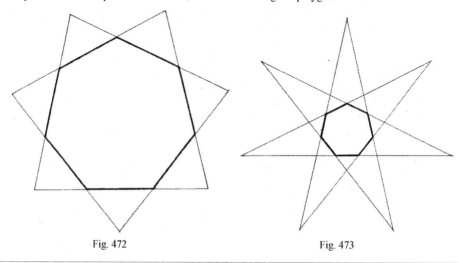

Fig. 472   Fig. 473

The regular octagon also has two stellated forms, although the first (fig. 474) is no more than a combination of two squares.   The second stellation is a true polygon, an octagram, with eight intersecting sides which can be traced in a continuous line (fig. 475).

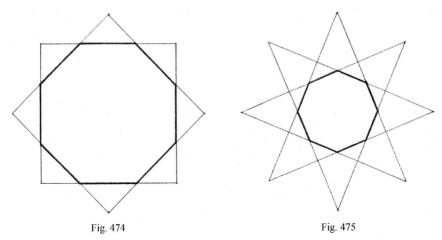

Fig. 474   Fig. 475

The regular enneagon, *alias* the "nonagon", with nine sides, is the simplest polygon to have three stellated forms (figs. 476, 477 and 478).   The first and the third of these are true polygons, but the second (fig. 477) is a combination of three equilateral triangles.

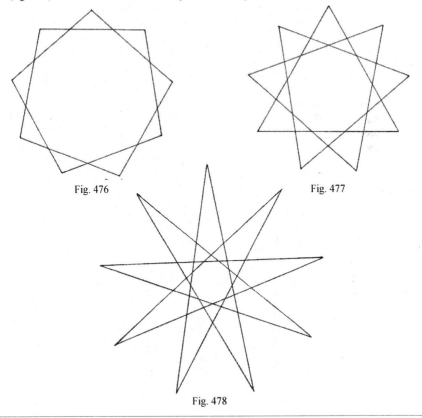

Fig. 476   Fig. 477

Fig. 478

Fig. 479

It is left to the reader to analyse the three stellations of the regular decagon, shown together in fig. 479; to identify the simplest polygon to have four stellations; and to find a way of determining how many stellations a particular polygon will have, and which of these stellations will be "true" polygons and which will be combinations of other polygons. The following paragraphs may help provide answers to some of these questions.

Schläfli Symbols

In chapter 2, page 5, we allotted a Schläfli symbol of the form $\{p, q\}$ to each of the five Platonic solids, where p is the number of sides of a polygonal face and q the number of faces meeting at each vertex. For example a cube, with four sides to a face and three faces meeting at a vertex, has the Schläfli symbol $\{4, 3\}$. Cundy and Rollett, *op. cit.*, label all their polyhedra with a modified Schläfli symbol of the form p^q, so that a cube, for example, is labelled not $\{4, 3\}$ but 4^3.

Now we may normally determine the number of sides of a regular polygon simply by counting but, should this prove difficult, we may *calculate* the number of sides by dividing the exterior angle of the polygon into 360°, recalling that the exterior angle is also the angle which each side of the polygon subtends at the centre. Thus a regular pentagon, with an exterior angle of 72°, must have $360 \div 72 = 5$ sides. The exterior angle of a regular *pentagram*, however, is 144°, and $360 \div 144 = 2.5$, which suggests somewhat oddly that a pentagram has only 2½ sides. Cundy and Rollett, *op. cit*, page 83, explain: "Since each side of a regular polygon of p sides subtends an angle of $2\pi/p$ at the centre, whereas the side of a pentagram subtends $4\pi/5$ [= 144°], it is convenient to call the pentagram $\{5/2\}$..." [I.e., $4\pi/5 = 2\pi/(5/2)$.] "(A polygon) is a stellated polygon of n sides, enclosing the centre d times, if p is a fraction n/d in its lowest terms." So, for instance, Cundy and Rollett label the small stellated dodecahedron $\{5/2\}^5$, since in this solid five faces in the shape of pentagrams meet at each vertex (see fig. 482, page 188).

We can see what is meant by "enclosing the centre" by studying the stellated polygons shown above. If we travel round the sides of the regular pentagon, we reach our starting point after one circuit of 360°, to enclose the centre once. If we do the same on the pentagram, we make two circuits before we return to the start, enclosing the centre twice, and so the pentagram is labelled {5/2}. In the third stellation of the enneagon (fig. 478), we make four circuits and so this stellation has the label {9/4}.

Stellated Polyhedra

The notion of "stellation" can be extended to polyhedra, but whereas a polygon is stellated by extending its *sides*, a polyhedron is stellated by extending its *faces*. As we have already mentioned, stellation adds extra cells to a polyhedron and so in a sense can be thought of as the opposite process to faceting, which removes cells.

Stellation produces new polyhedra. We have already met on page 147 the *stella octangula*, which is the only stellation possible of the regular octahedron. Each face of the octahedron is extended until it meets the extensions of two other faces. These three extensions are triangular in shape and together they make up three faces of a regular tetrahedron, so that a stella octangula, as well as being a regular compound of two interpenetrating regular tetrahedra, can, as we have seen earlier (page 147), be regarded as a regular octahedron with a regular tetrahedron attached to each face. The view of the solid as a compound of two regular tetrahedra is analogous to the view in fig. 471, page 184, of the two-dimensional stellation of the regular hexagon which is a compound of two intersecting equilateral triangles. However the stella octangula can also be regarded as a single solid having eight triangular faces which *interpenetrate*. In fig. 480 the triangle ABC is one such face, with its visible parts shaded, these being the three extensions of one (hidden) face of the octahedron. AB and BC are single edges of the stella octangula; A, B and C are true vertices of the solid; while D is a false vertex, since vertices are defined as points where the *ends* of edges meet. The solid has 12 edges, 8 faces and 8 vertices, and so incidentally does not obey Euler's rule (see page 33).

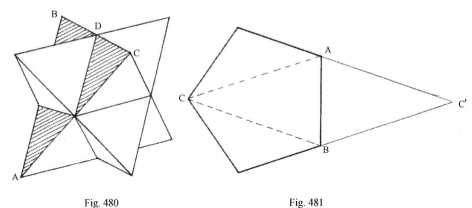

Fig. 480   Fig. 481

Stellations of the Regular Dodecahedron

Neither the regular tetrahedron nor the cube can be stellated, as their faces will not meet when extended. The regular dodecahedron however can be stellated three times in succession to give three new polyhedra. These are the small stellated dodecahedron (fig. 482), the great dodecahedron (fig 486), and the great stellated dodecahedron (fig. 487).

The small stellated dodecahedron is formed when each face of the regular dodecahedron is extended to meet the extensions of four other faces. Each face becomes a pentagram, consisting of the original pentagonal face with five triangles added. The triangle ABC' added to any side AB of the pentagon in fig. 481 is a reflection in AB of the triangle which is formed by joining the ends of AB to the opposite corner C of the pentagon. Both AC and BC are diagonals of the pentagon, so AC', BC' and AB are in the ratio of ø:ø:1 (see page 197). The triangular extensions of the faces form pentagonal pyramids (fig. 483).

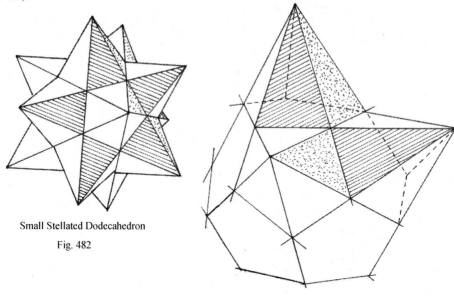

Small Stellated Dodecahedron

Fig. 482

Fig 483

In fig. 483 each pair of triangles with similar shading belongs to the same pentagram face, while the central pentagonal part of this face lies beneath a pyramid. The five sides of each pentagram lie along five edges of the stellated solid, which has twelve pentagram faces, thirty edges, and twelve vertices. It was discovered by Kepler in 1619, and is one of the *Kepler-Poinsot* polyhedra, counting alongside the Platonic solids as a regular polyhedron. It can best be made by sticking a pentagonal pyramid to each of the twelve pentagonal faces of the dodecahedron. The net of one such pyramid is shown in fig. 484.

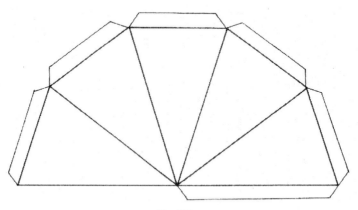

Fig. 484

The pentagram faces of the small stellated dodecahedron can themselves be extended. Fig. 485 shows how this is done. When these extended faces meet we find that the gaps between their "points" have been "filled in" with a wedge-shaped cell so that the twelve faces have once more become regular pentagons. These twelve (intersecting) pentagons form the great dodecahedron, another Kepler-Poinsot polyhedron (fig. 486). Like the regular dodecahedron, this has twelve pentagonal faces and thirty edges, but since five faces meet at each vertex, it has only twelve (true) vertices. Cundy and Rollett, *op. cit.*, page 93, show a net for making the great dodecahedron.

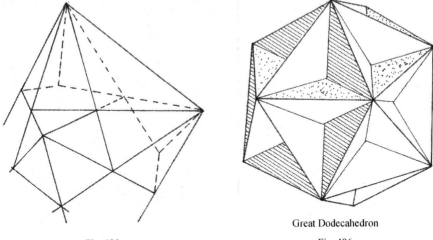

Great Dodecahedron

Fig. 485   Fig. 486

The twelve pentagonal faces of the great dodecahedron can be extended to give the third and final stellation of the regular dodecahedron. The faces become pentagrams once again, and three of these meet at each vertex of the great stellated dodecahedron (fig. 487). This has twelve faces, thirty edges, and twenty vertices, and is another of the Kepler-Poinsot polyhedra.

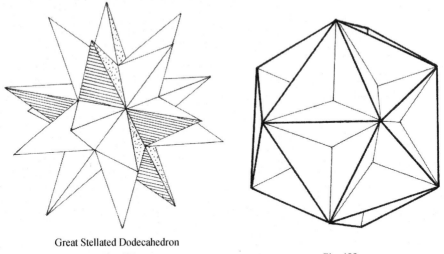

Great Stellated Dodecahedron

Fig. 487   Fig. 488

Both the small stellated dodecahedron and the great dodecahedron have twelve vertices, as does the regular icosahedron. It should be clear from studying figs. 482 and 486 that both these dodecahedra can be contained within a regular icosahedron. But the relation extends a little further than this. The great dodecahedron can readily be seen to be a regular icosahedron from which some cells have been removed, leaving pyramidal depressions where the faces were (fig. 488). That is to say, the great dodecahedron is also a faceted regular icosahedron. Each cell removed has the form of a triangular pyramid, called by Cundy and Rollett an "indented trihedron", with a (missing) equilateral triangle as its base and three 36°-36°-108° faces.   The small stellated dodecahedron is also a faceted regular icosahedron, from which the same triangular pyramids have been removed, together with the wedge-shaped cells which stellation added to the solid to make the great dodecahedron.

The great stellated dodecahedron has twenty vertices, and can be contained within a regular dodecahedron.   It can also be regarded as a faceted regular dodecahedron, the cells removed being of a variety of shapes.

The great stellated dodecahedron can be built by fixing a triangular pyramid to each face of a regular icosahedron.   This is the method favoured by Cundy and Rollett, *op. cit.*, page 95.   In this pyramid each triangular slant face is part of a pentagram whose central pentagon is a face of an antiprism of the icosahedron (see page 106) so that (in theory) the faces of the stellated dodecahedron cut into the body of the icosahedron (fig. 489).

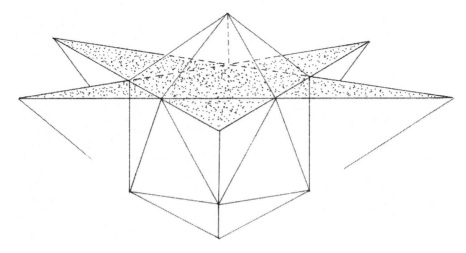

Fig. 489

Fig. 490 shows schematically how the faces of the stellated dodecahedra grow.   At the centre is the pentagonal face of the regular dodecahedron; this face is the centre of the pentagram which is the face of the small stellated dodecahedron; this pentagram is inscribed in the regular pentagon which is the face of the great dodecahedron; and this pentagon is the centre of the pentagram which is the face of the great stellated dodecahedron.

Fig.490

Stellations of the Regular Icosahedron

The number of stellations of the regular icosahedron extends in all to 59 (= 27 + 32). We do not intend to describe any of these here, although we look briefly at the great icosahedron (fig. 491), which has twenty interpenetrating faces in the shape of equilateral triangles, and which is the last of the Kepler-Poinsot polyhedra. Otherwise all we shall do is refer to other sources of information.

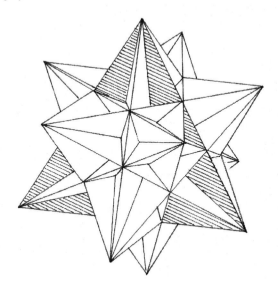

The Great Icosahedron

Fig. 491

The definitive book is Coxeter, DuVal, Flather and Petrie, *The Fifty-nine Icosahedra*, whose third (1999) edition is published by Tarquin Publications. Wenninger, *op. cit., passim*, gives illustrations of many of these beautiful and fascinating stellations of the icosahedron.

Cundy and Rollett, *op. cit.*, pages 97-99, give instructions on how to build a model of the great icosahedron. Their fig. 97 on page 97 is a portion of fig. 3 on page 17 of Coxeter, etc. Their fig. 100 on page 98 is a drawing of another stellation of the icosahedron, labelled no. 26 by Coxeter, no. 28 by Wenninger, and called the "third stellation of the icosahedron" by Jenkins and Wild in *Make Shapes*, book 2. This is also of course a simple faceted form of the regular dodecahedron, while the great icosahedron itself is a faceted form of a regular icosahedron.

In their *Make Shapes* series, Jenkins and Wild also give cut-out nets for the small stellated dodecahedron (book 1); for the great dodecahedron and great stellated dodecahedron, (book 2); and in book 3 for the "ninth stellation of the icosahedron", numbered 30 in Coxeter and 34 in Wenninger. It is left to the reader to consult the literature if he wishes to take the study of stellations of the icosahedron any further.

Cundy and Rollett also devote some space (pages 127 f. and 149 f.) to the stellations of the rhombic dodecahedron, and to the building up of solids from smaller units, in a section called "Unitary Construction" (page 145 f.). These topics are well enough covered there to require no further comment here.

Geodesics

We have referred earlier to the truncated icosahedron, to buckminsterfullerene, and to the work done by Buckminster Fuller in connection with the development of the *geodesic dome*. The whole topic of geodesic domes is covered very fully, with background theory as well as cut-out models, in *Geodesic Domes* by Borin van Loon (Tarquin), and so this topic also requires no further comment here, beyond the observation that in the building of these domes, the study of the Platonic solids and their related forms has found another practical application!

Further reading

This book has attempted to cover work which may be done (and which has been done successfully) in the classroom with pupils of secondary school age. If any reader wishes to extend this work, then Cundy and Rollett's *Mathematical Models* is a rich source both of practical suggestions and of theoretical background. Beyond this are two important founts of wisdom and insight into the theory of the Platonic and other solids. The first is W. W. Rouse Ball's *Mathematical Recreations and Essays*, especially chapter V, "Polyhedra", which owes a lot however to H. S. M. Coxeter's eleventh edition of the book. The other is Coxeter's own *Introduction to Geometry*, which contains valuable material on the Platonic solids, on the Golden Section, on geodesics, on the close-packing of spheres and on honeycombs.

Appendix A

THE REGULAR PENTAGON

In chapters 8 and 9, on the regular dodecahedron and the regular icosahedron respectively, we made frequent mention of the regular pentagon, with its five equal sides and five equal angles. We also mentioned the "Golden Ratio". In this Appendix we discuss ways of drawing the regular pentagon, and we look at its geometry. We also study in some detail the geometry and the arithmetic of the Golden Ratio.

Drawing a Regular Pentagon

Elsewhere in this book we have described special methods of drawing the equilateral triangle, the square, the regular hexagon and the regular octagon. All these polygons, and any other regular polygon of *n* sides (a regular *n-gon*), can also be drawn inside a circle, the *circumcircle* of the polygon, using the following general method.

1. Draw a circle of suitable radius.
2. Within this circle draw *n* radii, the angle between each pair of radii being $(360/n)°$.
3. Join adjacent points where the radii meet the circumference of the circle to obtain a regular *n*-gon.

For the regular pentagon, $n = 5$, so the angle between radii is $(360/5)° = 72°$.

To draw a regular pentagon whose length of side is not specified, first draw a circle centre O, of large enough radius to contain the pentagon. (A radius of, say, 5 cm will give a pentagon of side 5.9 cm.)

1. Draw a radius from O to the top of the circle at A..
2. Turn the paper so that OA is horizontal. Place a protractor with its centre on O and its bottom line along OA.
3. Measuring along the scale which has its zero near A, mark 72° and 144° (= 2 x 72°) at the edge of the protractor.
4. Turn the paper upside down and repeat the process, again measuring along the scale which starts at A. If the marks made do not lie exactly on the circle, lay a ruler from O through each mark in turn, and mark where the ruler crosses the circle. There will now be a radius OA within the circle and four other points, B, C, D and E, on its circumference (fig. 492).
5. Carefully join each of the points A, B, C, D and E to its neighbours to obtain a regular pentagon (fig. 493). Rub out the circle and the radius OA.

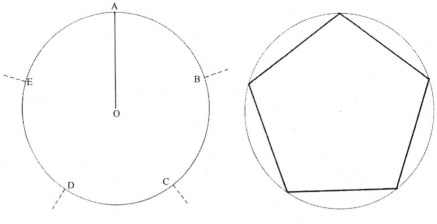

Fig. 492   Fig. 493

It is not easy to draw a regular pentagon with a high degree of accuracy, but drawing a pentagon in a circle is as accurate a method as any. Note that if the pentagon is to have a given length of side, it will

193

be necessary first to calculate what radius to use for the circumcircle.

Fig. 494 shows the isosceles triangle AOB taken from fig. 492. P is the mid-point of AB. The angle OPA is a right angle, and the angle AOP is half the angle AOB, so <AOP = (72/2)° = 36°. If AO is one unit long, then AP = 1 x sin 36° ≈ 0.587785 and hence AB is 2 x sin 36° ≈ 1.176 units long. (This number 1.176 was used above to calculate the length of AB when the radius was 5 cm: 5 x 1.176 ≈ 5.9.)

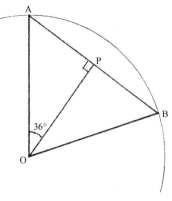

Fig. 494

To calculate the radius of the circle which will contain a pentagon of a given length of side, we either *divide* the length of the side by 1.176 or we multiply it by the *inverse* of 1.176, that is by 1/(2 sin 36°) ≈ 1/1.176 ≈ 0.85. For a pentagon of side, say, 7 cm, we will require a circle with radius 7 x 0.85 (= 7 ÷ 1.176) = 5.95 cm.

A Look Ahead - Calculating with Functions of ø

The number which we have written above as 1.176 (≈ 2 sin 36°) is an approximation to 1.17557... which is $\sqrt{(3 - ø)}$ where ø (the Greek letter *phi*) is the Golden Section or Golden Ratio (≈ 1.61803: see page 196). This means that sin 36° = $\frac{1}{2}\sqrt{(3 - ø)}$, while the number 0.85 used above to calculate the radius of the circumcircle is an approximation to 0 85075... = $1/\sqrt{(3 - ø)}$.

The number ø has a number of curious properties, as will be seen shortly, and it so happens that 1.17557... is also the value of $\sqrt{(ø + 2)/ø}$. In calculations in the body of this book we tend to use this latter function of ø in place of $\sqrt{(3 - ø)}$, partly through preferring a positive to a negative relation, but more particularly because $\sqrt{(ø + 2)/ø}$ lends itself more easily to simplification in calculations of volume, etc. It follows that 0.85075...(= 1/1.17557...) is the value not only of $1/\sqrt{(3 - ø)}$ but also of $ø/\sqrt{(ø + 2)}$.

A Regular Pentagon with a Given Length of Side

To draw a pentagon with a given length of side, say, 6 cm, we may either first calculate the radius required for the circumcircle (6 cm x 0.85 = 5.1 cm) and then proceed as above, or we may use the following method, which given sufficient care is no less accurate.

The outside, or exterior, angle of the regular pentagon is equal to the angle subtended by a side at the centre of the pentagon, that is to say, each is one-fifth of a full circle or (360/5)° = 72°. Each inside, or interior, angle is (180 – 72)° = 108°. The following construction again requires the use of a protractor.

1. Draw the base AB of the pentagon 6 cm long.
2. Place the centre of the protractor on A and its bottom line along AB. Measuring on the scale which shows 0 near B, mark an angle of 108° (on the other scale this will mark the *exterior* angle, 72°). Join this mark to A with a straight line.
3. Move the protractor along to the right so that its centre is on B and its bottom line still along AB, and mark 108° from the 0 near A. Join this mark to B (fig. 495 opposite).
4. Check that both the lines which have been drawn from A and B are at least 6 cm long. If they are not, then make them a little longer, say, 6.5 cm long.
5. Placing the compass point on A and the pencil on B, draw an arc to cut the line from A at C.
6. Place the compass point on B (and the pencil on A) and draw an arc to cut the line from B at D (fig. 496). This ensures that AC = BD = AB.

7. Two more lines of the same length as AB complete the pentagon. Placing the compass point first on C and then on D, draw two arcs of radius AB to cut at E. Then ACEDB is a regular pentagon of side 6 cm (fig. 497).

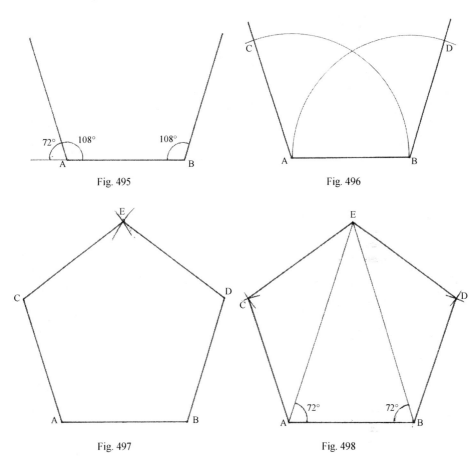

Fig. 495   Fig. 496

Fig. 497   Fig. 498

Another Method

We may also draw the pentagon by measuring angles of 72° instead of 108° from A and B, to give two lines meeting at E, a third corner of the pentagon. These two lines will be diagonals of the pentagon. Two arcs of radius AB, centred on A and B respectively, drawn to cut two arcs of the same radius centred on E will give the positions of two more corners of the pentagon at C and D (fig. 498). However, since AE and BE meet at a relatively small angle, 36°, this allows a degree of inaccuracy to creep in. For example, an error of only half a degree in measuring the 72° angles will result in an error of 2 mm in the length of AE. This means that although all five sides of the pentagon will be equal in length, the five angles may not all be equal.

Even More Methods

On page 90 we described a method of constructing six small regular pentagons inside a larger regular pentagon; and on page 201 f. we give various methods of constructing a regular pentagon using ruler and compasses only.

The Golden Ratio and the Golden Rectangle

The "Golden Section" or, as we shall call it from now on, the "Golden Ratio", is introduced in most textbooks by means of a "Golden Rectangle". This is a rectangle which has the unique property that, if a square section is removed from one end, the rectangle which remains is similar to the original rectangle. So in fig. 499 ACDF is the original "Golden" rectangle, ABEF is the square to be removed, and BCDE is the rectangle remaining: BCDE is similar to ACDF.

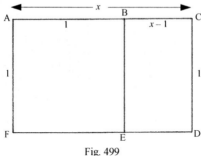

Fig. 499

If we take AF = 1 unit and AC = x units, then AB = 1, BC = $x - 1$, and CD = 1. Since ACDF and BCDE are similar, then AC/AF = CD/BC $\Rightarrow$ $x/1 = 1/(x - 1)$ $\Rightarrow$ $x(x - 1) = 1$ $\Rightarrow$ $x^2 - x - 1 = 0$. The positive root of this equation is $\frac{1}{2}(1 + \sqrt{5}) \approx 1.618$, which is the "Golden Ratio".

The Golden Ratio and the Regular Pentagon

Fig. 500 shows a regular pentagon ABCDE with sides 1 unit long and with three diagonals drawn. We take AC to be x units long. Since, by the symmetry of the pentagon, all diagonals are the same length, BD and CE are also x units long.

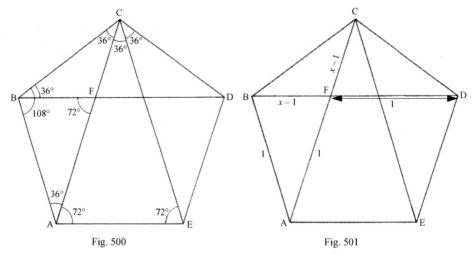

Fig. 500   Fig. 501

We now calculate some angles. The angle ABC is 108° and ABC is an isosceles triangle, so <BAC = <BCA = $\frac{1}{2}(180 - 108)° = 36°$. By rotational symmetry the angles CBD and ECD are both 36°, and so <ACE = $(108 - \{2 \times 36\})° = 36°$ also. The angle CAE is $(108 - 36)° = 72°$.

The angle ABF is $(108 - 36)° = 72°$, and <BFA = $(180 - \{36 + 72\})° = 72°$ also, so the triangle ABF is isosceles. Hence AF = AB and since each is 1 unit long and AC is x units long, it follows that CF must be $(x - 1)$ units long (fig. 501). The triangle BCF is also isosceles and so BF = CF = $(x - 1)$ units

long. From this it follows that FD is $x - (x - 1) = 1$ unit long.

Since the two triangles ABC and BFC are similar, it follows that BF/BC = AB/AC $\Rightarrow (x - 1)/1 = 1/x$ $\Rightarrow x(x - 1) = 1 \Rightarrow x^2 - x - 1 = 0$. Referring back to the section on the Golden Rectangle above, we see that here again we have the equation whose positive root is $\frac{1}{2}(1 + \sqrt{5}) \approx 1.618$, the "Golden Ratio". This means that the lengths of the diagonal of a regular pentagon and of its side are in the ratio of ø:1.

Note also that the alternate angles BFA and FAE are both 72°, so BD is parallel to AE. All the sides of the quadrilateral AFDE are equal (all 1 unit long), and at least two opposite sides are parallel, so AFDE is a rhombus.

The Golden Ratio ø

The number 1.618034..., the value of x above, has in the past been known as τ, the Greek letter "tau", but more recently it has become widely known as ø, the Greek letter "phi", and we shall use ø in this account. Like π, ø is an unending decimal number, with 1.618 being a good working approximation to its true value.

The number ø has some interesting properties.

a) $ø^2 = ø + 1$.
From the equation $x^2 - x - 1 = 0 \Rightarrow ø^2 - ø - 1 = 0$ it follows directly that $ø^2 = ø + 1$. [$1.618^2 = 2.618 = 1.618 + 1$.]

b) $1/ø = ø - 1$.
Dividing $ø^2 = ø + 1$ through by ø we have $ø = 1 + 1/ø \Rightarrow 1/ø = ø - 1$. [$1/1.618 = 0.618 = 1.618 - 1$.]

c) $1/ø^2 = 2 - ø$.
By "completing the square" on $ø^2 = ø + 1$, we have $ø^2 - 2ø + 1 = ø + 1 - 2ø + 1 = 2 - ø$, so $(ø - 1)^2 = 2 - ø$. But $ø - 1 = 1/ø$ so $(ø - 1)^2 = (1/ø)^2 = 1/ø^2 = 2 - ø$. [$0.618^2 = 0.382 = 2 - 1.618$.]

Powers of ø

Every integral power of ø can be expressed as a linear function of ø. Every power can also be expressed as a linear function of $\sqrt{5}$, which is not so surprising when we recall that ø itself is a function of $\sqrt{5}$.

For example, $ø^2 = [\frac{1}{2}(1 + \sqrt{5})]^2 = \frac{1}{4}(1 + 2\sqrt{5} + 5) = \frac{1}{4}(6 + 2\sqrt{5}) = 1\frac{1}{2} + \frac{1}{2}\sqrt{5} = 1 + \frac{1}{2}(1 + \sqrt{5}) = 1 + ø$: and $ø^3 = ø.ø^2 = ø(1 + ø) = ø + ø^2 = ø + ø + 1 = 2ø + 1$. Also $ø^2 = \frac{1}{4}(1 + 2\sqrt{5} + 5) = \frac{1}{4}(2\sqrt{5} + 6) = \frac{1}{4} \times 2(\sqrt{5} + 3) = \frac{1}{2}(\sqrt{5} + 3)$.

The table of equivalents begins :

n	$ø^n$	$ø^n$
2	ø + 1	$\frac{1}{2}(\sqrt{5} + 3)$
3	2ø + 1	$\frac{1}{2}(2\sqrt{5} + 4)$
4	3ø + 2	$\frac{1}{2}(3\sqrt{5} + 7)$
5	5ø + 3	$\frac{1}{2}(5\sqrt{5} + 11)$
6	8ø + 5	$\frac{1}{2}(8\sqrt{5} + 18)$
7	13ø + 8	$\frac{1}{2}(13\sqrt{5} + 29)$
8	21ø + 13	$\frac{1}{2}(21\sqrt{5} + 47)$
9	34ø + 21	$\frac{1}{2}(34\sqrt{5} + 76)$
10	55ø + 34	$\frac{1}{2}(55\sqrt{5} + 123)$

and so on.

The whole numbers in the table of equivalents on the previous page are to be found in two "Fibonacci" sequences. In these sequences each term is the sum of the two previous terms, i.e., $F_n = F_{n-1} + F_{n-2}$. The main Fibonacci sequence begins 1, 1, 2, 3, 5, 8, 13..., and we find, for example, looking at $ø^7 = 13ø + 8$, that 13 is the 7th number (F_7) in this Fibonacci sequence and that 8 is the 6th number (F_6). Generally $ø^n$ will be $F_nø + F_{n-1}$ where F_n is the nth Fibonacci number.

Again this connection of ø with the Fibonacci numbers is less surprising when we recall that $½(\sqrt5 + 1)$ (= ø) is the limiting value, as n approaches infinity, of the ratio of any Fibonacci number F_n to its immediate predecessor F_{n-1} in the sequence. For example 55/34 = 1.6176... which already gives a three-figure correspondence, while the next pair of numbers give 89/55 = 1.61818..., and the next pair give 144/89 = 1.61797.... The further along the sequence we go, the closer the ratios of successive terms converge on the true value of ø.

In the third column of the table on page 197 we have a mixed pattern. The coefficients of $\sqrt5$ are the same Fibonacci numbers as the coefficients of ø in the second column, but the other numbers inside the brackets are "Lucas" numbers. Lucas numbers come from another Fibonacci sequence, different from the main sequence, starting 1, 3, 4, 7, 11, 18, 29,... Numbers in the Lucas sequence have the same properties as those in the main sequence: each term is the sum of the two preceding terms, and the ratio of any one term to its predecessor approaches the value of ø in the limit. The Lucas numbers are connected to the numbers in the main Fibonacci sequence by the relation $L_n = F_n + 2F_{n-1}$. The Lucas sequence has a particular connection with *powers* of ø, in that the nth Lucas number is also equal to the value of the nth power of ø rounded to the nearest integer. For example $ø^7 = 13ø + 8 \approx 21.034 + 8 \approx 29.034$, and $L_7 = 29$.

Incidentally, it is of interest that high integral powers of ø approximate very closely to an integer and the higher the power, the closer the approximation. Odd powers round down; for example, $ø^{13} = 521.0019...$, $ø^{15} = 1364.0007...$ ($L_{13} = 521$, $L_{15} = 1364$), while even powers round up; $ø^{14} = 842.9988...$, $ø^{16} = 2206.999...$ ($L_{14} = 843$, $L_{16} = 2207$).

The pattern of linear equivalents for *negative* powers is also interesting. The two we meet most often are $ø^{-1} = ø - 1$ and $ø^{-2} = 2 - ø$ The first ten of these are offered for inspection with no further comment.

n	$ø^n$	n	$ø^n$
-1	$ø - 1$	-6	$13 - 8ø$
-2	$2 - ø$	-7	$13ø - 21$
-3	$2ø - 3$	-8	$34 - 21ø$
-4	$5 - 3ø$	-9	$34ø - 55$
-5	$5ø - 8$	-10	$89 - 55ø$

Trigonometrical Ratios and ø

In fig. 502 we have taken the triangle ACE from fig. 500, have turned it on its side, and have drawn a median CH to bisect both AE and <ACE, so dividing the isosceles triangle into two right-angled triangles. It is immediately clear that sin 18° (= EH/CE) = ½/ø = 1/2ø. [Note the difference in this text between $½ø = ½ \times ø$ and $1/2ø = 1 ÷ 2ø$.]

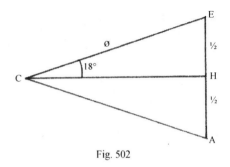

Fig. 502

We can calculate cos 18° as $\sqrt{(1 - \sin^2 18°)} = \sqrt{(1 - 1/4\o^2)}$, but to simplify this and similar expressions we have to be prepared to use various substitutions. These substitutions are primarily those we have met earlier, namely, $\o^2 = \o + 1$; $1/\o = \o - 1$; and $1/\o^2 = 2 - \o$.

Cos 18° $= \sqrt{(1 - 1/4\o^2)} = \sqrt{(1 - \frac14\{1/\o^2\})} = \sqrt{(1 - \frac14\{2 - \o\})} = \sqrt{(1 - \frac12 + \o/4)} = \sqrt{(\o/4 + \frac12)} = \sqrt{(\{\o + 2\}/4)} = \frac12\sqrt{(\o + 2)}$.

From sin 36° = 2 sin 18° x cos 18°, we can calculate sin 36° as 2 x $1/2\o$ x $\frac12\sqrt{(\o + 2)} = \sqrt{(\o + 2)}/2\o$.

Cos 36° $= 2\cos^2 18° - 1 = 2\{\frac12\sqrt{(\o + 2)}\}^2 - 1 = 2\{\frac14(\o + 2)\} - 1 = \frac12(\o + 2) - 1 = \frac12\o + 1 - 1 = \frac12\o$.

At this point we are in a position to write down or calculate the sine, cosine and tangent of any angle which is a multiple of 18°, using the facts that sin θ = cos (90° − θ) and *vice versa,* and that tan θ = sin θ/cos θ. The following table shows the three ratios for four such angles, two of which appear in fig. 500.

Angle	*sine*	*cosine*	*tangent*
18°	$1/2\o$	$\frac12\sqrt{(\o + 2)}$	$1/\o\sqrt{(\o + 2)}$
36°	$\sqrt{(\o + 2)}/2\o$	$\o/2$	$\sqrt{(\o + 2)}/\o^2$
54°	$\o/2$	$\sqrt{(\o + 2)}/2\o$	$\o^2/\sqrt{(\o + 2)}$
72°	$\frac12\sqrt{(\o + 2)}$	$1/2\o$	$\o\sqrt{(\o + 2)}$

It must be noted that, as we observed earlier, these are not the only ways in which we may express these ratios in terms of ø. For example sin 36° is also $\frac12\sqrt{(3 - \o)}$, while tan 72° is also $\sqrt{(4\o + 3)}$. It can in fact be quite a challenge to find the simplest function of ø which gives a particular trigonometrical ratio. The value of 2 − ø is 0.381966... but this is also the value of $(\o - 1)^2$ and of $1/\o^2$ and of $\sqrt{(5 - 3\o)}$, to name but a few. To emphasise this range of choice, some lines of the same length appear with different labels in fig. 503.

Fig. 503 shows a regular pentagon of side 1 unit with its diagonals, which are all ø units long. These diagonals form a star with a smaller regular pentagon inside. Some sections of the diagonals are marked with their lengths in various equivalent functions of ø. Using our knowledge of area factors of enlargement, which are the square of scale factors, we can work out that the small pentagon has an area of $(2 - \o)^2$ $= 1/\o^4 = 5 - 3\o \approx 0.146$, measured as a fraction of the area of the large pentagon. We note also that each diagonal divides two other diagonals in the Golden Ratio.

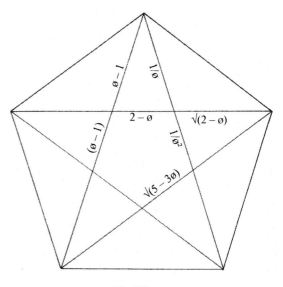

Fig. 503

We can express both the area of the pentagon and the radius of its circumcircle in terms of ø. In fig. 504 ABCDE is a regular pentagon; AB is 1 unit; O is the centre both of the pentagon and of its circumcircle; F is the mid-point of AE; and C, O and F all lie on the same straight line. The angle AFO is a right angle; AF = ½ unit long and <OAF = ½<BAE = ½ x 108° = 54°.

a)   AO, the radius of the circumcircle, is ½/cos 54° = ½/{√(ø + 2)/2ø} = ø/√(ø + 2) ≈ 0.85 units, as we calculated earlier (page 194).

b)   OF = ½ tan 54° = ½ ø²/√(ø + 2)units.

c)   The area of the triangle AOE is ½.AE.OF. Since AE = 1, the area is ½.1.½ ø²/√(ø + 2) = ¼ ø²/√(ø + 2) ≈ 0.344 square units. Since five of these triangles make the whole pentagon, the area of the pentagon is 5/4 x ø²/√(ø + 2) ≈ 5 x 0.344 = 1.72 square units.

d)   The "height" of the pentagon, CF, will be ½ tan 72° (see fig. 500, page 196) = ½ ø√(ø + 2) ≈ 1.54 units.

e)   FG = AH = cos 18° = ½√(ø + 2) ≈ 0.951 units: CG = sin 36° = √(ø + 2)/2ø ≈ 0.588 units.

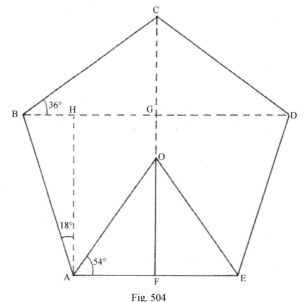

Fig. 504

In our study of the regular dodecahedron we needed to know the ratio in which the diagonal BD of the pentagon divides the height CF. By similar triangles this ratio must be the same as that in which the diagonal BD divides the diagonal AC in fig. 501, page 196, which is (ø – 1):1. In fig. 504, CG:FG = sin 36°:cos 18° = √(ø + 2)/2ø:½√(ø + 2) = 1/2ø:½ = 1/ø:1= (ø – 1):1.

Occasionally we have found the need to "divide a given line in the Golden Ratio". This we do by measurement rather than by construction. If the line is ø units long, we divide it in the Golden Ratio by marking a point 1 unit from one end. If the line is 1 unit long, we mark a point 1/ø units from one end. This is a point 0.618 (= 1/ø) units from one end, which will therefore be 0.382 (= 1/ø²) units from the other end. We may check that 0.618/0.382 = 1.618, and that (1/ø)/(1/ø²) = ø. If the line were, say, 6 cm long, a mark 6 x 0.618 cm = 3.7 cm from one end would divide it in the Golden Ratio (fig. 505).

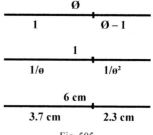

Fig. 505

Constructing a Regular Pentagon

It is possible to draw a regular pentagon by *construction*, using ruler and compasses only, without measuring directly either lengths or angles. We give three methods here.

Method 1

This method, for drawing a regular pentagon in a circle, is given by H. E. Dudeney in his *Amusements in Mathematics*, first published in 1917.

1. Draw a circle, centre O, with two diameters AB and CD at right angles to each other (fig. 506).
2. Find E, the mid-point of OB (see page 13).
3. Place the compass point on E and the pencil on C, and draw an arc of radius EC to cut AO at F.
4. With compass point on C and pencil on F, draw an arc to cut the circle at G and again at H. The chords CG and CH are two sides of a pentagon.
5. With radius CG, draw two arcs centred on G and H to cut the circle again at I and J. CHJIG is a regular pentagon.

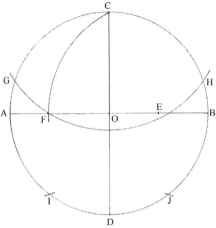

Fig. 506

It is easy to check the accuracy of this method. If the radius of the circle is taken to be 2 units, then the length of one side of the pentagon must be 4 x sin 36° (see fig. 494, page 194) = 4 x ½√(ø + 2)/ø (see page 199) = 2 x √(ø + 2)/ø units. However, on this occasion it is more helpful to use sin 36° = ½√(3 − ø) (see p. 194), so that the side of the pentagon must be 2√(3 − ø) units long.

By Pythagoras CE is √5 units, and OF is therefore √5 − 1 = √5 + 1 - 2 = 2ø − 2 = 2(ø − 1) = 2/ø units. Again by Pythagoras, CF = √(4 + 4/ø²) = 2√(1 + 1/ø²) = 2√{1 + (2 − ø)} = 2√(3 − ø) units. By construction, CG = CF and is also 2√(3 − ø) units, so that this method of drawing a regular pentagon, unlike many other methods proposed over the centuries, is exact.

Method 2

This method allows us to choose the length of side of the pentagon.

1. Draw a horizontal line AB one unit long as one side of the pentagon.
2. With centre A and radius AB, draw an arc to continue above and somewhat to the left of A (fig. 507 overleaf).
3. With centre B and radius AB, draw an arc to cut the first arc at C.
4. With centre C and radius AB, draw an arc to cut the first arc at D
5. Draw two arcs with any equal radius and centred at C and D to cut at E.

6. Draw EA to cut the arc BCD at F. AF = AB and <FAB = 90° (cf. fig. 30, page 15).
7. Draw a line from A passing through and beyond C, that is, at an angle of 60° to AB.
8. With centre B and radius BF (= √2 by Pythagoras) draw an arc to cut this line at G. AG is
   ½(1 + √5) = ø units long.

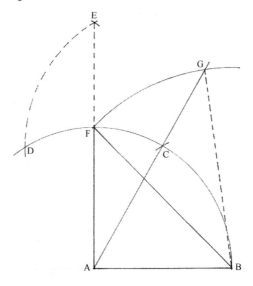

Fig. 507

It is not easy to see at a glance why AG is ø units long, but the result can be checked by using the cosine rule in the triangle AGB. The angle GAB is 60°, AB = 1, BG = √2, and AG is taken to be a units long. Then $(\sqrt{2})^2 = 1^2 + a^2 - 2.1.a.\cos 60° \Rightarrow 2 = 1 + a^2 - a \Rightarrow a^2 - a - 1 = 0$, an equation one of whose roots we have already seen (page 196) is ½(1 + √5) = ø.

To draw the pentagon, draw two arcs of radius AG centred on A and B respectively to cut at H (fig. 508). Two pairs of arcs of radius AB, one pair centred on A and H, and the other on B and H, will cut at I and J respectively, the other two corners of the regular pentagon AIHJB.

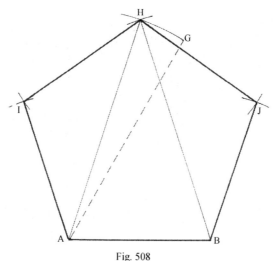

Fig. 508

Method 3

First draw two lines whose lengths are in the Golden Ratio, that is in the ratio ø:1. Cundy and Rollett explain how to do this on page 69 of *Mathematical Models*, and their explanation is reproduced below.

1. Draw a line AB 2 units long.
2. At B, draw another line BC at right angles to AB, 1 unit long.
3. Join AC. By Pythagoras, AC is √5 units long.
4. With the compass point on C, draw an arc of radius CB (1 unit) to meet AC at D. AD is (√5 − 1) units long.
5. With centre A, draw an arc of radius AD to cut AB at E (and to continue some way below E for the next part of the construction) (fig. 509).

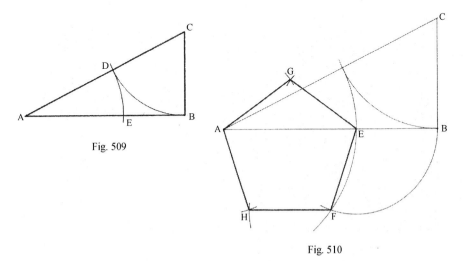

Fig. 509

Fig. 510

AE and EB are in the ratio of ø:1, since EB is 2 − (√5 − 1) = 3 − √5 units long and AE/EB = (√5 − 1)/(3 − √5) = {(√5 − 1)(3 + √5)}/{(3 − √5)(3 + √5)} = (2 + 2√5)/4 = ½(1 + √5) = ø.

To draw the pentagon we use the fact that an isosceles triangle whose sides are in the ratio of ø:ø:1 is the central triangle of a regular pentagon, formed by two diagonals and a side.

Extend the arc drawn through E with centre A and radius AD to cut another arc with centre E and radius EB at F. The triangle AEF is the central triangle of the pentagon (fig. 510). Two arcs of radius EB and centred at A and E will intersect at G, a fourth corner of the pentagon, while two similar arcs centred at A and F will give the fifth corner, H, to complete the pentagon AGEFH.

Even though the greatest care may be taken, any lengthy construction using pencil and compasses may well fall short of absolute precision. A slight error made at an early stage will be magnified in later stages, and although in theory a carefully drawn pentagon should be perfectly regular, in reality it may not be so.

To test the accuracy of any of the above pentagon constructions, find the centre O of the pentagon by joining the mid-points of any two sides to the opposite corners. A circle with centre O and radius OA should pass exactly through all five corners of the pentagon (fig. 511).

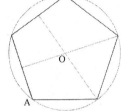

Fig. 511

The Golden Rectangle - A Postscript

We have just seen how we may divide a line in the Golden Ratio by construction. We may use the same method to divide the sides of a square in the Golden Ratio, the points we obtain in this way being the corners of a Golden Rectangle.

In fig. 512, ABCD is a square.

1. Find E, the mid-point of BC, and join AE.
2. With the compass point on E and radius EB, draw an arc to cut AE at F.
3. With the compass point on A and radius AF, draw an arc to cut AB at G. Then G divides AB in the Golden Ratio. (AG:GB = ø:1.)
4. With the compass point first on B and then on D, and with radius BG, draw arcs to cut BC at H, and DC and DA at I and J respectively. Then GHIJ is a Golden Rectangle. (JG:GH = ø√2:√2 =ø:1.)

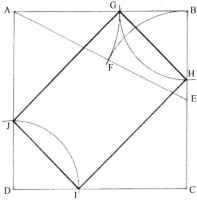

Fig. 512

We referred to fig. 512 when we came to look at the relationship between the regular octahedron and the regular icosahedron (page 152).

We may also add a Golden Rectangle to a square to obtain another Golden Rectangle. In fig. 513 ABCD is a square, and E is the mid-point of DC.

1. Draw an arc with centre E and radius EB to cut DC produced at F.
2. Draw FG perpendicular to DF, with G on AB produced. Then both BGFC and AGFD are Golden Rectangles. This construction dates back to Euclid.

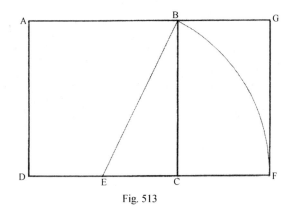

Fig. 513

Appendix B

MORE ABOUT THE CUBE

Cutting Cubes from Cubes

On pages 17 and 18 we described how to make and colour a cube so that it appeared to be made from $3 \times 3 \times 3 = 27$ small cubes (fig. 37), and we asked questions about it. We reproduce fig. 37 here in fig. 514. If alternate cubes are coloured green (shaded) and yellow, then 14 cubes in all will be green, while the other 13, including the single cube inside at the centre, will be yellow. Martin Gardner in *Mathematical Puzzles and Diversions*, Pelican, page 32, poses a problem based on such a cube.

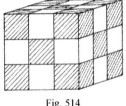

Fig. 514

He asks: "A carpenter, working with a circular saw, wishes to cut a wooden cube, three inches on a side, into 27 one-inch cubes. He can do this easily by making six cuts through the cube, keeping the pieces together in the cube shape (fig. 515). Can he reduce the number of necessary cuts by rearranging the pieces after each cut?"

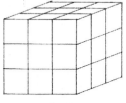

Fig. 515

We can best approach this problem by considering a $2 \times 2 \times 2$ cube, to be cut into 8 small cubes, using a hand saw rather than a circular saw. First we cut, let us say, vertically downwards through the middle of the cube. This gives us two pieces $2 \times 2 \times 1$. We stack these pieces flat one on top of the other, and cut again down through the middle. We now have four pieces, $2 \times 1 \times 1$. Finally we turn these pieces on their sides, keeping them together, and again cut down the middle, to finish with eight small cubes. Fig. 516 shows the cuts in the order they were made (but not the stacking pattern), together with the end result. No matter how we arrange the pieces after each cut, we need a minimum of three cuts.

Alternatively we can argue that each cube is attached to three others and so three successive cuts are needed to separate each cube from its neighbours.

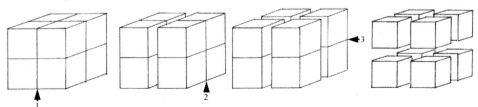

Fig. 516

[If we have or can lay our hands on a set of Dienes' blocks or other multi-base arithmetic blocks, we can demonstrate the process using $2 \times 2 \times 2$ blocks, with their associated "flats" and "longs", and so also for larger cubes. At one time such blocks were a necessary part of the classroom equipment of any up-to-date mathematics teacher.]

For a $2 \times 2 \times 2$ cube we needed three cuts. How many cuts shall we need for a $3 \times 3 \times 3$ cube, assuming that after each cut we may stack the pieces in any way we like?

We shall find that we shall need at least six cuts, so that the carpenter in the problem could not have solved it with fewer cuts, no matter how he rearranged the pieces after each cut. The key lies in the single cube situated at the centre of the large cube. Each face of this cube needs a separate cut to free it from its neighbour; the cube has six faces, so six cuts are needed. No amount of ingenious stacking will allow us to do the job with fewer than six cuts.

On the other hand, stacking will certainly help us cut up a 4 x 4 x 4 cube. First we cut the cube down the middle into two pieces (fig. 517). We place one piece on top of the other and cut down the middle again (fig. 518). We now have four slices 4 x 4 x 1. We stack these slices flat one on top of the other, and cut down the middle (8 pieces). We stack four of these eight on top of the other four and cut down again to give 16 rods 4 x 1 x 1. We turn these rods around, cut down the middle again, (32 pieces) and finally stack and cut again to obtain 64 small cubes. As with the 3 x 3 x 3 cube, the whole process takes only six cuts. How many cuts shall we need for a 5 x 5 x 5 cube?

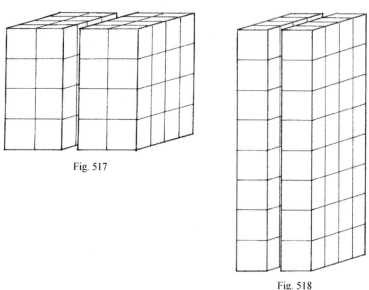

Fig. 517

Fig. 518

Let us leave this problem for a moment and jump to consider an 8 x 8 x 8 cube. Eight is a power of 2, being 2^3, and we shall find that three cuts down the middle with stacking after each cut will be enough to give us eight 8 x 8 x 1 slices. Stacking these slices and cutting and stacking three more times will give us sixty-four 8 x 1 x 1 rods; and three more cuts with stacking will be enough to cut these up into 512 small cubes. The whole process takes nine cuts, so presumably a 5 x 5 x 5 cube will need somewhere between 6 and 9 cuts. How many will it need in fact?

We can certainly do the job in nine cuts by pretending the 5 x 5 x 5 cube is an 8 x 8 x 8 cube with a lot of small cubes missing, and proceed as before. We in fact do best to make the first cut only 2 cubes in from one edge (fig. 519); we can stack the two pieces but now we need two more cuts to give us five 5 x 5 x 1 slices. Three more cuts will give us 25 rods each 5 x 1 x 1, and three more cuts, a total of nine, will give 125 small cubes.

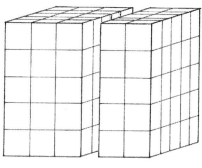

Fig. 519

Martin Gardner (*op. cit.*, page 39) suggests that "if at each piling (i.e., stacking) you see that every piece is cut as nearly in half as possible, the minimum number of cuts will be achieved. In general, for an *n* x *n* x *n* cube, the minimum number of cuts is 3k where k is defined by $2^k \geq n > 2^{k-1}$."

So for n = 4 = 2^2, the number of cuts needed was 2 x 3 = 6, and so also for n = 3. For n = 8 = 2^3, the number of cuts needed was 3 x 3 = 9. Since for n = 5, 6, and 7, $2^3 > n > 2^2$, 9 cuts will also be needed for these values of n. The reader may check that according to this rule, if n = 64 = 2^6, only 6 x 3 = 18 cuts will be needed, while as few as 30 cuts will divide up a 1000 x 1000 x 1000 cube.

Cube Numbers

Fig. 520 shows twenty-five dots arranged in a square array of five lines, each containing five dots, illustrating why twenty-five is commonly called a "square number". The sequence of square numbers is 1, 4, 9, 16, 25, 36,..., the nth term of which is n x n = n^2. Analogous to this sequence is the sequence of "cube numbers", 1, 8, 27, 64, 125, 216,..., the nth term of which is n x n x n or n^3. The name "cube number" reflects the fact that, say, 27 objects can be arranged in a cubic array with three layers, each layer in the form of a square made up of three rows of three objects each, while 64 objects can be arranged in four layers, each made up of four rows of four objects. We saw how the folding cube in fig. 37 on page 18 appeared to be built up from 27 smaller cubes in three layers, with nine cubes in each layer. The cube shown in fig. 521 appears to be built from four layers, each containing 4 x 4 = 16 small cubes, and 4 x 16 = 64. Therefore 64 follows 27 in our sequence of cube numbers.

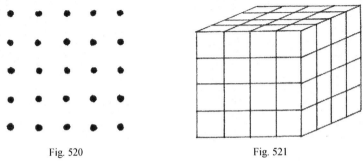

Fig. 520   Fig. 521

The fact that cube numbers have their own special name suggests that they may be of some significance mathematically, and this is in fact so.

1. ***Cubic measure*** The property that cubes possess of being able to fill space without leaving gaps makes them a natural choice as a measure of volume. The statement that a solid has a volume of 20 cubic centimetres implies that, if it is hollow, it can be filled completely with 20 cubes of some substance, each originally of edge 1 centimetre and of volume 1 cubic centimetre, but each capable of being deformed if necessary to fit the shape of the solid; or that it takes up exactly the same amount of space as those 20 cubes.

2. ***Enlargement*** Cube numbers also measure *volume factors of enlargement*. If we take a cube and double the length of its edges, each face becomes a square with $2^2 = 4$ times the area of the original face. The volume of the enlarged cube is 2 x 2 x 2 = 2^3 = 8 times the original volume. If we make the edges three times as long, the area of each face increases by a factor of $3^2 = 9$, while the volume increases by a factor of $3^3 = 27$. It is easy to check that this is true by counting how many unit cubes are needed to build larger cubes. What is not so easy to understand is that this increase in volume happens no matter what the original shape of the solid may be. We can check easily enough that if a 2 x 3 x 4 cuboid, with a volume of 24 (cubic units), is enlarged by a *linear* or *scale* factor of enlargement 3, it becomes a 6 x 9 x 12 cuboid, with a volume of 648 = 24 x 27, its volume having increased by a factor of 27. We have no easy means of checking that when, as happens on page 147, we double the length of the edges of a regular tetrahedron, the enlarged tetrahedron has in fact a volume eight times that of the small one. We simply accept that it is so, helped by certain considerations. For instance, as we saw on page 148, a regular tetrahedron can be made to fit snugly inside a cube. If we enlarge both the cube and the tetrahedron by the same scale factor, the tetrahedron

will occupy the same proportion of space inside the cube as it did formerly and therefore its volume must have increased by the same volume factor.

It must be noted that we are not restricted to whole numbers for the scale factor when we enlarge a solid, and the volume factor of enlargement, although always the cube of the scale factor, may not itself be a cube number. Nevertheless it will help generally if we think first in terms of cube numbers when approaching most enlargement problems.

3. **The metric system**   This system is built upon powers of 10, and cubes figure prominently in definitions. A cube of edge 10 centimetres has a volume of $10^3 = 1000$ cubic centimetres (cm^3) and will hold one *litre* of liquid. We use "litres" for measuring the capacity of a car engine: a 2.3 litre engine has a capacity of 2.3 x 1000 = 2300 cm^3. A cube of edge 1 centimetre, with a volume of 1 cubic centimetre, will hold one *millilitre* of liquid. A millilitre of water has a mass of 1 gram, while a litre of water has a mass of $10^3 = 1000$ *grams*, which is 1 *kilogram*.

A cube with edge 100 cm = 1 metre, will have a volume of 1 cubic metre or $100^3 = 1\,000\,000\ cm^3$, a million cubic centimetres. Its capacity will be 1000 litres and this volume of water has a mass of 1000 kilograms, or 1 *tonne*.

4. (a) There still lingers a faint folk-memory that 1728 ($= 12^3$) cubic inches make one cubic foot, and even that 27 ($= 3^3$) cubic feet make one cubic yard.

   (b) The number of different outcomes possible when we throw three ordinary dice is 6 x 6 x 6 = $6^3 = 216$.

   (c) The third line of Pascal's Triangle (see page 212) is 1 3 3 1, and $11^3 = 1331$.

5. We obtain cube numbers when we split up the sequence of odd numbers in the following manner: 1 + (3 + 5) + (7 + 9 + 11) + (13 + 15 + 17 + 19) + (21 + 23 + 25 + 27 + 29) + ... = 1 + 8 + 27 + 64 + 125 +... (adding the numbers in the brackets). The next *six* odd numbers will add to $6^3 = 216$, and so on.

6. In the traditionally set out multiplication square (fig. 522), the numbers in successive (reversed) L-shaped portions of the table add up to successive cube numbers: 1, 2 + 4 + 2 = 8, 3 + 6 + 9 + 6 + 3 = 27, 4 + 8 + 12 + 16 + 12 + 8 + 4 = 64, etc.

1	2	3	4
2	4	6	8
3	6	9	12
4	8	12	16

Fig. 522

7. The diagram in fig. 523 contains five squares and four rectangles, a total of 9 in all, while that in fig. 524 contains 14 squares and 22 rectangles, a total of 36 in all. These diagrams introduce the general problem of how many squares and rectangles are contained in a n-by-n square, divided into *unit* squares.. The answer is $[½n(n + 1)]^2$, which is the square of the nth triangular number (from the sequence 1, 3, 6, 10, 15,...: see page 211). Each successive extension of the side of the square by one unit increases the number of squares and rectangles by a cube number; for example 36 – 9 = 27.

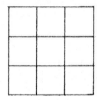

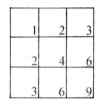

Fig. 523   Fig. 524   Fig. 525

We may approach this problem by writing at each intersection of the grid (fig. 525) the number of squares and rectangles which have their bottom right-hand corner at that intersection. We see at once that this method generates the pattern of the multiplication table in fig. 522 above. The successive numbers in the solution to the problem are 1^2, 3^2, 6^2, 10^2, 15^2,... = 1, 9, 36, 100, 225,... and $9 - 1 = 8$, $36 - 9 = 27$, $100 - 36 = 64$, $225 - 100 = 125$. Generally if T_n is the nth triangular number, $T_n^2 - T_{n-1}^2 = n^3$.

8. Successive sums of the sequence of odd cubes $1^3 + 3^3 + 5^3 + 7^3 + 9^3 + 11^3 + 13^3 + ...$ include all the *perfect* numbers except 6. Perfect numbers are those numbers whose factors add up to the number itself: $6 = 3 + 2 + 1$, $28 = 14 + 7 + 4 + 2 + 1$; etc. The next perfect numbers are 496 and 8128, and the sequence of odd cubes sums successively to 1, *28*, 153, *496*, 1225, 2556, 4753, *8128*,...

9. It is well known that the expressions $a^2 - b^2$ and $a^3 - b^3$ both have a factor $(a - b)$, the other factors of these expressions being $(a + b)$ and $(a^2 + ab + b^2)$ respectively. However the expression $a^2 + b^2$ does not have a factor $(a + b)$, whereas the expression $a^3 + b^3$ does have $(a + b)$ as a factor, the other factor being $(a^2 - ab + b^2)$. If a, b and c are consecutive integers, then $a^3 + b^3 + c^3$ has a factor $(a + b + c)$, and if a, b, c and d are consecutive integers, then $a^3 + b^3 + c^3 + d^3$ has a factor $(a + b + c + d)$. Also $3^3 + 4^3 + 5^3 = 6^3$. These facts and the reasons behind them could form the subject of a fruitful mathematical investigation, but further consideration of them falls outside the scope of the present book.

Cubes of Various Sizes

However, we can continue to look at the relationship between cubes of various sizes, which generates problems such as the following.

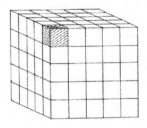

Fig. 526

1. How many small cubes are visible in the view in fig. 526 of a 5 x 5 x 5 cube?

(a) We can count the visible cubes. One cube is shaded; each edge meeting at the shaded cube contains four more cubes; each face shows 4 x 4 = 16 cubes not already counted. The total is $1 + (3 \times 4) + (3 \times 4^2) = 1 + 12 + 48 = 61$. If we generalise this result for a similar view of an n x n x n cube, the number visible is $1 + 3(n - 1) + 3(n - 1)^2$. This simplifies to $3n^2 - 3n + 1$ or $3n(n - 1) + 1$. For the 5 x 5 x 5 cube this is $(15 \times 4) + 1 = 61$ and for a 6 x 6 x 6 cube will be $(18 \times 5) + 1 = 91$.

(b) We can argue that each face in fig. 526 shows 25 cubes, so 3 x 25 = 75 are visible. However, we have then counted the shaded cube three times and twelve of the others twice, so the total is only $75 - 12 - 2 = 61$. Generalising for an n x n x n cube, this is $3n^2 - 3(n - 1) - 2 = 3n^2 - 3n + 1$ as before.

(c) If we strip away all the visible cubes, we shall expose a 4 x 4 x 4 cube lurking behind them, so the total visible is $5^3 - 4^3 = 125 - 64 = 61$. Since, as we have seen earlier, $a^3 - b^3 = (a - b)(a^2 + ab + b^2)$, $5^3 - 4^3$ is also $(5 - 4)(5^2 + [5 \times 4] + 4^2) = 25 + 20 + 16 = 61$. For a 6 x 6 x 6 cube the total visible will be $6^2 + (6 \times 5) + 5^2 = 36 + 30 + 25 = 91$.

2. A 6 x 6 x 6 cube is painted on its outside and is then divided into 216 separate cubes. How many of these will be painted on three faces, how many on two faces, how many on a single face, and how many will not be painted at all?

The 8 cubes at the vertices, each of which belongs to three faces, will be coloured on three of their faces. If these cubes are removed, there remain four cubes along each edge which are coloured on two faces, that is 4 x 12 = 48 in all. If these cubes are removed then there remains a square block of 4 x 4 = 16 cubes on each face coloured on one face only, a total of 6 x 16 = 96 in all. Removing these cubes leaves behind a 4 x 4 x 4 cube which formed the interior of the original cube, none of whose 64 small cubes is coloured at all. We can check that all the cubes are accounted for: $8 + 48 + 96 + 64 = 216$.

209

3. How many unit cubes must be added to an n x n x n cube to make an (n + 1) x (n + 1) x (n + 1) cube?

First we must add an n x n square slab of unit cubes to each of three faces; then we must add a row of n unit cubes to each of three edges; and finally we must add one unit cube to a vertex (fig. 527). This gives the result $(n + 1)^3 = n^3 + 3n^2 + 3n + 1$, which can be shown to be true by multiplying out the left-hand side. We may extend this result to show that $(n + 2)^3 = n^3 + 6n^2 + 12n + 8$, and so on.

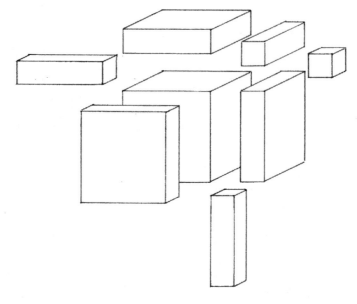

Fig. 527

Other Problems

Among other problems concerning cubes are some which appear in the *Mathematical Curiosities* series by Jenkins and Wild (Tarquin). In *MC* 1 pages 3 and 5 appear nets for a model of "Folding and Unfolding Cubes"; in *MC* 2 page 29 is a net of a "magic cube"; while on page 31 of *MC* 3 there is the net of a hollow cube which can with skill be turned inside out.

On page 203-205 of *Mathematical Models*, Cundy and Rollett describe three puzzles which involve the building of cubes from pieces which themselves are made of smaller cubes. One is the "Soma Cube" puzzle, which is marketed under that title by Tarquin, and to an examination of which Martin Gardner devotes chapter six of his *More Mathematical Puzzles and Diversions*. A second puzzle is Steinhaus' dissection of the cube; and the third originates in the fact noted above that $3^3 + 4^3 + 5^3 = 6^3$. From seven of its eight pieces, leaving out a 3 x 3 x 3 cube, can be made a 4 x 4 x 4 cube and a 5 x 5 x 5 cube, or, using all the pieces, a 6 x 6 x 6 cube. Tarquin markets this third puzzle under the title of "The Three Cubes Cube".

Appendix C
MORE ABOUT THE REGULAR TETRAHEDRON
Tetrahedra and Dice

In the past dice in the form of regular tetrahedra have occasionally been used for gambling . Such dice are fair in the sense that the symmetry of the solid makes it unlikely that the die will fall more often on one face than on another. The only drawback to using tetrahedral dice is that when one of these is thrown no single face is uppermost, so that the score is usually taken to be the number marked on the hidden face on which the die rests. If tetrahedra are used as dice, this problem may be overcome by writing around the opposite vertex the number on the hidden face (fig. 528).

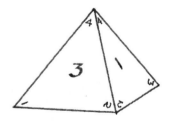

Fig. 528

Tetrahedral Numbers

Tetrahedra are linked numerically with ordinary cube dice. If we throw four ordinary dice together, the number of possible outcomes is 6 x 6 x 6 x 6 = 6^4 = 1296. Of these outcomes just one (1,1,1,1) will give the minimum possible score of 4. Four outcomes, (1,1,1,2), (1,1,2,1), (1,2,1,1), (1,2,1,1), will give the next highest possible score of 5, while ten outcomes, (1,1,1,3), (1,1,3,1), (1,3,1,1), (1,3,1,1), (1,1,2,2), (1,2,1,2), (1,2,2,1), (2,1,1,2), (2,1,2,1), (2,2,1,1), will give the next highest possible score of 6. These numbers 1, 4, 10,... are part of the sequence of *tetrahedral* numbers 1, 4, 10, 20, 35, 56,..., which are the partial sums of the sequence of *triangular* numbers 1, 3, 6, 10, 15, 21,..., (e.g., 20 = 1 + 3 + 6 + 10), which themselves are the partial sums of the sequence of natural numbers 1, 2, 3, 4, 5, 6,... (e.g., 15 = 1 + 2 + 3 + 4 + 5). A triangular number counts the number of items arranged in the form of an equilateral triangle. In fig. 529 we see ten touching circles arranged in this manner; four circles lie along each side; and ten (= 1 + 2 + 3 + 4) is the fourth triangular number.

We now take the circles in fig. 529 to represent a layer of spheres. We can place a second triangular layer of six spheres on top of this first layer, each sphere touching three spheres in the layer below. Fig. 530 shows a plan view of this arrangement. On top of this second layer we can place a third layer of three spheres, and finally we can top off the pile with a single sphere. Fig. 531 shows a side view of this pile of 20 spheres. The pile is in the shape of a regular tetrahedron, and this fact justifies our giving the name *tetrahedral numbers* to the sequence 1, 4, 10, 20, 35, 56,... of which 20 is the fourth term.

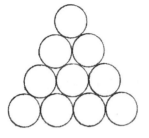

Fig. 529

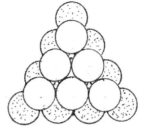

Fig. 530

Fig. 531

The algebraic formula which generates the tetrahedral numbers is an extension of the formula for generating triangular numbers. The nth triangular number is $n(n + 1)/2! = \frac{1}{2}n(n + 1)$, while the nth tetrahedral number is $n(n + 1)(n + 2)/3! = n(n + 1)(n + 2)/6$. The sequence of tetrahedral numbers appears in Pascal's triangle below in the diagonal next to the sequence of triangular numbers, and it is well known that in this triangle each diagonal leading downwards to the right is made up of the partial sums of the numbers in the diagonal next to its right.

$$
\begin{array}{c}
1\\
1\quad 1\\
1\quad 2\quad 1\\
1\quad 3\quad 3\quad 1\\
1\quad 4\quad 6\quad 4\quad 1\\
1\quad 5\quad 10\quad 10\quad 5\quad 1\\
1\quad 6\quad 15\quad 20\quad 15\quad 6\quad 1\\
1\quad 7\quad 21\quad 35\quad 35\quad 21\quad 7\quad 1\\
1\quad 8\quad 28\quad 56\quad 70\quad 56\quad 28\quad 8\quad 1\\
1\quad 9\quad 36\quad 84\quad 126\quad 126\quad 84\quad 36\quad 9\quad 1\\
1\quad 10\quad 45\quad 120\quad 210\quad 252\quad 210\quad 120\quad 45\quad 10\quad 1
\end{array}
$$

[Note that the next "extension" of the formula for triangular numbers is $n(n + 1)(n + 2)(n + 3)/4! = n(n + 1)(n + 2)(n + 3)/24$. This formula for n = 1,2,3,4,... gives the sequence 1, 5, 15, 35,...which appears in the diagonal next to the left below that of the tetrahedral numbers. These further sequences however have no special names linking them to geometrical patterns or structures.]

The tetrahedral numbers tell us the number of possible outcomes when four ordinary dice are thrown for any score from 4 up to and including 9. Each set of outcomes can be represented as a tetrahedral pile of spheres. There are, for example, 56 ways of scoring 9 on four dice (and also by symmetry 56 ways of scoring 19). However there are not 84 ways of scoring 10 on four dice but only 80, since the four outcomes (1,1,1,7), (1,1,7,1), (1,7,1,1), (7,1,1,1) cannot result from throwing dice whose faces are numbered only from 1 to 6.

We can imagine these four "impossible" outcomes to be placed one at each vertex of the tetrahedron, where they will appear as gaps, or as "truncations" of the tetrahedron (see page 153, fig. 410). By a similar argument we can calculate that instead of there being 120 possible ways of scoring 11 on four dice, there will be 120 − (4 x 4) = 104. The total of impossible outcomes is 16, and these can be removed from the vertices of the tetrahedron as four tetrahedral numbers, each worth 4. The total number of ways of scoring 12 will be 165 − (4 x 10) = 125. (Pursuing this argument for higher scores, we find that the tetrahedra we remove from the vertices eventually overlap, so that we have then to reinstate extra tetrahedral numbers incorrectly removed, but this is outside our present study!)

Volumes

We can take tetrahedral numbers generated by the formula $n(n + 1)(n + 2)/6$ to measure in some degree the *volume* of tetrahedra, but only if we take great care. If we make n very large, then the constants 1 and 2 in the product $n(n + 1)(n + 2)$ become insignificant, and the value of this product approaches n^3 as n approaches infinity, while the value of the tetrahedral number $n(n + 1)(n + 2)/6$ approaches $n^3/6$, suggesting that a regular tetrahedron has one-sixth the volume of a cube with the same length of edge. However we have seen on page 50 that the volume of a regular tetrahedron is slightly less than one-eighth that of a cube with the same length of edge, and one-eight is significantly different from one-sixth. Nevertheless the tetrahedral numbers will measure approximately the volume of a tetrahedral pile in which each sphere rests on only one sphere in the layer below and not on three; and in which each layer is in the shape of a right-angled triangle instead of an equilateral one (fig. 532). We then have a pyramid three of whose faces are half-squares, that is, right-angled isosceles triangles (fig. 533), and it is true that such a pyramid, with a base area of $\frac{1}{2}n^2$ and with height n, has a volume $\frac{1}{3}$ x $\frac{1}{2}n^2$ x n = $n^3/6$, which is one-sixth the volume of the cube which contains it. [Can six of these pyramids be fitted together to form a cube? Can any number of such pyramids be fitted together to form any other regular solid? See fig. 209, page 70, for the net of such a pyramid.]

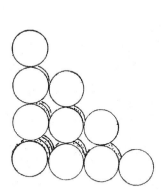

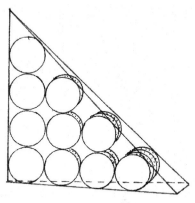

Fig. 532   Fig. 533

In chapter 13, page 147, we made use of the fact that a tetrahedron (or any solid) whose edges are doubled in length undergoes an eightfold increase in volume. Now the twentieth tetrahedral number, 1540, is not eight times the tenth tetrahedral number, 220, but only seven times; but as we take larger and larger numbers, the ratio of the 2nth number to the nth number increases. We are looking at the quotient $[2n(2n + 1)(2n + 2)/6]/[n(n + 1)(n + 2)/6]$, and as n approaches infinity the constant terms in the brackets lose their significance, so that the quotient approaches a limiting value of $[(2n \times 2n \times 2n)/6]/[(n \times n \times n)/6]$ or $8n^3/n^3 = 8$. This result bears out what we know of the volume factor of enlargement when the scale factor of enlargement is 2.

Puzzles and Diversions

Construction Puzzles.

It is possible to buy construction puzzles based on tetrahedra. One of these, marketed in a slightly different form by Tarquin under the title "Pyramid Puzzle", consists of twenty wooden spheres joined in the following way (fig. 534):

 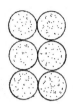 

Fig. 534

These spheres have to be put together in the shape of a regular tetrahedron, as in fig. 531, page 211. One way of thinking out the solution is to draw separate layers of the tetrahedron as in fig. 535. One of the 3 by 2 pieces (hatched) contributes to the bottom layer and to the next layer up; the other (speckled) is placed on end and contributes two spheres to each of the bottom three layers. The other two strips of four will supply (plain) the rear base edge and (cross-hatched) the front sloping edge. Such a puzzle can also be made by joining together table-tennis balls or small spheres of expanded polystyrene.

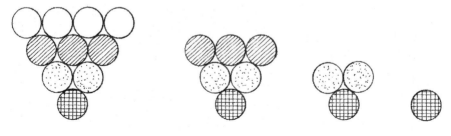

Fig. 535

A Problem

Three points can be drawn on a plane surface so that each is exactly the same distance from the other two only if they are at the corners of an equilateral triangle.

Can four points be placed so that each is the same distance from the other three? To solve this problem we move into three dimensions, and place the points at the four vertices of a regular tetrahedron. This means that, for example, if four points on the surface of a sphere are equidistant from one another, they must occupy the vertices of a regular tetrahedron inscribed in the sphere (fig. 536). Placed in this way, they will be equidistant not only in the sense that straight lines joining them and passing through the interior of the sphere will be the same length, but also that the (great circle) distances between points across the surface of the sphere will be equal. How far apart would four such points be if they were points on the Earth's surface?

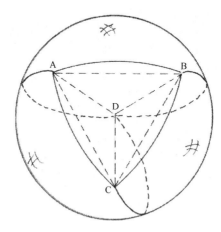

Fig. 536

Bibliography

W. W. Rouse Ball & H. S. M. Coxeter, *Mathematical Recreations and Essays*, Dover 1987

H. S. M. Coxeter, *Introduction to Geometry*, John Wiley & Sons 1961

H. S. M. Coxeter and others, *The Fifty-Nine Icosahedra*, Tarquin Publications 1999

H. M. Cundy and A. P. Rollett, *Mathematical Models*, Tarquin Publications 1981

H. E. Dudeney, *Amusements in Mathematics*, Thomas Nelson 1949

M. Gardner, *Mathematical Puzzles and Diversions*, Pelican 1965

M. Gardner, *More Mathematical Puzzles and Diversions*, G. Bell 1963

G. Jenkins and M. Bear, *Stellated Polyhedra*, Tarquin Publications 1997

G. Jenkins and A. Wild, *Make Shapes, (Series 1-3)*, Tarquin Publications 1990

G. Jenkins and A. Wild, *Mathematical Curiosities, 1-3*, Tarquin Publications 1989-90

M. Kline, *Mathematics in Western Culture*, Penguin 1972

B. van Loon, *Geodesic Domes*, Tarquin Publications 1994

H. Steinhaus, *Mathematical Snapshots*, O. U. P. 1983

D. Wells, *The Penguin Dictionary of Curious and Interesting Geometry*, Penguin 1991

M. J. Wenninger, *Polyhedron Models*, Cambridge University Press, London-New York 1971

INDEX